ROMANTIC ORPHEUS

Romantic Orpheus

PROFILES OF CLEMENS BRENTANO

JOHN F. FETZER

University of California Press / Berkeley / Los Angeles / London

University of California Press
Berkeley and Los Angeles, California

University of California Press, Ltd.
London, England

Copyright © 1974, by
The Regents of the University of California

ISBN: 0-520-02312-9
Library of Congress Catalog Card Number: 72-85527
Printed in the United States of America
Designed by Jim Mennick

Hier, unter Schwindenden, sei, im Reiche
der Neige,
sei ein klingendes Glas, das sich im Klang
schon zerschlug.
R. M. Rilke, *Sonette an Orpheus*

Contents

Preface   ix

Abbreviations of Commonly Cited Works   xi

Prospect   1

1. Proteus-Brentano: The Crisis of Continuity   5
   The Musicalization of Literary Criticism   8
   Brentano's Musical Muse   13

2. Orpheus-Brentano: The Crisis of Conscience   28
   Variations on Orphean Figures   31

3. The Musicalization of Life   65
   The Legacy of Orpheus' Lyre: Instrumental Symbolism   66
   The Ethos of Harmony   80
   The Pathos of Love and Death   99
   Musica Naturata—Musica Naturans   121
   The Cosmos and Chaos of the Dance   137
   Metamorphosis and Catharsis: "Singen—Lobsingen"   149

4. The Musicalization of Literature   179
   Synthesizing the Senses: Synaesthesia   183
   Synthesizing the Arts: The Syn-Aesthetic   186
   Lyric Musicality   204

5. Chandos-Brentano: The Crisis of Communication   262

Retrospect   273

Appendix: Chronology of the Life and
   Major Writings of Clemens Brentano   293

Selected Bibliography   297

Index   305

Preface

THE principal aim of this study is to introduce to English and American audiences the German writer Clemens Brentano (1778–1842), a leading representative of the Romantic tradition from its inception (ca. 1797) through the approximately three decades of its hegemony on the literary scene, from a perspective which is most congenial to his poetic disposition as well as to the temperament of his entire generation: the relationship between music and literature. Since a specialized interpretation such as this cannot presuppose in the reader familiarity with the relevant facts of the poet's life or fluency in the language in which he wrote, these obstacles were broached in the following manner. Pertinent biographical data together with the titles of Brentano's major writings (in the original German and in English translation) are given in a chronological table in an appendix; all German quotations have been translated into English—prose directly in the text and poetry in the footnotes.

Since virtually nothing by Brentano has been translated into English, this task proved to be particularly awesome. In both prose and poetry the primary goal was accuracy of both the spirit and the letter of the original, with a minimum of error and a maximum of comprehensibility. Credit for any success in translation must be given to several dedicated graduate students of the University of California at Davis, most notably Mr. Richard Hacken; censure for any gross blunders that may occur is exclusively mine. I owe a special debt of gratitude to my university for its patience and continued support—financial and moral—during the long, long period of gestation, to the American Philosophical Society for its generosity, and finally to the Freies Deutsches Hochstift in Frankfurt am Main (and its director, Dr. Detlev Lüders) for allowing me to peruse unpublished manuscripts and other documents that will one day be included in the definitive edition of Brentano's works.

Of course, no study built on the Orpheus myth would really be complete without a personal Eurydice to spur the writer on when he faltered on the brink of success, when the pressures of academia became too great or when the burdens of routine commitments threatened to stifle intellectual pursuits. So it is to this Eurydice, who crosses the threshold of my life each day in the guise of my wife Henriette, that I dedicate these profiles of that poet whom I have chosen to call the Romantic Orpheus.

Abbreviations of Commonly Cited Works

BP   *Biographische Porträts von Varnhagen von Ense.* Leipzig: F. Brockhaus, 1871.

EL   *Clemens Brentano: Briefe an Emilie Linder.* Ed. Wolfgang Frühwald. Bad Homburg: Gehlen, 1969.

F   *Clemens Brentanos Frühlingskranz.* Ed. Heinz Amelung. Leipzig: Insel, 1921.

FDH   Unpublished documents held by the Freies Deutsches Hochstift.

GS   Brentano, Clemens. *Gesammelte Schriften.* 9 vols. Frankfurt am Main: J. D. Sauerländer, 1852–1855.

L   *Clemens Brentano und Minna Reichenbach: Ungedruckte Briefe des Dichters.* Ed. W. Limburger. Leipzig: Insel, 1921.

LB   *Clemens Brentanos Liebesleben.* Ed. Lujo Brentano. Frankfurt am Main: Frankfurter Verlags-Anstalt, 1921.

S   *Clemens Brentano: Briefe.* Ed. Friedrich Seebaß. 2 vols. Nürnberg: Hans Carl, 1951.

SB   *Briefwechsel zwischen Clemens Brentano und Sophie Mereau.* Ed. Heinz Amelung. 2 vols. Leipzig: Insel, 1908.

SW   Brentano, Clemens. *Sämtliche Werke.* Ed. Carl Schüddekopf et al. 10 vols. Munich and Leipzig: Georg Müller, 1909–1917.

U   *Das unsterbliche Leben: Unbekannte Briefe von Clemens Brentano.* Ed. Wilhelm Schellberg and Friedrich Fuchs. Jena: Eugen Diederichs, 1939.

W   Brentano, Clemens. *Werke.* Ed. Friedhelm Kemp et al. 4 vols. Munich: Hanser, 1963–1968.

Prospect

𝕴N the foreword to his study of 1950, *Orpheus: Der Dichter und die Toten*, Walther Rehm writes:

> The power and depth of the Orpheus symbol, whose significance, due to very specific philosophical and historico-religious reasons, was lost to the centuries after Christ and which, indeed, had to be lost or at least had to retain its meaning only in an allegorical context, became comprehensible, indicatively enough, only after 1800 with Novalis, with Hölderlin, and a full century later especially with Rilke. It is Rilke himself who can be viewed as the new creator of the Orpheus symbol; of course, at the same time, one must also perceive the pain and sadness which are necessarily connected with the reawakening of the old symbol.[1]

As the title of Rehm's book suggests, the author was primarily interested in the relationship between poetry and death, between the poet and the dead ("The inner, unalterable correlation of poetry and death, of the poet and the dead").[2] Whereas this aspect of the Orpheus myth is indispensable for an understanding of its literary and musical manifestations over the ages, there is another facet of the legend that makes the revival of the Greek singer-poet's story by German writers from the turn of the nineteenth century to Rilke's monumental cycle of sonnets in the twentieth particularly appealing to the modern audience. This feature, which will be referred to henceforth as the "threshold condition," derives from Orpheus' unprecedented conquest of the realm of death through the power of music and his subsequent forfeiture of this victory on the very brink of success. None of the various accounts of the Orpheus legend is explicit with regard to the exact cause of this predicament. Whatever the basis for his failure might be—whether it is attributable, in the final analysis, to a basic human flaw or to the decrees of a higher power—the fact remains that this development leads to a "crisis" in the career of the poet-singer. "Crisis," as defined

---

[1] Walther Rehm, *Orpheus: Der Dichter und die Toten* (Düsseldorf: L. Schwann, 1950), p. 9.

[2] Rehm, p. 10. All subsequent references to "Rehm" in the footnotes apply to his Orpheus study.

by *Webster's International Dictionary*, is "a psychological or social
condition characterized by unusual instability caused by excessive
stress and either endangering or felt to endanger the continuity of
the individual or his group."[3] Can Orpheus, one is tempted to ask,
after fulfilling the impossible dream and then losing out in the nightmare that followed, continue to regard either his art or himself in
the same confident spirit as before? Will the aftermath of doubt and
despair surrounding what might have been mar the execution of what
now has to be? This perplexing aspect of the Orphean figure is particularly applicable to a contemporary of Novalis and Hölderlin whom
Rehm does not treat in *Orpheus: Der Dichter und die Toten*, but with
whom this critic, judging by his other publications,[4] is intimately familiar: Clemens Brentano (1778–1842).

Considered from a purely chronological standpoint, Brentano and
his Romantic generation found themselves in many a "threshold"
condition; those writers and thinkers who matured around 1800 stood
at the crossroads of numerous historical and intellectual currents. For
example, in the political arena, the "old order" had been overthrown
in France during the last decade of the eighteenth century, and the new
superstructure of society was groping its way through the quagmire
of revolution. This particular type of "threshold" situation finds symbolic expression on several levels in Brentano's *Die Gründung Prags*
(1814).[5] Not only does this lyrically tinged dramatic spectacle occupy
an intermediary position between the literary genres, but it also treats
as its subject an age of transition in the course of human history, tracing the dilemmas that confronted one segment of mankind in its progression from a matriarchal to a patriarchal culture, from an agrarian
to an urban civilization. Even the name given to the capital of this
new nation—Prague—is noteworthy, since Brentano based his conception of the work on the widely accepted pseudomythical derivation

---

[3] *Webster's Third New International Dictionary of the English Language*, ed.
Philip B. Gove (Springfield, Mass.: G. & C. Merriam, 1961), p. 538.

[4] For instance, Rehm's article "Brentano und Hölderlin" in the *Hölderlin
Jahrbuch* (1947), pp. 127–178 (also contained in the author's collected essays
Begegnungen und Probleme [Bern: Francke, 1957], pp. 40–88) or his very pene-
trating "Nachwort" to *Clemens Brentanos Romanfragment 'Der schiffbrüchige
Galeerensklave vom Todten Meer* in *Abhandlungen der Deutschen Akademie der
Wissenschaften*, Philosophisch-historische Klasse (1948), No. 4, pp. 15–54.

[5] The dates given in this study for Brentano's works are taken from the critical
apparatus found in each of the volumes of Brentano's *Werke*, ed. Friedhelm Kemp,
4 vols. (Munich: Hanser, 1963–1968). For fuller information concerning this
edition, see n. 19 of chapter 1.

of the Czech word "Praha," meaning "threshold."[6] This play, in addition, was to form the introduction to an entire cycle of dramas. But having brought his creative skills to the "brink" of this grandiose conception, Brentano let the project fall—the continuity of design necessary for a successful execution deserted him. This situation of faltering on the threshold of success is paradigmatic for Brentano's entire career, and therefore provides the basis for the following "profiles" of the author and his role as a—if not *the*—romantic Orpheus.

Chapter 1 focuses attention on the "identity" crisis surrounding the figure of Brentano and examines his qualifications as the singer-poet par excellence in German literary history. It investigates the extent of his actual musicality within the context of his acknowledged protean malleability and personal idiosyncrasies. Chapter 2 contains a detailed analysis of those poet-singers in his works who exhibit traces of the Orphean gift of song and who experience the Orphean destiny in varying degrees of intensity. This phase of the discussion culminates in a portrayal of a female Orpheus, Rosadore from the *Romanzen vom Rosenkranz*, whose development best illustrates the "crisis of conscience" which Brentano seems to have regarded as symptomatic of the *malheur d'être poète*. The central chapter of this investigation—the third—is entitled "The Musicalization of Life" and examines the manner in which Brentano, by means of musical metaphor and image, infused the spirit of song and beautiful sound into almost every phase of human activity (ranging from instrumental symbolism, the concepts of harmony and discord, the dance, to liturgical singing). At the same time, this phase of the analysis does not lose sight of the central concern of the original Orpheus legend (the interrelationship of music, love, and death—for which constellation the three corresponding Greek terms: Melos-Eros-Thanatos are used) and, concomitant with this, the "crisis of conscience" that results from regarding every aspect of existence from a two-dimensional perspective. Chapter 4 concentrates on the thorny issue of the "musicalization of literature" (a trend which some critics regard as the hallmark of modernism)[7] and attempts to pinpoint how the originally synthesized activities of creating a form of song that was a unique amalgam of poetry and

[6] For a full account of this derivation, see Hans Taeschler, '*Die Gründung Prags,' Eine Interpretation*, Diss. Zürich (Zürich: Juris Verlag, 1950). pp. 10–12.

[7] See the chapter "Music and Existence" in Walter H. Sokel, *The Writer in Extremis: Expressionism in 20th-Century German Literature* (Stanford, California: Stanford University Press, 1959).

melody enjoyed a renaissance under the aegis of the Romantic writers in general and Brentano in particular. The theme of chapter 5—the "crisis of communication"—can be regarded, at least in part, as an outgrowth of some of the procedures and poetic techniques applied in the process of musicalization. Even this development reveals Brentano in a "threshold" situation—at the point of intersection between a naïve faith in the uninhibited power of song suggested by the Orpheus legend and the complete skepticism of many modern poets who share the sentiments of the writer of the Lord Chandos letter at the outset of the twentieth century, maintaining that the spoken word is incapable of conveying little but the nonessentials of life. The closing section of this study—"Retrospect"—presents, in lieu of the customary summary and conclusions, a recapitulation of the major findings of chapters 1–5 from a radically altered perspective: that of the anti-Orpheus faction or, to use Brentano's own terminology, the philistine. What emerges then from this mode of disillusionment or debunking is the impression that Brentano himself had no qualms about demeaning or destroying those very same values which the Orphean artist had created. This self-destructive attitude, however, would be in accord with the challenge hurled at the modern age by Rilke, who wrote in his own _Sonette an Orpheus_: "Hier, unter Schwindenden, sei, im Reiche der Neige, / sei ein klingendes Glas, das sich im Klang schon zerschlug."[8]

[8] Rainer Maria Rilke, _Sämtliche Werke_, ed. Rilke-Archiv (n.p.: Insel, n.d.), I, 759. "Here, amidst the transitory, be, in the realm of decline, / Be a resonant glass, that shattered while yet ringing."

1. Proteus-Brentano: The Crisis of Continuity

CRITICS are of many minds concerning the literary significance of Clemens Brentano and the course of his personal development. Although Brentano died in 1842, there has never been a complete, critical edition of his works. And because no such authoritative edition exists, we possess today no comprehensive interpretation of his writings, no all-encompassing analysis of his life.[1] To be sure, Brentano's unruly mode of living and his quixotic manner of writing dictated that his works would be transmitted in haphazard fashion, that taboos would be placed on much of what he said, and that circumspect editors would delete numerous passages that offended the aesthetic sensibility of their readers or that brought embarrassment to later generations of the Brentano family.[2] One result of these arbitrary deletions and emendations has been the emergence of divergent Brentano images, the evolution of diffuse assessments of his poetic gifts. The persistence of this multilayered Brentano portrait has led some commentators to compare him with the master of metamorphosis in Greek mythology: the sea-god Proteus.[3] Today, with the prospect of a historically critical edition soon to be published under the auspices of the Freies Deutsches Hochstift of the Goethe-Museum

---

[1] For a survey of the secondary literature on Brentano see my article "Old and New Directions in Clemens Brentano Research (1931–1968)" in the *Literaturwissenschaftliches Jahrbuch* (im Auftrag der Görres-Gesellschaft), 11 (1970): 87–119; 12 (1971): 113–203.

[2] For an excellent account of the history of the *Gesammelte Schriften* (which, although published during the 1850s of the preceding century, is still indispensable for Brentano's work) see Henning Boetius' article "Zur Entstehung und Textqualität von Clemens Brentanos 'Gesammelten Schriften,'" *Jahrbuch des Freien Deutschen Hochstifts* (1967), pp. 406–457. In his article "Zu neueren Brentano-Ausgaben," *Literaturwissenschaftliches Jahrbuch*, 5 (1964): 361–380, Wolfgang Frühwald gives a sketch of recent editions.

[3] Joseph von Eichendorff's comment in his essay "Brentano und seine Märchen" of 1847 (reprinted in *Aurora*, 24 [1964]: 14–20) that the poet was "an inexplicable Proteus pure and simple" (p. 16) has persisted in the most current interpretations.

in Frankfurt, one can hope that the aura of myth and mystery surrounding the man and his works will eventually be dispelled.[4]

Even to his friends and contemporaries, Brentano's way of life seemed chimeric and chameleonic. To some, he epitomized the gay roué, the childish prankster, the jaunty minstrel strumming a guitar and singing seductive love songs, or the devil-may-care satirist whose supple wit and glib tongue poked fun at friend and foe alike.[5] Conversely, others saw in him a "poète maudit," a star-crossed lover, a crabbed misanthrope, or an apostate Catholic who, following a radical volte-face in 1817, ended his life completely out of step with the times, a recluse propagandizing for the Church and preaching adherence to official dogma to an age that was impatient with religious orthodoxy and intent upon debunking Christian mythology.[6]

Similar conflicts of opinion persist with regard to Brentano's literary stature and artistic accomplishments. Whereas many critics see in him only a carefree improviser or a conscious imitator,[7] others proclaim him to be a careful artisan and conscientious innovator.[8] Questions pertaining to the influences on as well as the influence of his works abound. Does Brentano's poetry and prose simply hark back to the medieval folk song and chronicle, to the baroque mannerists and mystics, or do his lyrics introduce techniques that anticipate the practices of the Symbolists,[9] and does his narrative craft augur develop-

---

[4] An excellent account of the format for the critical edition of Brentano's works being prepared by the Freies Deutsches Hochstift is provided by the joint report of Jürgen Behrens, Wolfgang Frühwald, and Detlev Lüders "Zum Stand der Arbeiten an der Frankfurter Brentano-Ausgabe," *Jahrbuch des Freien Deutschen Hochstifts* (1969), pp. 398–426, and by Frühwald's supplement "Frankfurter Brentano-Ausgabe" in the *Jahrbuch für Internationale Germanistik*, 1, No. 2 (1969): 70–80.

[5] For instance, Werner Hoffmann in *Clemens Brentano: Leben und Werk* (Bern and Munich: Francke, 1966), p. 77, points out that the poet's contemporaries coined such terms as "Demens" and "der Angebrannte" (the man on fire) when referring to his mercurial temperament.

[6] Heinrich Heine, for example, in *Die romantische Schule* of 1836, considered Brentano "immured in his Catholicism" and "a corresponding member of Catholic propaganda." Heine, *Sämtliche Werke*, ed. Ernst Elster (Leipzig and Vienna: Bibliographisches Institut, n.d.), V, 308–309.

[7] Friedrich Gundolf, in his Brentano discussion found in *Romantiker I* (Berlin: H. Keller, 1930), pp. 283–291, stresses these features.

[8] The meticulous craftsmanship behind the production of some of Brentano's poetry has been analyzed by Hans Magnus Enzensberger in *Brentanos Poetik* (Munich: Hanser, 1961), and more recently, the "artistic consciousness" of the poet has been studied by Wolfgang Frühwald in his essay "Clemens Brentano" in *Deutsche Dichter der Romantik*, ed. Benno von Wiese (Berlin: Erich Schmidt, 1971), pp. 280–309.

[9] The affinity of Brentano with the Symbolist movement was already noted

ments that were later to become the hallmark of modernity?[10] In short, are his modes of literary production reactionary or revolutionary? Is his lyricism best characterized by the term "lilting musicality"[11] or by the phrase "labored monotony"?[12] Are his prose creations time-bound or still timely today? And finally, should one relegate his stage works to the category of unplayable closet-dramas, or do some of them constitute avant-garde pieces which simply have not yet found their proper theatrical medium?

The impression one gains of Brentano's personal life depends, to a large extent, upon the particular biography one reads and the religious[13] or psychological bias[14] of its author. Similarly, one's appreciation of Brentano's artistry is often contingent upon the controlled sampling with which the literary critic undergirds his premises. In both instances, the erratic state of Brentano philology during the century and a quarter since his death has contributed the lion's share in blurring the contours and distorting our perspective. The mass of previously unpublished material which the new edition will place at the disposal of scholars may enable them to trace a line of unity and continuity in his career and creative writings, which, up to now, has been missing. On the other hand, the abundance of additional documentary evidence could make the already elusive and enigmatic nature of the poet even more pronounced. One might discover, for instance, that Brentano played the role of a romantic Proteus to the hilt, donning and discarding even more disguises than critics up to the present have suspected. The only consistent factor in the course of his lifetime may indeed prove to be a protean malleability.

---

at the end of the nineteenth century by Alfred Kerr in the introduction to his study *Godwi: Ein Kapitel deutscher Romantik* (Berlin: Georg Bondi, 1898), p. vi.

[10] Frühwald, in "Clemens Brentano," p. 286, speaks of the "late works" (1816–1842) exhibiting "a level of language virtually independent from the period and its style,... a modern idiom which alone has exerted an effect on the writing of the current age."

[11] Walther Killy in *Wandlungen des lyrischen Bildes*, 3rd. ed. (Göttingen: Vandenhoeck & Ruprecht, 1961), p. 69, speaks of "the sheer music of Brentano's verses."

[12] Hermann August Korff in *Geist der Goethezeit*, IV (Leipzig: Koehler & Amelang, 1953), p. 206, comments that many of Brentano's poems never move from the spot ("das Nicht-vom-Fleck-Kommen").

[13] For instance, Josef Michels' interpretation *Clemens Brentano: Irrtum des Herzens—Einkehr bei Gott*, (Münster: Regensbergsche Verlagsbuchhandlung, 1948) assesses the literary works from a markedly Catholic viewpoint.

[14] Werner Hoffmann, *Clemens Brentano*, draws heavily upon Freudian psychology and terminology in his analysis of the poet's "mother fixation" (p. 29) and, to a lesser extent, for Brentano's attitude toward his father.

The Musicalization of Literary Criticism

Some of the dilemmas plaguing Brentano scholarship, however, should not be ascribed solely to the philological shortcomings of the extant editions; rather, they are attributable to handicaps which the poet's interpreters have inflicted upon themselves. Certain methodological practices have become so entrenched over the course of the last century that one is inclined to accept them wholeheartedly instead of examining them critically. Perhaps no other aspect of analysis has been invoked more and investigated less than the question of Brentano's "musicality." In spite of the fact that almost every critical study dealing with the poet has recourse to such terms as "musicality," "melody," "the music of language," or "a composer with words," the actual extent of Brentano's involvement with and commitment to the field of music has received only scant and peripheral attention. Consequently, the confused and confusing relationship of this poet to the art of music represents *in nuce* the crisis besetting Brentano criticism *in toto* due to a combination of intrinsic and extrinsic factors. By throwing some light on this restricted—but relevant—phase of his life and work through the utilization of the conventional primary sources together with recently published correspondence and previously inaccessible material,[15] the following investigation seeks to determine whether Brentano's attitudes changed radically each time the "winter of discontent" set in, or whether he remained, in spite of the "slings and arrows of adversity," a man for all seasons.

The causes for ambiguity and ambivalence with reference to the nature of Brentano's "musicality" can be traced to two principal sources: the poet's habit of discussing important aspects of life and art (personal affiliations, emotional and intellectual issues, modes of poetic creativity) in terms of vague musical analogy and imagery; the tendency of his interpreters to emulate him in this practice by adopting similar abstruse terminology when speaking of his career and his writings. Of course, the use of the musical frame of reference by both the poet and his critics may stem from the attempt to articulate a condition or verbalize a state of mind for which no other mode of dis-

---

[15] Some of the unpublished documents currently held by the *Freies Deutsches Hochstift* have been utilized for this study; excerpts from these manuscripts will be indicated in the text by the abbreviation FDH.

course is felt to be adequate.[16] Under these circumstances, the musical image would correspond to the "objective correlative" in the sense in which T. S. Eliot defines the concept:

> The only way of expressing emotion in the form of art is by finding an "objective correlative"; in other words, a set of objects, a situation, a chain of events which shall be the formula of that *particular* emotion; such that when the external facts, which must terminate in sensory experience, are given, the emotion is immediately evoked. . . . The artistic "inevitability" lies in this complete adequacy of the external to the emotional.[17]

For example, the following passage from a letter of Brentano's to Rahel Varnhagen (1813) contrasting the existential condition of the writer and of the recipient respectively in terms of musical phenomena might serve as an illustration of the "objective correlative" as Eliot intended the term:

> My appearance is . . . a musical one; I sing the melody, and when the orchestral accompaniment completely deserts me and the *forte* is lacking, I just carry on with the melody; but when everything gets out of beat, I close my eyes and ears and start dancing. . . . But in you, dear friend, there is no melody at all, so that the beat comes forth wonderously and often sounds like a drum to the silent, exquisite music of your hidden soul.[18]

Whereas the musical analogy in the above passage is particularly apropos, there are numerous occasions when such "musicalizations" either fail to ring true or even cause confusion in the mind of the reader because of imprecise terminology. In the following excerpts, for instance, one has the impression that Brentano simply may be availing himself of the "mask" of music either to avoid full commitment, to conceal flaws in his thinking, or to pay lip service to contemporary fads: "Is a poet conceivable who is no musician?"[19] "What I like best

---

[16] German Romantic writers, from Wackenroder to E. T. A. Hoffmann, consistently maintained that music alone could make the ultimate statement. For a compendium of their views on the subject, see Willi Reich's anthology *Musik in romantischer Schau: Visionen der Dichter* (Basel: Amerbach-Verlag, 1946).

[17] From the essay "Hamlet and His Problems" in *The Sacred Wood*, 3rd. ed. (London: Methuen, 1932), p. 100.

[18] *Biographische Porträts von Varnhagen von Ense* (Leipzig: F. Brockhaus, 1871), p. 99. Henceforth: BP (page given in the text).

[19] Clemens Brentano, *Werke*, 4 vols. (Munich: Hanser, 1963–1968), II. 1230. Vol. I (1968), ed. Wolfgang Frühwald, Bernhard Gajek, and Friedhelm Kemp; vols. II (1963), III (1965), IV (1966), ed. Friedhelm Kemp. Henceforth: W (volume and page given in the text).

about him [Tieck] is his musicality."[20] "The dear, musical heart [of Arnim] has probably not been made to dance in more noble beats of a joyful self-awareness" (S I 300). Since none of these statements is amplified by concrete details in the context in which they occur, they serve merely as provocative and promising asides, replete with problems and puzzles.

A random sampling from both the older and the more recent research will indicate how the tendency to indulge in vague musico-poetic imagery has also infiltrated Brentano scholarship, proceeding from Nietzsche's apodictic pronouncement of 1882 ("Of the German poets, Clemens Brentano has the most music in him")[21] and extending to the most current analyses.[22] Max Preitz, for instance, in his introduction to the 1914 edition of Brentano's *Werke* alludes to "the musical structure of his [Brentano's] spiritual being."[23] Felix Scholz points to "the musical soul of Brentano, soaring in constant feeling,"[24] while Hans Rupprich declares categorically: "The final, basic form of every human and spiritual experience for Brentano was music."[25] With reference to Brentano's language—especially in his lyric poetry—the amount of musical allusion is even more striking. To Friedrich Gundolf's mind, Brentano possessed "the natural melodiousness of a verbal musician,"[26] while for René Guignard the poet exhibited "a very exact sense of the musical character of lyricism."[27] Whereas Hermann A. Korff stresses "the virtually unique talent of Brentano for . . . word music,"[28] Werner Vordtriede, in the postscript to his anthology of selected Brentano poems, conjectures: "As an actual composer with words, he created romantic music decades before Schu-

[20] *Clemens Brentano: Briefe*, ed. Friedrich Seebaß, 2 vols. (Nürnberg: Hans Carl, 1951), I, 192. Henceforth: S (volume and page given in the text).

[21] Friedrich Nietzsche, *Gesammelte Werke*, ed. R. and M. Oehler and F. Würzbach, XI (Munich: Musarion Verlag, 1924), 283.

[22] Ian Hilton, for example, in his article "Clemens Brentano" in *German Men of Letters*, ed. Alex Natan (London: O. Wolff, 1969), V, 51–74, speaks of composers who have set Brentano's poetry to music and adds "but his verse of course with its rhythms and colour produces its own musicality" (p. 69).

[23] Clemens Brentano, *Werke*, ed. Max Preitz, 3 vols. (Leipzig and Vienna: Bibliographisches Institut, 1914), I, 22.

[24] *Clemens Brentano und Goethe* (Leipzig: Mayer and Müller, 1927), p. 152.

[25] *Brentano, Luise Hensel und Ludwig von Gerlach* (Vienna: Österreichischer Bundesverlag für Unterricht, Wissenschaft und Kunst, 1927), p. 12.

[26] *Romantiker I*, p. 327.

[27] *Un poète romantique allemand, Clemens Brentano (1778–1842)*, Diss. Paris, 1933 (Paris: Les Belles Lettres, 1933), p. 110.

[28] *Geist der Goethezeit*, IV, 219.

bert, Schumann, and Wagner; the eternal melody that moves onward from tone to tone, from image to image."[29]

The eclectic selection of examples could be augmented ad infinitum. Yet the amassing of additional quotations would not conceal but rather would reveal that such musico-poetic parallels are very tempting to draw but extremely difficult to demonstrate. Whereas judicious application of overlapping nomenclature from one aesthetic discipline to another may sometimes contribute to the "reciprocal illumination of the arts,"[30] indiscriminate and unsubstantiated usage of similar—but not necessarily synonymous—designations can often cloud rather than clarify the relationship. The following excerpt from Richard Benz's stimulating book *Die Welt der Dichter und die Musik* will illustrate this contention:

> Brentano was, as far as we can observe, the only German for whom language was music whenever he opened his mouth to say something ... a perfect, highly gifted existence expresses itself here, a life filled with the music of language.... His word is not of this world: it is not the mundane word of the poets who realistically describe and relate or who classically measure and count; it is not the logically dissected word, and it is not the plastically formed and forming word—it is the musical word, imbued only with the tone and rhythm of its content.[31]

Since neither of these assertions is substantiated by the analysis of a single line of poetry, they do little to enhance the reader's appreciation of Brentano's alleged verbal musicality. The critic has, in this case, presupposed a priori what he should have proved a posteriori.

The prevalence of such obscurities in secondary literature dealing with Brentano and other writers has induced some scholars to qualify—and even question—the nature of the phenomenon generally known as "musical" style.[32] The Brentano discussion in the book by Johannes Mittenzwei entitled *Das Musikalische in der Literatur* offers ample

[29] *Clemens Brentano: Gedichte,* ed. Werner Vordtriede (Frankfurt am Main: Insel, 1963), p. 65.

[30] Oskar Walzel, *Gehalt und Gestalt im Kunstwerk des Dichters* (1929; reprinted, Darmstadt: Wissenschaftliche Buchgesellschaft, 1957), pp. 265 ff.

[31] *Die Welt der Dichter und die Musik* (Düsseldorf: Diederichs Verlag, 1949), pp. 97–98.

[32] In their *Theory of Literature,* 3rd. ed. (New York: Harcourt, Brace & World, 1962), pp. 126 ff., Austin Warren and René Wellek express strong doubts that "poetry can achieve the effects of music."

proof of why such reservations are justified.[33] Although Mittenzwei proclaims this poet to be "the musical language-artist of Romanticism,"[34] he never comes to grips with the central issue of what constitutes "das Musikalische" in literature per se, or what, with respect to Brentano, makes his poetry more musical than the lyrics of a host of other authors. Herein lies the crux of the problem: that imprecise articulation which compounds the "crises" already manifest in Brentano's enigmatic personality and latent in his works because of the sporadic and arbitrary manner in which they have been transmitted.

Not only is there a lack of precision and documentation among critics in delineating the nature and extent of Brentano's transfer of musical features to literature, but there is also a faction which denies that he possessed the requisite knowledge to make any correlation of the two arts meaningful. Wolfgang Pfeiffer-Belli, for instance, in his biographical monograph *Clemens Brentano*, subscribes to the general consensus of opinion by designating the author a "musician of the word,"[35] but he finds him in all other respects no musician, no "initiate of music."[36] Apparently some distinction must be made between literal and literary musicality, since the two attributes, although they may exhibit certain elective affinities, can also be mutually exclusive.

No one has helped more to widen the gap further between Brentano the musician and Brentano the exponent of musicality in literature than the poet himself. On several occasions he confessed his deficiencies in the field ("music, about which I know nothing" [S II 37]), and one has the impression that such statements are not meant to be a mere *captatio benevolentiae*. In Brentano's remarks concerning E. T. A. Hoffmann's *Phantasiestücke in Callots Manier* one can detect a trace of envy on the part of the dilettante for the proficiency of the expert: "All of the musical elements in it are uncommonly thorough, yet at the same time simple" (S II 167). And yet Brentano allies himself with that ironically named figure of Hoffmann's—the "foe of music"—who actually possesses a deep understanding for the essence of the art: "You know which music your foe of music (my favorite) loves, yes, you appear to be in accord with him. I am he—completely" (S II 164).

In spite of such discrepancies and dissenting views, the mystique

[33] *Das Musikalische in der Literatur* (Halle/Saale: VEB Verlag Sprache und Literatur, 1962), pp. 143–161.
[34] Ibid., p. 143.
[35] *Clemens Brentano* (Freiburg im Breisgau: Herder, 1947), p. 155.
[36] Ibid., p. 115.

of Brentano's musicality still persists. Emil Staiger's challenge of 1939 has gone virtually unheeded: "And certainly only then will we completely understand the language of Brentano when the meaning of music in his poetic world becomes clear."[37] Consequently, the following investigation will examine this "meaning of music" and its ramifications in both the empiric and the poetic sphere, not under the misapprehension that there is necessarily a direct, causal link between the two, but rather because of the conviction that Brentano's exposure to actual musical stimuli was not totally irrelevant for his literary career. And even if no clearly demonstrable ties can be established between "life" and "art," one still cannot discount the possibility that reciprocity may be implicit rather than explicit.

Brentano's Musical Muse

When one considers the musical facts of Brentano's life, it becomes evident that his "training" in this field was sparse and undisciplined, that his acquaintance with the theoretical principles of composition remained minimal. As a result, he never progressed beyond the stage of the amateur as either a performer, a composer, or a critic. And yet his contemporaries found his musical renditions fascinating. In the brief biographical sketch preceding volume eight of the *Gesammelte Schriften*, for instance, we read: "The young poet enchanted everyone with his singing and his guitar playing."[38] Joseph von Eichendorff found Brentano's mode of oral presentation particularly effective "when he sang to the accompaniment of his guitar—and often in impromptu fashion—tunes which he had composed himself."[39]

The environment of the Brentano household in Frankfurt am Main during the poet's childhood was undoubtedly conducive to fostering musical interest in the family. Brentano's mother, Maximiliane (Goethe's "Maxe" of his *Werther* period), as well as several of his sisters played the piano.[40] In a moment of levity he declared to his

[37] *Die Zeit als Einbildungskraft des Dichters* (1939; reprinted, Zurich: Atlantis, 1953), p. 44.

[38] Clemens Brentano, *Gesammelte Schriften*, 9 vols. (Frankfurt am Main: J. D. Sauerländer, 1852–1855), VIII (1855), 44. Henceforth: GS (volume and page given in the text).

[39] *Sämtliche Werke*, ed. Wilhelm Kosch and August Sauer (Regensburg: J. Habbel, n.d.), X, 423.

[40] In a letter to his wife, Sophie Mereau, Brentano mentions the possibility of acquiring the piano "on which my mother played, and on which all my sisters

sisters in 1797 that even when his travels took him far away from home, he could not forget "the melodies, sighs, trills . . . which . . . set the resounding echoes of the Brentano vaulted ceiling into motion."[41] On more than one occasion, Maximiliane urged her son to take up an instrument of his own choosing, and when he proved reluctant to do so voluntarily, she explicitly suggested one.[42] Following her death in 1794, Brentano seems to have taken her suggestion to heart, for his correspondence from later years reveals that he intended to study alternatingly the violin, (U 92), clarinet, (U 69), flageolet, (U 91), and zither, (U 111). The inability to settle on a single instrument, and the inclination to dabble amateurishly on several simultaneously, reflect not only Brentano's lack of direction after his mother's death but also his facile skills and eclecticism. Even he grew impatient with his own shortcoming in music, however: "You cannot imagine how much I regret not being able to play any music; it would greatly sweeten my loneliness" (U 72). Ultimately the guitar caught his fancy, and it was this instrument—which he once labeled an "awkward traveling orchestra" (S I 278)—that became his companion for the remainder of his life and won him considerable popular acclaim.

Brentano's musical insight was greatly enriched through contact with his younger sister, Bettina. The latter was trained in the fundamentals of music theory. She also played the guitar, composed songs and chamber music, studied the history of Hebrew music, corresponded with Beethoven, and later in life, made the acquaintance of Spontini, Liszt, Schumann, and Brahms.[43] The exchange of letters between brother and sister (1800–1803), which Bettina edited somewhat arbitrarily and published in 1844 under the title Clemens Brentanos Früh-

---

learned" (Briefwechsel zwischen Clemens Brentano und Sophie Mereau, ed. Heinz Amelung, 2 vols. [Leipzig: Insel, 1908], II, 95). Henceforth: SB (volume and page given in the text).

   [41] Das unsterbliche Leben: Unbekannte Briefe von Clemens Brentano, ed. Wilhelm Schellberg and Friedrich Fuchs (Jena: Eugen Diederichs, 1939), p. 82. Henceforth: U (page given in the text).

   [42] Since Maximiliane's question of 1792: "Papa a permis que vous appreniez un instrument, lequel avez-vous choisi?" went unanswered, she pressed the point in German: "Papa fragt immer nach Dir, er will haben, daß Du etwas geigen lernen sollst, damit wenn Du einst zurückkömmst wir dann und wann ein klein Konzert halten können." These quotations are taken from Reinhold Steig, Achim von Arnim und die ihm nahe standen, 3 vols. (Stuttgart: J. G. Cotta'sche Buchhandlung, 1894–1913), I (Achim von Arnim und Clemens Brentano, 1894), pp. 11 and 14 respectively.

   [43] Mittenzwei (n. 33 above), pp. 161–179.

lings-kranz (aus Jugendbriefen ihm geflochten), illustrates how the poet's knowledge of *musica practica* was enhanced by this close contact with her. Brentano reports at one point that her melodies prompted him to play and brought him the plaudits of his friends: "With my guitar and your melodies I am acquiring a considerable reputation. Every evening I sit with some group or other until late into the night and sing and play in such a way that they all admire me."[44] Bettina, in turn, found inspiration for some of her compositions in Clemens' poetry, and she was constantly encouraged by him to further her musical training (S I 78, F 11).

Undoubtedly many of Bettina's digressions on the intricacies of the "thorough-bass" (which proved to be her musical nemesis) (F 199), and her fondness for weaving technical jargon into the fabric of the discussion, grew tedious for Clemens. He was not familiar enough with the *termini technici* to reply to comments such as this: "The diminished seventh chord is built on the leading tone of the fundamental" (F 141). As he indicated to an acquaintance at this time, he instinctively rebelled against an analytical approach to music or any attempt to probe its magical effects by scientific means: "No . . . I am not the type . . . that reduces everything down to its basic parts . . . that rips the resonant tongue out of tones in order to trace everything . . . to the wave length of some gut strings through which the secret spirits of music are conjured up" (S I 153). Yet in spite of his layman's nontheoretical attitude toward music, Brentano was not deterred from embarking into two areas of this art that presuppose at least a minimal background in fundamentals: composition and criticism.

According to Emma von Niendorf's memoirs, Brentano is reputed to have declared in 1841: "I have composed many melodies, but in every instance only on the street or when I am sad."[45] References to the creation of impromptu melodies can also be cited from earlier periods. For instance, he writes to Arnim in 1802: "I am composing melodies for your songs and will send them to Bettina to sing" (S I 146), and notes in a letter to Bettina: "Today I wrote Arnim a little poem and a nice melody for it" (F 338). One of Brentano's melodies— the tune he composed for the folk song "Da droben auf jenem Berge"—

---

[44] *Clemens Brentanos Frühlingskranz*, ed. Heinz Amelung (Leipzig: Insel, 1921), p. 330. Henceforth: F (page given in text).

[45] Emma von Niendorf, *Aus der Gegenwart* (Berlin: Duncker, 1844), p. 90.

is supposed to have inspired Goethe to write the poem "Schäfers Klagelied."[46] A comment of Brentano's in a letter to Bettina from Düsseldorf (1802) reveals his intention of pursuing the study of composition more seriously now that he has found a suitable instructor: "the capable music director, for whom I intend to compose an opera, and who, in turn, will instruct me in composition" (F 227–228). However, nothing seems to have come of this project, for he notes some time later that he is still providing the melodies which this colleague then scores and orchestrates: "Even late in the evening I think up melodies for my verses, which Ritter, with generous acknowledgement, then assimilates into the opera" (F 263).

Unfortunately for the modern reader, most of the spontaneous songs and original tunes created by Brentano have been lost. Because of the improvisory nature of their conception and the impromptu circumstances of their performance, these melodies were seldom written down and, as a result, have disappeared almost without a trace. Two exceptions, however, are the songs that Brentano devised for his chauvinistic pageant *Viktoria und ihre Geschwister*,[47] and a melody ascribed to him in the *Liederbuch für deutsche Künstler*.[48] To an 1817 edition of the "musical play" *Viktoria* Brentano appends the following ambiguous comment: "The enclosed melodies are partly reminiscences, partly singable ideas which a friend set to music."[49] In all probability, Brentano sang his tunes for this anonymous friend, who then harmonized and transcribed them. Examples 1, 2, and 3 give some impression of the rudimentary character of these songs.

Most of the pieces for *Viktoria* have a sprightly rhythmic vigor in keeping with the martial tenor and militaristic spirit of the play. However, except for traces of an elementary A-B-A song-form in the "Singweise zum wohlriechenden Franziskerl," these melodies are de-

---

[46] Reinhold Steig, "Schäfers Klagelied von Goethe," *Euphorion*, 2 (1895): 814.

[47] *Viktoria und ihre Geschwister* (Berlin: Mauersche Buchhandlung, 1817), three pages of musical supplement.

[48] *Liederbuch für deutsche Künstler*, ed. Franz Kugler and Robert Reinick (Berlin: Vereins-Buchhandlung, 1833), p. 201.

[49] Brentano, *Viktoria*, p. xv. A remark of Hedwig von Staegemann's (a member of the Berlin group to which Brentano read aloud selections from this work) supports the contention that the melodies for *Viktoria* were actually composed by the poet. "He composed," she writes, "several marvellous melodies himself and sang selections from them to us." This quotation is taken from a letter of Hedwig von Staegemann's quoted by Hubert Schiel in his study *Clemens Brentano und Luise Hensel: Mit bisher ungedruckten Briefen* (Aschaffenburg: Paul Pattloch, 1956), p. 16.

Example 1

Example 2

Example 3

void of standard structural features of the "Lied" or of genuine musical development. The lyric flow of the "Lied beim Scharpiezupfen," however, is lilting and not too much disrupted by certain awkward details (such as the division of "zo-gen" in the fifth and sixth measures) or even by more "serious" compositional flaws (the fact that the song concludes in the dominant instead of the tonic key). The charming melodic strain at the outset of "Theodor Körner an Viktoria," on the other hand, is hardly in accord with the abrupt manner in which the song comes to a close.

These selections from Brentano's original melodies have been presented in order to indicate that this poet may have possessed the gift for tuneful inventiveness to a limited degree, but he did not—at least not with reference to the available scores—expand or develop his "singable ideas" beyond the confines of a few phrases. The same may be said with regard to the melody that appears under his name in the above-mentioned *Liederbuch für deutsche Künstler* (see Example 4).

Example 4

When one examines this tune for such criteria as thematic development or rhythmic subtlety, the evidence at hand supports Pfeiffer-Belli's contention that Brentano was, in the final analysis, no musician, no "initiate of music." The latter shortcoming comes blatantly to the fore with reference to Brentano's efforts in the field of music criticism. In view of his dearth of training and his antianalytical bias, one must regard Brentano's excursion into this territory as an act either of daring enterprise or of sheer foolhardiness.

For the most part, Brentano's comments on musical performances are restricted to amateurs rather than professionals; likewise, his mode

of expression is geared more toward the lay audience than the professional critic or the connoisseur. Usually, his critiques are liberally
spiced with colorful asides and clever anecdotes. For example, he describes a concert which he heard in Schönbeck (1797) to his sister,
Sophie, as follows: "They also play the piano, to be sure, but pure
hodge-podge, and they sing, but like genuine cheese-thread; it sounds,
on the whole, as if they were fiddling on their shin-bones with strands
of hair" (U 69). In a similar vein, he writes concerning Bettina's singing
on the occasion of Tieck's visit to Heidelberg in 1806:

> She sang to him so wonderfully well, the wild beat of her soul, no
> *aria brillante* as she had formerly sung. . . . With regard to her singing,
> that is, her extemporaneous performance . . . he [Tieck] assured us,
> that because of her, he, the church musician, now felt for the first time
> that his conception of music had been expanded . . . that he now knew
> how music had originated. But she also sang in a manner that we have
> never heard from her before! (S I 334).

The majority of critical judgments pronounced by Brentano on
serious composers and their works is based essentially on extrinsic
factors rather than intrinsic criteria. For instance, his remarks on the
works of Johann Friedrich Reichardt (1752–1814), one of the most
celebrated musicians of the period, illustrate this contention and must
be examined *cum grano salis* and, above all, in conjunction with Brentano's attitude toward the personality of the composer.[50] During the
years 1804–1810 Reichardt not only set several of the *Wunderhorn*
songs and a number of Brentano's lyric poems to music, but he also
composed the musical score for the latter's two cantatas (the first in
commemoration of the death of Queen Luise of Prussia in 1810, the
second celebrating the dedication of the University of Berlin in the
same year). Whereas Brentano admits in a letter of 1805 to Arnim that
Reichardt's setting for the song "Die Rose" is "quite nicely composed"
(S I 273), he immediately qualifies this laudatory comment with the
following reservation:

> Reichardt's style is not my favorite: In his simplicity there is too much
> consciousness, in his inventiveness too much that is well known, in his
> innocence too much purpose, and in all his songs he vacillates between
> the folk idiom and the opera, such that his taste is—enough, I can't

[50] For a detailed analysis of Brentano's approach to musical criticism, see
my article "Clemens Brentano on Music and Musicians," *Studies in Romanticism*,
7 (1968): 220–223.

say it. His best song is still "Kennst du das Land," because it actually can't be composed any differently. (S I 273)

In this critique Brentano inadvertently and indirectly confesses more than he realizes and praises more than he intends. The phrase "enough, I can't say it" reveals a kind of helplessness on the part of the poet when he is confronted with the task of articulating the essentials of musical style. The complex question whether this inability to verbalize those specific features of Reichardt's music which result in a negative value judgment stems from the ineffable nature of the object (the ultimate mystery surrounding the art of music) or from the deficient knowledge on the part of the analyzing subject, seems, in the case of this simple song, to be resolved in favor of the latter alternative. On the other hand, the observation concerning Reichardt's setting of Goethe's poem could also be construed as the highest compliment; one simply could not have done it otherwise. However, a few lines later in the same letter Brentano, with tongue in cheek, proposes a method whereby Reichardt might improve his technique: "Ask Reichardt if he doesn't sometimes accept music from strangers too; if so, I would send him some of my songs" (S I 273–274). This quip, in turn, is followed by the hope that the same composer might collaborate with them on their "inexpensive book of folk songs" (S I 274), an indication that Reichardt was to share in what would become a joint undertaking of the first magnitude—*Des Knaben Wunderhorn*.

Judging from the foregoing remarks on Reichardt's music, one would surmise that Brentano viewed the composer's efforts with mixed emotions—at least during the early years of their acquaintanceship. What eventually transformed this ambivalence into manifest distaste was not so much the music as the man. When the paths of the two artists crossed in Kassel in 1807, Brentano let it be known that he resented Reichardt's vanity and garrulity—for which attribute he devised the double-edged phrase "Die gänzliche Inkurabilität seines Musikantendurchfalls" (S I 350).

The incurability may refer to either of the two meanings of "Durchfall": "failure" (in the aesthetic sense as an artist) or "diarrhoea" (Reichardt's overindulgence in idle chatter was "medically" speaking irremediable). Not only the composer's predilection for gossip, but also his failure to judge human nature—that of his superiors and his fellow artists, and his own—aroused Brentano's ire:

I don't have any illusions at all about a person such as Reichardt. Particularly in his constitution he exhibits something that distresses me; he certainly cannot judge others at all, yet he's still very peremptory. . . . He thinks he is making himself agreeable, but everywhere he makes himself repulsive. . . . He is often apt to tell how this person or that has treated him with benevolent deference, while that very person is whispering behind his back just how disagreeable he finds him . . . his music I feel is more wearisome and vacuous each day—just yesterday he even accused Beethoven of insanity.[51]

Undoubtedly there is a dash of envy contained in Brentano's cutting comments. The pomp and ceremony with which Reichardt paraded about and performed at court grated on the nerves of the poet (in whom contemporaries detected similar proclivities) and elicited invectives such as the following addressed to Arnim:

You will not be able to imagine what he [Reichardt] is *en wix*; he's incessantly at court, procures the masks for the queen, composes dances, she performs them for me, I don't like them, he derives pleasure from how much she is said to have liked them, he drills the royal family in the dances, they dance to them as well as can be expected. The next day Lepel tells Jordis that his dances were utter failures. In general, he has the misfortune of being led astray by his own supposed charm and social success, when he has actually achieved just the opposite. (S I 353–354)

A very characteristic trait of Brentano's musical criticism becomes evident in these excerpts: the habit of mingling praise and condemnation in such a way that a kind of evaluative stalemate results. Thus, when lauding Reichardt's talents in one area (such as his conducting: "He danced the chaps neatly into the passage; it was absolutely heart-gripping the way he flew into passion and set everything into action")[52] or discussing the composer's works, Brentano invariably appends a derogatory coda to his remarks. On other occasions, he reverses this procedure by first creating a negative impression and then interspersing, almost parenthetically, positive asides: "Reichardt . . . has set to music my cantata to the queen, already sung and snorted it for me; on the whole it will have a great effect, even if some of it is unbelievably wretched and other parts of it quite well done, though not at all as I had conceived it" (S II 59).

[51] Steig, *Achim von Arnim*, p. 233.
[52] Ibid, p. 232.

Another prominent feature of Brentano's approach to Reichardt's music is the tendency to revoke earlier value judgments, to take back previous pronouncements (especially favorable ones). Note, for instance, the depreciatory overtones in the remark to Arnim concerning Reichardt's arrangement of Mignon's song, which he had once praised enthusiastically: "But to me the most ridiculous composers are those who compose your songs and don't care to; these are the type of composers that write the notation on songs: Mignons Sehnsucht by Goethe and Reichardt, and that repulses me" (S I 358). The extent to which extramusical factors distorted Brentano's assessment of Reichardt's music can be illustrated by examining the former's critique of the opera *Das blaue Ungeheuer*. The composer is chided for bungling Gozzi's libretto and transforming a brutal tyrant into a theater buffoon. This blunder in the adaptation of the text convinces Brentano that Reichardt's works will never attain the "romantic" ideal espoused by his contemporaries:

> Granted, his light music is pleasing enough and he is not without talent, as his musical plays prove, but he lacks a sense for the romantic. Indeed, I feel that his views on poetry already indicate that his music does not take, and will not take, the new romantic step in art. He has only touched upon it in a few melodies, which he will perpetually repeat, whereas Mozart, Paer, Winter have done it, albeit with inferior models, without really knowing it. (S I 360)

Whereas one may pardon Brentano for his ambiguity with regard to the term "romantic" or overlook his generous appraisal of Paer (a verdict which, incidentally, he would also rescind later) and Winter, one cannot subscribe to his contention that Reichardt's music would never attain comparable stature because of the composer's dramatic shortcomings. Even though Brentano was correct in his estimation of Reichardt's mediocrity and, at the same time, proved to be clairvoyant in recognizing Beethoven's significance for the history of music, he was, in the final analysis, right for the wrong reasons. He regarded Reichardt's works with jaundiced eye because he could not tolerate the man and his behind-the-scene chicaneries; he extolled Beethoven's music because of the composer's valiant struggle against just such devious machinations. It is, therefore, no mere coincidence that, according to Brentano, Reichardt's opinion of Beethoven ("just yesterday he accused Beethoven of insanity") is shared by that brand of individual against whom the poet and his Romantic contemporaries waged perpetual warfare: the philistine. "The philistines," he was to note later, "have a feeling only for music that is insipid, frivolous, or stiff-as-a-board; they consider Beethoven to be completely insane" (W II 998).

To be sure, the passages cited above as examples of Brentano's mode of musical criticism do not necessarily fall into this category, since they are opinions gleaned from his correspondence and thus are intended for private not public consumption. However, the basic approach manifested in his letters persisted later during his brief tenure (1815) as music critic for the *Spenersche Zeitung* in Berlin. His commentaries tend to analyze music not qua music, but rather in connection with some nonmusical or extramusical factors (the personality of the composer, the literary qualities of the operatic libretto, and so forth).[53] Consequently, Beethoven is praised for composing music that transcends the intrigues contrived by the hostile factions to sabotage his opera (*Fidelio*), while Paer is chided for conforming to the exigencies of the moment and catering to the whims of the prima donna. Throughout Brentano's reviews one encounters again and again a fundamental inability to articulate the essential features of musical style and structure. Instead of coming to grips with the music in concrete terms, Brentano skirts the periphery of genuine criticism and concentrates on interesting but basically superfluous factors, sometimes in clever, sometimes in cumbersome fashion.

The evasive tactics employed by Brentano when he endeavors to pinpoint exactly what aspects of a given composition appeal to his aesthetic sensibility, or what, conversely, disturbs his sense of artistic taste, may simply be a manifestation of that widespread dilemma confronting his entire generation. The paradox can be formulated as follows: If music represents the apex of the arts, if it makes the ultimate statement (as is claimed by Tieck, Wackenroder, Novalis, E. T. A. Hoffmann, and others), how could poetry, whose medium—language—ranked so much lower on the artistic hierarchy of expression because of its inescapable ties with the tangible, "real" world, ever presume to compete with pure, tonal articulations? Brentano's reticence, on the other hand, may stem from the fear of revealing to a knowledgeable audience his basic ignorance about the subject on which he was commenting. The following "confession," attributed to Brentano and found in manuscript form among his posthumous papers under the

[53] Fetzer, "Clemens Brentano on Music and Musicians," pp. 224–229.

heading "Various Thoughts at Operas. By someone who knows nothing, as they say, about music" (W II 1230), dovetails both possibilities
outlined above:

> When I say that I know nothing about music and yet think all sorts
> of things when hearing operas, then I mean that I certainly know the
> tones and what is intended when they proceed in this manner or that;
> I know them like the countenance of a man or of any creature agitated
> or at peace. But I don't know them as the countenance of frozen masks
> which have an accepted, statutory, and fixed meaning in a traditional
> arabesque order, which the composer usually employs in such a man-
> ner as all before him, because it appears just as difficult to him not to
> find a particular style of clothing lovely as it is impossible to be able to
> find naked man himself lovely. Of the arts, music is the freest, and
> therefore the attempts to bind it and to bring it before the senses are
> more brutal than in any other art. (W II 1230)

The contrasting pair "countenance of man" and "countenance of froz-
en masks" are clearly metaphors for two distinct approaches to the art
of music. The first implies an empathic, the second an analytic attitude.
One might paraphrase the respective positions as sympathetic versus
didactic, emotional as opposed to rational, amateur (in the best sense
of the term) in contradistinction to professional. Whatever dichotomous
pairs one selects to characterize these divergent viewpoints, it is obvious
from the foregoing evidence that Brentano's allegiance would lie in
the realm of empathy and emotionalism. Doubtlessly, this critical stance
results as much from his innate attitude toward artistic analysis in
general as from his ineptitude toward music in particular. Furthermore,
it should be noted that the musical genres which he prefers to treat—
the song, the opera, and program music—all have strong affiliations
with literature. Brentano's observations on absolute music, on the other
hand, are both rare and inconsequential.[54]

   Included in the above essay on opera are the following rhetorical
questions posed in chiasmatic form: "Is a musician conceivable who is
no poet? Is a poet conceivable who is no musician?" (W II 1230). Although the first of these queries is only of marginal relevance for this
study, the second is quite germane to those issues raised throughout
the preceding discussion. Whereas the writer of these random thoughts
on opera might have had in mind the same form of dual talent found
in the medieval minnesinger (who supplied both text and melody—

[54] Ibid, p. 224.

"wort unde wîse"), in contemporary poet-musicians such as Hölderlin, Jean Paul, E. T. A. Hoffmann, and Franz Grillparzer, or in later composer-authors (Wagner, Nietzsche), he may also be alluding to a unique breed of verbal musician or an unusual brand of literary "musicality." Since the figure of the Greek singer-poet Orpheus serves as a kind of mythical archetype for this form of musico-poetic creativity, the following chapters will examine Brentano's affiliations with this most illustrious predecessor.

2. Orpheus-Brentano: The Crisis of Conscience

THE first chapter of this investigation compared Brentano—albeit obliquely—with the mythological Proteus insofar as the conflicting and often contradictory profiles of the poet that have emerged during the last century and a half for a variety of reasons (editorial censorship, religious prejudice, lack of proper documentation, and so forth) leave the reader with the impression that there were perhaps many "Brentanos" hiding behind a variety of masks. One manifestation of this confusing situation was illustrated with reference to the poet's relationship to music, for whereas some commentators ranked his musicianship quite highly, others felt him to be a rank amateur in the field. A closer examination of Brentano's extant compositions and his musical criticism led to the conclusion that he did not progress beyond the stage of the dilettante in those areas requiring technical knowledge and training. On the other hand, he perpetuated the practice—inaugurated by Tieck, Wackenroder, and Novalis—of employing musical analogy and imagery to express certain existential situations and aesthetic conditions for which no other mode of articulation was deemed adequate. Brentano's critics followed in his footsteps by drawing upon musical metaphor and simile to characterize both his life and his works. The end product of this predilection was, unfortunately, a blurring rather than a clarifying of perspective, and the growing suspicion that recourse to "musicality" often proved to be a convenient scapegoat, a bit of hollow verbiage full of "sound and fury," signifying nothing of value.

The second chapter of this study brings Brentano into contact with a major mythical figure from Greek lore: the Thracian singer-poet Orpheus. In this instance, the affinity is much more deep-seated, extending from biographical details to basic artistic convictions. Before drawing these parallels, however, it would be helpful to summarize briefly those phases of the Orpheus legend which will later be applied to Brentano's career and creativity. The following synopsis of the myth is based on several divergent—and sometimes conflicting—sources.[1]

The crux of the Orpheus legend is the episode involving his descent into the underworld in order to win back his beloved, Eurydice, after her death from the bite of a serpent. Orpheus hopes to placate the guardian of the realm of shades through his powerful and persuasive song. His tones so charm the goddess Persephone that she consents to Eurydice's return to the upper realm on condition that Orpheus precede her on the journey and not look back. Because of either a lack of confidence in the efficacy of his song, or impatience, or doubts concerning Eurydice's fidelity, the singer, on the brink of success, does turn around, and this single glance causes him to forfeit forever that prize which his lilting melodies had wrested from the realm of death. The remainder of Orpheus' life is spent in mourning his lost beloved and in founding a religious cult, which incorporates elements of Apollonian ritual and Dionysian rite.

The details of Orpheus' death are shrouded in mystery: according to some versions of the myth, he was torn apart by the maenads in a bacchanalian orgy at the instigation of Dionysus, who had been vexed by the singer-priest's stubborn adherence to the rival deity, Apollo.[2] In other accounts, the reason for the slaughter of Orpheus by the bacchantes was his disdain for all women after Eurydice's banishment to the nether region.[3] The final incidents in the career of the Thracian bard indicate that after his scattered limbs had been buried by the Muses, his severed head, having been cast into the Hebrus river, floated—still singing in harmony with the tones of his lyre—to the isle of Lesbos, where an oracle was established in his memory and whence there descended a long line of lyric poetesses. Ultimately, Orpheus' lyre was borne up to heaven, where it was transformed into

[1] The account of the Orpheus legend presented in this chapter is based on a composite from five sources: Paulys *Realencyclopädie der classischen Altertumswissenschaft*, ed. Georg Wissowá, XVIII: 1 (Stuttgart: J. B. Metzler, 1939), column 1200–1316. Oskar Seyffert, *Dictionary of Classical Antiquities*, ed. Henry Nettleship and J. E. Sandys, 3rd. ed. (1894; reprinted, Cleveland: Meridian, 1961), p. 438. *Encyclopedia Britannica*, XVI (Chicago: William Benton, 1971), 1116–1117. Padraic Colum, *Orpheus: Myths of the World* (New York: Macmillan, 1930), pp. 80–83. W. K. C. Guthrie, *Orpheus and Greek Religion*, 2nd. ed. (London: Methuen, 1952), pp. 25–68.

[2] For an interesting interpretation of this phase of the Orpheus myth and its application to literature, see Ihab Hassan, *The Dismemberment of Orpheus* (New York: Oxford University Press, 1971). "Prelude: Lyre without Strings," pp. 3–23.

[3] Guthrie, pp. 49–50.

a constellation, thereby perpetuating his memory as part of the music of the spheres.

To this skeletal outline of the feats and fate of Orpheus one must add certain significant details: the fabled power of his lyre's tones to move trees and rocks, to tame wild beasts and calm the raging sea, to cure the sick and induce a state of beneficial sleep. In his *Tragische Literaturgeschichte*, Walter Muschg makes some penetrating observations concerning Orpheus' later life:

> He returns to earth with his mission unfulfilled, and it is precisely this failure that becomes the cause of his poetic renown. The terrible "almost" of his victory over death, the realization of his guilt, the despair about his failure make him into what he meant to the Greeks. For only now did the classical version of his legend begin. The song of the guilt-ridden and despairing wanderer acquired something universally moving, something that men had never been conscious of before. . . . The futile journey into the realm of the dead is Orpheus' poetic initiation. . . . Everything responds to his anguish, everything moves according to his will, he is as omnipotent as God, but not in reality, just in song.[4]

In addition to the aforementioned accomplishments recorded in Greek and Roman sources, Orpheus, as the son of the Muse of epic song Calliope and the river-god Oiagros (in some instances he is the offspring of Apollo), is also remembered for his role as the singer who rescued the Argonauts from the lure of the sirens by outdoing them in song.[5]

Certain significant alterations were made in the original conception of the Orpheus myth when it was revived during the postclassical Christian era, especially in the period from the Renaissance to the age of Romanticism. Walther Rehm summarizes these changes as follows:

> However, the fact that Orpheus, during the post-Christian era, enters immediately and unhesitatingly into inner confrontation with Christ, the "verus Orpheus," intensifies his symbolic power and his unique aura, but at the same time places particularly grave burdens upon him. The poet as redeemer, as the other redeemer: basically the Orpheus symbol *post Christum natum* claims no more than this.[6]

[4] *Tragische Literaturgeschichte*, 2nd. ed. (Bern: Francke, 1953), p. 31.
[5] Seyffert, p. 438.
[6] Walther Rehm, *Orpheus: Der Dichter und die Toten* (Dusseldorf: L. Schwann, 1950), p. 10.

Just as Orpheus ... himself is considered a *sacer interpres deorum*, now [1800] the poets become renewers, interpreters, and expounders of his pensive manner, of the figure of the "sublime god of primordial song," and thereby interpreters and expounders of their own selves.[7]

Even though Rehm's book does not treat Brentano in detail, the above quotations touch upon two fundamental areas of concern in which this poet became embroiled and which, owing to his inability to extricate himself from the situation, constitute the "crisis of consciousness" in his life. The first of these problem areas centers around the clash of the Graeco-Roman tradition with the Judaeo-Christian heritage (in Rehm's terms: "the poet as redeemer" and "the other redeemer"). The second aspect is expressed by the phrase "interpreters and expounders of their own selves" and entails the excessive preoccupation of the artist with the nature of his own person and that of his artistic medium. In conjunction with this latter phase of the problem Rehm cites Kierkegaard's polemic against the poet for aestheticizing his suffering instead of enduring it in all its existential anguish: "For it no doubt signifies a crisis when poets and their poetry after 1800 become, under the symbol of Orpheus, their own theme, their own problem."[8] The manner in which Brentano treats this "crisis" situation in a series of variations on the Orpheus theme and the extent to which he develops motifs associated with the singing and suffering of his Greek prototype will provide the framework for the succeeding chapters.

Variations on Orphean Figures

The interrelationship of music (or art), love, and death (the constellation "Melos-Eros-Thanatos") forms the nucleus or nexus of the Orphean legend, just as it was the central concern of Brentano's life. In the empiric sphere, for instance, one might show that Brentano "lost" his Eurydice (Sophie Mereau) during the period of their estrangement (1800–1803) only to win her back after much soul searching and a "descent" to the depths of his own heart. Although Sophie, in true Eurydicean fashion, followed him to and beyond the threshold of a new life, Brentano's nagging suspicions and persistent cross-question-

[7] Rehm, pp. 9–10.
[8] Rehm, p. 11. The most recent account of Kierkegaard's views on Romanticism can be found in Gerhard vom Hofe, *Die Romantikkritik Sören Kierkegaards* (Frankfurt am Main: Athenäum, 1972).

ing during their hectic marriage (1803–1806) contributed as much to her eventual demise as did the rigors of childbirth, which actually put an end to her physical existence.

On a more figurative level, one could trace a similar ambivalent destiny with regard to another "beloved" in Brentano's life: poetry itself. After having acquired renown as a lyric singer of no mean skill (1797–1803), Brentano experienced an eclipse of his poetic genius during the years of marriage with Sophie when what he termed their mutual suicide ("we are killing each other in our vain attempt to be man and wife" [S I 245]) extinguished the creative spark in his soul. Then, after actually losing Sophie Mereau, Brentano plunged into a veritable underworld—the hell he entered following his precipitous union with the "After Circe"[9] Auguste Bußmann in 1807—only to undergo, as a result of his mental and spiritual torment, a revival of his lyric powers. However, when the poet, on the threshold of a new life in 1817, "looked back" to survey his accomplishments during the preceding decade, his probing glance resulted in the discreditation of art and the denunciation of the artist. An intensive analysis of the aesthetics of poetry and the ethics of the poet led to the rejection of both. Thus Brentano's "crisis of conscience" at this point would have won Kierkegaard's stamp of approval, since it was experienced intensely on the "existential" plane. On the other hand, Brentano also succeeded in incorporating elements of this probing introspection and meticulous scrutinization of his art into a poetic mold which occasionally resulted in his writing most eloquently about the futility of writing and the impropriety of this craft.[10]

Even though the course of Brentano's life has certain parallels with the career of Orpheus, he makes very few direct allusions to his illustrious prototype in his works and correspondence. The majority of references to Orpheus are, for the most part, incidental and parenthetical. For example, Brentano notes in his *Erklärung der Sinnbilder auf dem Umschlage dieser Zeitschrift* (1812) (the periodical is *Hesperus*): "Behind the genius rests the lyre of Orpheus; he tamed the animals

---

[9] Whereas the implication of the name "Circe" in this composite as a sorceress who transforms men into beasts is clear, the force of "After" in German is manifold and ambiguous. Invariably derogatory in tone, this prefix can mean anything ranging from "late," "false," "pseudo," or "semi" to "posterior" and "waste matter."

[10] For a recent interpretation of this central problem in both Brentano's life and works, see Wolfgang Frühwald, "Clemens Brentano," in *Deutsche Dichter der Romantik*, ed. Benno von Wiese (Berlin: Erich Schmidt, 1971), pp. 294–295.

with the power of his tones, he molded men, he made stones fly together into walls, the woods followed him and the fountains ceased to
flow in order to listen to his formative melodies" (W II 1050). This
brief account is notable for two reasons: the attributing to Orpheus of
feats not normally ascribed to him, and the omission of any reference
to the Eurydice episode. According to most sources. Amphion and not
Orpheus caused the stones destined for the walls of Thebes to fly into
place through the power of music.[11] Whereas it is a common literary
phenomenon to attribute to a single, dominant figure deeds that originally were credited to lesser known individuals (as, for instance, the
bulk of lore and legend that coalesced around Doctor Faustus in the
sixteenth century), the deliberate avoidance of Eurydice in the above
passage is more difficult to explain. Biographical factors, however, may
have played a role here, since Brentano had just obtained a divorce
decree from Auguste Bußmann after considerable legal wrangling
(1811). Consequently, he may not have been too intent about winning
back his erstwhile Eurydice through song. In fact, as he indicated in
the autobiographical allegory in the "Prologue" to *Die Gründung Prags*
(1812), it was only through the intercession of another legendary
singer of the past that he had been able to escape from Auguste's
clutches: "Und lieh Arion mir zur Flucht Delphinen, / Der After-
Circe Spielen nicht zu dienen" (W IV 547).[12] Aside from this brief
account of Orpheus and a number of passing allusions to his singing,
there are only two occasions in Brentano's work when this figure appears in a context of more than peripheral significance. The first of
these comes in the early novel *Godwi oder Das steinerne Bild der Mutter* (1801); the second occurs in a letter of 1839 to the painter Eduard
von Steinle.

Although the elegy "An Clemens Brentano," which concludes
the second volume of *Godwi*, was allegedly written by August Winkelmann rather than by Brentano himself (W II 1187) and is generally
regarded as being of inferior aesthetic quality, its inclusion in the novel
as a final tribute to the now deceased "author" Maria (Brentano's
pseudonym) makes it a focal point of interest and underscores its thematic importance. This apostrophe urges Brentano to carry on Maria's
work, to take up the cause of youth and love, and as the now departed

---

[11] Seyffert, p. 28.

[12] "Arion lent me dolphins to flee away / That I not serve the whim of the
Circean creature."

champion of art had done, to rescue the poetry of life from the restrictive shackles imposed upon it by a pedestrian society:

> Schon ergreifst du die Leier, zu rächen, zu retten die Liebe,
> Und ein neues Geschlecht dankt dir den freien Genuß.
> Wie du hinunter jetzt steigst in das Dunkel des irrenden Lebens,
> In die Tiefe der Brust kehrst du begeistert zurück,
> Dort die verlorne Jugend umringt von Schatten zu finden,
> Kühn bezwingend den Tod führst du die Dichtung zurück.
> Also zum Orkus hinab stieg einst der thrazische Orpheus,
> Suchte, die er geliebt, fand sie dem Tode vertraut,
> Aber die göttliche Leier bezwang des Tartarus Mächte,
> Seinem Gesange vermählt kehrt die Geliebte zurück.
> Ja, schon lächelt das Licht, doch an der Schwelle des Lebens
> Faßt ihn des Zweifels Gewalt, raubt ihm den schönen Besitz.
> Unglückseliger Mann! sie war dem Vertrauen gegeben,
> Was dir der Glaube gewährt, kann es der Zweifelnde sehn?
> Doch was fürchtetest du, dir nahe tötend der Zweifel
> Und dir mißlänge dein Werk, kühn zu gestalten den Schmerz?
> Dir bewahret die Liebe der Guten das schöne Vertrauen,
> Und der kindliche Sinn schützt dir das kindliche Glück.[13]

(W II 459)

Those familiar with the course of Brentano's later life cannot share
the optimism of this writer. Only too often "the forces of doubt"
took hold of him at the threshold of success and deprived him of his
most precious possessions: his "poetic existence" with Sophie on the
one hand, and his conviction of the validity and value of "poetry" on
the other. Winkelmann's choice of the term "Zweifel" (doubt) is
symbolically significant because of the etymological root of the German word in "zwei," or "two" (as in "Verzweiflung"—despair).[14] Al-

---

[13] "You grasp the lyre to avenge, to save all love, / And a new generation
thanks you for its free use. / As you now descend into the darkness of erring
life, / Inspired, you will return into the depth of your breast, / To find there lost
youth surrounded by shadows; / Boldly vanquishing death, you lead poetry back.
/ Likewise down to Orcus once descended the Thracian Orpheus, / Sought the
one he loved, found her promised to death, / But the divine lyre overcame the
powers of Tartarus; / Wedded to his song, the beloved returns. / Indeed, the
light begins to smile, yet on the threshold of life / The forces of doubt seize him,
rob him of his fair possession. / Miserable man! She was entrusted to faith, /
Whatever faith may grant you, can the doubter see it? / Yet what do you fear,
with doubt nearly destroying you, / That your work—to boldly depict pain—
should fail you? / The love of the good woman maintains that sweet trust for
you, / And the child-like mind protects your child-like bliss."

[14] Friedrich Kluge, *Etymologisches Wörterbuch der deutschen Sprache*, 19th
ed., ed. Walther Mitzka (Berlin: W. de Gruyter, 1963), p. 897.

though the writer may not necessarily have been thinking along these lines, the implication of duality and dichotomy clearly presents itself here. Brentano's "crisis of conscience" in each of these two realms—the erotic and the aesthetic—comes to the fore, as does his penchant for linking the two spheres. Woman as well as art occupied an intermediary and mediating position between the sensual and the spiritual, "between heaven and earth," as he later phrased it,[15] and both, therefore, had to maintain a delicate—and consequently precarious—balance between extremes so that the pendulum would not swing too far in either direction and distort. Too much spirituality would transcend human comprehension (as, for instance, can be seen in the figure of Otilie in Part I of the novel *Godwi*), while an overabundance of sensuality would be an offense to the reader's sensibility (the Countess in Part II of the same work). It is, however, precisely at this critical juncture—the balancing point, or, in terms of the Orpheus myth, the "threshold of life"—that Brentano falters, loses faith, and falls. In desperation, he "looks back" to see whether his companion is dutifully following him, or, in the aesthetic sphere, he "looks over his own shoulder," as it were, to make certain that his poetic endeavors are in accord with his austere, self-imposed restrictions. In both cases, the inevitable result was doubt and despair.

The second Orpheus quotation stems from a letter of 1839 and comments on the quality of the work produced under contrastive conditions: "A great musician and singer is not an Orpheus every day; on one occasion he composes and sings with freshness, gusto, and imagination, on another he harps to himself an old popular ditty as if it were heaven-sent from the Milky Way" (S II 370). Certainly these words could be applied to Brentano's own poetic production, which ranges in scope and quality from the sublime to the ridiculous. However, this passage does not stress the intrinsic ambivalence of art, the ultimate paradox that even the most perfect work, owing to its inherent nature, contains not only the fruits of the pure conception, but also the seeds of its own destruction. This congenital defect Brentano finds manifest even in the most "flawless" specimen; and whereas the mask of irony may have enabled him in his youth to cope with the situation, during his mature years he had recourse to denunciation and rejection.

[15] *Clemens Brentano: Briefe an Emilie Linder,* ed. Wolfgang Frühwald (Bad Homburg: Gehlen, 1969), p. 114. Henceforth: EL. See also GS VIII 330.

Between the chronological limits set by the above quotations (1801 and 1839 respectively) and the divergent range of artistic expression implied by the concepts of "divine lyre" and "street ballad," Brentano presented to his readers a host of poet-singers, who, although seldom compared with Orpheus explicitly, nevertheless share with him in varying degrees the magical power of music to transform or transcend the world, who experience the joys and sorrows of Melos-Eros-Thanatos in a variety of ways, and who undergo the "crisis of conscience" in different levels of intensity.

The least problematic of Brentano's Orphean performers are the protagonists of his fairy tales—both in the early fragments such as *Die Rose* (1800), where the minnesinger-knight, Margot, from the melodic land of Goren, performs (W II 481), and in the later "Rheinmärchen" in which Miller Radlauf holds his listeners spellbound with the music of his magical reed pipe. The lineage of Radlauf is reminiscent of that of Orpheus: as the son of a water sprite, Frau Lureley (who, in turn, is the offspring of Fantasy, and numbers among her siblings such musical figures as Harmony, Echo, and Rime), he readily acknowledges the influence which Father Rhine has exerted on his life and art:

> Mich aber lehrst du singen:
> Wenn dich mein Aug ersieht,
> Ein freudeselig Klingen
> Mir durch den Busen zieht;
>
> . . . .
>
> Ihr lieben Sterne, decket
> Mir meinen Vater zu,
> Bis mich die Sonne wecket,
> Bis dahin mahle du:
> Wirds gut, will ich dich preisen,
> Dann sing in höhern Weisen
> Ich dir ein Lied.[16]
>
> (W III 10)

The paternal ties of Radlauf with the Rhine River calls to mind Orpheus' lineage from the river-god Oiagros, while the linking of the

---

[16] "However, you teach me to sing; / Whenever my eye views you, / A joyful ringing / Moves through my bosom. / ... / Dear stars, cover up / My father, / Until the sun wakes me, / Til' then you / do the milling; / If it's done well, I will praise you, / Then I will sing in more exalted melodies / A song to you."

miller's song to the cosmic realm—the stars—and his promise of "more exalted melodies" later parallel the ascension of Orpheus' lyre to the firmament, where it functioned as a tonal component in the harmony of the spheres.

An even more familiar Orphean touch is the manner in which Radlauf rescues his future bride, Ameleya, from death (by drowning), only to lose her again. In this instance, the loss of the singer's beloved can be ascribed, not to any shortcomings on his part, but rather to the machinations of evil forces who also use Radlauf's instrument—a reed pipe—to wreak havoc. In a variation of the Pied Piper of Hamelin theme, Prince Mausohr induces the children of Mainz—including Radlauf's Ameleya—to dance to a watery grave in the Rhine. The terror in the hearts of his innocent victims at the insidious and yet irresistible power of these musical tones is captured, to a certain extent, by the lines in which they attempt to counteract this destructive force:

> Die Pfeife bläst du gar zu mild,
> Die Pfeife bläst du gar zu wild;
> Die Erde weicht, das Wasser schwillt
> Und uns mit Nacht die Augen füllt,
> Ach Pfeife! Pfeife! Pfeife![17]
>
> (W III 47)

In keeping with the happy-ending tradition of the fairy tale, however, the children of Mainz are ultimately restored to life, and Radlauf regains his bride. This sequence of events is marked by a significant change in instrumentation during the course of the narrative: the progression from Radlauf's hypnotic reed pipe to the tones of the harp. This shift in emphasis from the winds to the strings has important ramifications in the area of instrumental symbolism, a phase of Brentano's work to be discussed later. For the present, it will be sufficient to note that as the tragic rift which threatens to rend the fairy tale world asunder is repaired and poetic justice is restored, the irresistible melodies of the pipes decline in importance and eventually disappear.

The majority of Brentano's Orphean singers do not, however, share the good fortune of the fairy tale heroes. In the fragmentary story of 1801, *Der Sänger*, for example, we hear of the Eurydicean

---

[17] "You blow the fife too mildly, / You blow the fife too wildly; / The earth retracts, the water rises / And fills our eyes with night, / Alas, fife! fife! fife!"

destiny of the singer's beloved, Antonie, who was so constituted that the "pure image of her inner unity, of her grandeur and of her silent, unseen effect upon the world" became apparent "in the echo of her fleeting melody" (W II 484). Consequently, it is only through the lute melodies of the mysterious and restless singer (in whose embrace Antonie expired) that his beloved comes back to life—or better, that she really comes to life for the first time:

> There are faint, infinitely delicate songs that we do not hear when they leave the lips, but which must first, gripped by an echo, be spoken again, even as gold must be alloyed with other metals, and many things become well-known concepts to us only when clothed in symbols (W II 484). . . . Not until the faint song has died away and speaks to us from the other side is it formed for us; we once again give structure to the dissolution, and now we form the song that we sing and love, but it is always an elegy. (W II 485)

In a similar fashion the singer, through music and song, summons the spirit of his mother from her premature grave. The verses spoken by him as he embarks on a daring odyssey into the recesses of the past "on wings of song," so to speak, recall the situation of Orpheus as he emerged from his bold descent into the realm of Hades:

> Kann mir im Leben wieder Leben glühen,
> Kann Ruhe mir das krankende Gemüt
> Mit heiterm Sinn und Freudigkeit umziehen,
> So kehre ich und singe hier ein Lied,
> So werde hier an dieser ernsten Schwelle
> Die Aussicht in den frühen Tod mir helle.[18]
>   (W II 510)

The melancholy longing which characterizes the music of the singer as he straddles the borderline between life and death also pervades the singing of the harper, Werdo Senne, from the novel *Godwi* written at approximately the same time. The peculiar musical idiom of the latter's song stems from the fact that he simultaneously laments the demise of his beloved, Marie, and yet yearns for the peace of his own grave:

[18] "If life in life can glow for me again, / If peace can surround my sickened soul / With cheery feeling and with joyfulness, / Then I shall come and sing a song here, / Then here at this earnest threshold / Let the vision of her early death become clear to me."

Meiner Harfe Töne hallen
Sanfter durch die Felsen hier.
Aus der ewgen Ferne winken
Tröstend mir die Sterne zu.
Meine müden Augen sinken
Hin zur Erde, suchen Ruh.[19]

(W II 69)

The particular threshold on which Werdo Senne stands lies somewhere
between the transcendental (heavenly constellations hold the promise
of release from the burdens of life) and the terrestrial (his weary glance
falls upon the silent reminders of happier days):

Um die Harfe sind Kränze geschlungen,
Schwebte Lieb in der Saiten Klang:
Oft wohl hab ich mir einsam gesungen,
Und wenn einsam und still ich sang,
Rauschten die Saiten im tönenden Spiel,
Bis aus dem Kranze, vom Klange durchschüttert,
Und von der Klage der Liebe durchzittert,
Sinkend die Blume hernniederfiel.

.   .   .   .

Nie ertönt meine Stimme nun wieder,
Wenn nicht freundlich die Blüte winkt;
Ewig sterben und schweigen die Lieder,
Wenn die Blume mir nicht mehr sinkt.
Schon sind die meisten der holden entflohn;
Ach! wenn die Kränze die Harfe verlassen,
Dann will ich sterben; die Wangen erblassen,
Stumm ist die Lippe, verhallt der Ton.[20]

(W II 75)

At best, Werdo represents a passive Orpheus, a singer-poet who,
instead of taking the initiative and braving the bastions of death armed

---

[19] "The tones of my harp resound / More gently through the crags here.
/ From the distant eons the stars / Comfortingly wink at me. / My weary eyes
sink down / To earth, seeking peace."

[20] "Wreaths are slung about the harp, / Love soared in the sound of strings:
/ Indeed lonely have I often sung to myself, / And whenever I sang lonely and
silently, / The strings rustled with the resounding tune, / Til' from the wreath,
rocked by tone, / Made to tremble by love's complaint, / Sinking, the flower
tumbled down. / ... // Never again now shall my voice be heard, / If the blossom
does not cheerily nod; / Eternally shall the songs die and keep silent, / If the
flower sinks toward me no more. / Already most of the charming ones have
flown; / Alas! When the wreaths leave the harp, / Then I shall die; my cheeks
shall pale, / Mute become the lip, the tones die away."

solely with his powerful song, renounces singing completely and allows the forces of a higher order to make their decrees known through his instrument:

> Seufzer lispeln, Geisterhauch
> Rauschet bang durch meine Saiten,
> Horchend heb ich nun die Hand,
> Und es pochen, Trost im Leiden,
> Totenuhren in der Wand.[21]
>
>   (W II 70)

Werdo's reticence may be interpreted as a sign of utter frustration, as a hallmark of the modern counterpart of the Orphean singer; the former, unlike his spiritual progenitor, is no longer convinced of the efficacy—or even the propriety—of his artistic medium, especially when confronted with the most awesome of human encounters: death.

In contrast to the naïve confidence of the fairy tale singer, or to the passive resignation of performers such as Werdo Senne, stand the virtuosity and daring of two figures in Brentano's works who attain—on a different level—Orphean stature. The first of these is Michaly, the gypsy violinist from *Die mehreren Wehmüller und ungarischen Nationalgesichter* (1817), and the other is Rosadora, the "golden rose" maiden from the *Romanzen vom Rosenkranz*. Michaly, whose music provides a unifying motivic force linking the motley collection of novellas subsumed under the bizarre title, is one of the few performers in Brentano's works to be compared explicitly with Orpheus. His instrument, the violin, might be regarded as the modern representative of the string family tracing their lineage back to the Orphean lyre. Michaly's vivacious tones have the power to dispel the strife that develops among the heterogeneous groups of travelers from different nations as well as the squabbles that arise owing to the appearance of numerous doubles of the painter Wehmüller: "The gypsy seized his violin like a second Orpheus and . . . sang and played so movingly on his instrument that no one could resist and soon all grew quiet" (W II 673). The themes of Michaly's extemporaneous song are in keeping with the Orphean tradition: the lament for the death of a thousand gypsies and the plaintive tones of a bride for her fallen lover (W II 673–674). But not even the numerically imposing throng of victims

---

[21] "Sighs are murmuring, spirit-breath / Is swishing anxiously through my strings, / Listening, now, I raise my hand / And, comfort for sorrow, there are beating / Clocks of dead men in the wall."

nor the Melos-Eros-Thanatos complex can conceal the fact that Michaly's artistry is only a faint copy of that possessed by his fabled ancestor. By means of several deft touches throughout the tales, Brentano suggests that the Orphean charisma has become tarnished. For instance, at one point, the violinist, having been classified as a member of the "outlaw rabble" (W II 696), seizes his instrument in order to demonstrate his prowess, only to be silenced by the horn of the night watchman. Would Orpheus, one is tempted to ask, who competed note for note with the sirens, have been so easily intimidated? It is only when Michaly has been bolstered by the support of his sister, Mitidika, that some measure of his prestige is restored: "The charming creature (Mitidika) danced, beat the tambourine, and sang—and Michaly accompanied her—in such a wonderfully captivating fashion, that everyone was spellbound with astonishment" (W II 703).

Not only does Michaly's artistry stand in the shadow of his sister's talents, but it is also seriously challenged by the skill of another musician—Mores the Cat and his bagpipe. Since the entire plot of the Wehmüller cycle involves disguises, doubles, and other forms of identity concealment and confusion, one is not too surprised to discover that Michaly—essentially a figure from the "frame" narrative—has a musical competitor in the "framed" tales. Mores and his "musicalizing cat convention" (W II 674) are first introduced by the Croatian nobleman, a narrator whose pedestrian outlook on life is completely at odds with the bizarre subject of his story. The effect of such a unique amalgam of uninhibited fantasy and utilitarian calculation are already evident in the Croat's account of how he estimates the profit potential of the livestock on his estate:

> In summer I always have a kind of live winter wardrobe in my hunting grounds. Four pairs of stout leather breeches are always running about the place in the form of live billy-goats, and among them is a magnificent bagpipe which, even now as a live billy-goat, is displaying such musical talents that the candidates for the various trouser legs, the moment he comes bleating into their midst, begin dancing and keeping step with one another, as though they were already aware that they were destined one day to dance with my legs in Hungarian fashion to this same bagpipe.[22]

[22] This passage and the one following were translated by Jane B. Greene in *German Stories and Tales*, edited by Robert Pick (New York: Washington Square Press, 1954), pp. 214 and 216 respectively.

This passage not only serves as a comic postlude to Michaly's violin "Schariwari," which drove the girls from their beds to the inn and induced them to shout for joy and dance (W II 662), but it also functions as a prelude to Mores' diabolic nocturnal charivari:

> The whole tree was live with howling cats, and at the very top was enthroned my cat Mores, his back arched, playing in the most wretched fashion on a bagpipe, while the other cats, uttering bloodcurdling cries, were dancing about him in the branches.
>
> For a while I stood there transfixed with horror. But soon the sound of the bagpipe produced such a curious twitching in my legs that I too began to dance.... just then the church bell rang out through the starry night and I came to my senses. Seizing my rifle, I fired the entire load into the midst of the infamous dancing chorus.

As in the tales of the Rhine, the change in instrumentation from the strings (violin) to the winds (bagpipe) brings in its wake a radical shift in perspective. Any remnant of divine overtones that may have clung to Michaly's playing has been superceded by the diabolic undertone of Mores' art. And yet Brentano deliberately dilutes the malevolent potential of this satanical music. First of all, he labels the quality of this feline caterwauling "wretched"; second, the tolling of the church bells (suggestive of the world of Christianity) puts an abrupt end to such tomfoolery. Instead of experiencing a tragic death at the hands of enraged maenads, Mores is disposed of with a load of buckshot; his instrument, rather than ascending to the heavens and joining the music of the spheres, remains earthbound and becomes part of a prosaic gimmick with which to draw patrons to a local tavern. In its capacity as a wine container, this instrument gurgles perhaps its most mellifluous tones: "He brought it out; we placed the two pipes on our mouths and squeezed the full bag so gently to our hearts that the sweet wine flowed into our throats. Never has a bagpipe made such lovely music" (W II 683).

Brentano is not merely content with deflating the status of Michaly by contrasting his music with Mores' caterwauling both indirectly and directly (when Michaly later produces "such wild melodies on his violin," one member of the audience muses "whether Mores had not sounded this invitation to the dance" [W II 673]). Even Mores' performance undergoes a reduction—a virtual *reductio ad absurdum*—

when the chambermaid, a most delightful "Kammerkätzchen"[23] her-self, ponders whether or not she participated in the nocturnal cavort-ings (referred to as a "Teedansant" [W II 672]), and when the narrator of the suspense-filled tale of the accursed huntsman alludes to a do-mesticated kitten that suddenly assumes a menacing Mores-like pose and parodies the latter's music: "The cat . . . arched its back toward us, glared at us with fiery eyes and never stopped singing sol-fa" (W II 680).

In spite of Brentano's occasional debunking of the aura of mystery surrounding the playing of Mores, one must admit that in comparison with the latter's provocative bagpipe tones, Michaly's violin plays "second fiddle." The feline counterpart of the Orphean performer not only deprives Michaly of some of his luster, but at times threatens to usurp his musical prerogatives completely and become the focal point of interest. A similar situation prevails in the case of Brentano's most complex Orphean figure, the singer-dancer-harpist Rosadora from the unfinished cycle *Romanzen vom Rosenkranz* (1803–1812), a work which, although linked to the High Middle Ages by its chro-nology and setting, also incorporates musical concepts from the mytho-logical past and the fairy tale world, as well as the contemporary (that is, early nineteenth-century) scene.

Although each of the three "rose sisters" (Rosablanka, Rosarosa, Rosadora) in this symmetrically structured series of lyric-epic romances is musical, it is the "Golden Rose" (Rosadora, performing under the stage name "Biondette") who most closely resembles Orpheus and who shares his talents, his triumphs, and his tragedy. Since the gift of Orphean song has been transferred to the female artist, the part of the moribund beloved is played by a male figure: the university student Meliore. This interchange of roles reflects both Brentano's proclivity toward strong female characters in his works (for example, the Coun-tess in *Godwi*) and his tendency to play the passive partner to those women who dominated his life (such as Sophie Mereau).

The reader first learns indirectly of the overwhelming force of Rosadora-Biondette's music from the lips of Meliore when he declares that he no longer need attend the lectures of Apo (the necromancer and sometime professor) on "The might and wonder of tones" or

---

[23] A humorous designation in German for "chambermaid," the word literally means "house kitten."

"the art of the love-potion" (W I 669), since the "Golden Rose" has already introduced him to these miracles:

> Denn Meliore kennt die Wunder
> Harfenklanges und Gesanges.
>
> Denn es schlug die Liebeswunden
> Ihm Biondettens Wunderharfe,
> Die um Tanz und Sang und Tugend
> Man die heil'ge Sängrin nannte.[24]
>
> (W I 669)

This initial allusion to Biondette's artistry already touches upon both its profound and its problematical aspects. Walther Rehm had drawn attention to the conflict in postclassical times between Orpheus and Christ as the embodiment of mankind's redeemers on the terrestrial and transcendental planes respectively. Biondette, aware of the clash between the mundane and the divine aspects of music, seeks to resolve the conflict by renouncing the sphere of the profane—the aria of the opera—for the realm of the sacred—the "Gloria" of the convent. But the patterns of human destiny have become so complex and labyrinthine in the medieval-modern world which Brentano portrays in the *Romanzen* that such simplistic solutions are no longer possible.

It is evident from the lines cited above with reference to Meliore, for instance, that Biondette's "Wunderharfe" actually operates on two distinct but interdependent levels. The threads of secular life and religious devotion cannot be rent asunder, since they are inextricably interwoven in the fabric of existence. Meliore's language reflects his complex situation to the extent that the term "wounds of love," used to refer to the spiritual anguish he endures because of his contact with the "saintly songstress," could also be applied to the wounds inflicted upon the martyred Christ and the passion which the latter bore out of love for all mankind. Under such circumstances, love as both eros and caritas comes into play in this single concept. To this element of semantic ambiguity might be added ambivalence of plot. For instance, the cloister to be erected in memory of Rosarosa is envisioned by Biondette in a prophetic dream. This ecclesiastical structure, however, will rise on the very site where the songstress scored her greatest

---

[24] "For Meliore knows the wonders / Of harps set ringing and of singing. // For he was struck with the wounds of love / By Biondette's miraculous harp, / She, whom they called the holy singer / Because of her dance and song and virtue."

"worldly" triumphs: the now charred ruins of the opera house. The dilemma that ultimately confronts Biondette stems from the fact that a clear-cut line of demarcation can no longer be drawn between the hymns of the church and the fanfares of the theater. The two worlds, although ostensibly incompatible, are, nevertheless, inseparable. Life, as well as art, has become an immense oxymoron, marked by an uneasy but unavoidable coexistence of conflicting forces. Meliore inadvertently supplies the poetic formula for this paradox: "Der Gesang des süß'sten Mundes / War mir eine bunte Schlange" (W I 673).[25] A universe in which the sweetest song becomes a variegated serpent must indeed seem out of joint. The question remains: Is Biondette the artist to "set it right"?

The allusion to the "variegated serpent" in the above lines is also ambivalent. It not only evokes the biblical context in which the serpent functions as the embodiment of evil, the force of temptation, and the instigator of original sin, but also calls to mind the part played by the viper in the Orpheus legend as the force that terminated Eurydice's life and spurred the singer on to his most daring enterprise. Whereas Meliore's statement hints quite strongly that it may have been the songstress herself who fascinated him rather than the power of her music per se, a similar metaphoric complex used by Biondette with reference to her mentor and foster mother, Rosaläta (an errant nun who turned actress and who, in this capacity, performed under the name "Sirene"), stresses the same quality of serpentine sanctity as an innate attribute of song:

> Wenn um Mitternacht die Sterne
> Sinnend in dem Meere schwankten,
> Flocht mir durch den Traum Sirene
> Ihrer Lieder heil'ge Schlangen.[26]
>
> (W I 733)

The phrase "heil'ge Schlangen" suggests that song (and, by implication, all art) is destined by its very nature to function as a "sacred serpent," a force that can either elevate man to sublime spiritual heights or drag him down to the depths of depravity, depending upon a complex set of variables, some of which he might calculate, while others lie beyond the limits of his control.

---

[25] "The song of the sweetest mouth / Was as a variegated serpent to me."
[26] "Whenever the stars at midnight / Pensively swayed in the sea, / Sirene braided for me in a dream / Sacred serpents of her song."

The duality of art is, in the case of Rosadora-Biondette (whose twofold appellation reflects the dichotomy implicit in her nature and in her art), further complicated by a tripartite chronological overlay of historical-mythological referents. On the one hand, her musico-poetic feats link her with an illustrious triumvirate of Greek singers (Orpheus, Amphion, Arion), while, on the other, she is closely allied with one of the outstanding examples of song in the Judaeo-Christian tradition: "das Hohe Lied" (the Song of Songs). In addition, Brentano continually (and somewhat anachronistically) alludes to her role as a prima donna in the modern operatic world. These three strands of musical motifs—ancient Greek myth, Judaeo-Christian lore, and contemporary opera—do not run counter to one another nor are they depicted sequentially in the *Romanzen,* but rather are coincidental and reciprocal. The roots of Biondette's art coalesce in much the same manner as the reactions of her listeners, which derive from a combination of sensual delight and spiritual edification.

It was the awareness of this inevitable inextricability, the fusion of heterogeneous and often diametrically opposed traits in the aesthetic artifact, which induced Brentano to call into question the validity of the *Romanzen* when he was asked to consider their publication in 1826. On this occasion, he literally "protested too much," rejecting the romances as one of the "berouged, perfumed cosmetic sins of an unchristian youth" (GS IX 141) and devising such derogatory epithets for them as "the irksome potpourri" (GS IX 141) and "the moldy changeling of a melancholic glittering fantasy and a broken heart, pickled in tears, halfway between a bitter and a sweet orange or other similar fruits" (GS IX 141).[27] These harsh invectives were hurled at this work during the 1820s, a period when the author felt that he had found a secure haven from the vicissitudes of art in the stable confines of the church. The vehemence of his denunciation, however, leaves the impression that Brentano might actually be trying to convince himself that the step which he, like his heroine Biondette, had taken was indeed the proper one, that her renunciation of the opera in favor of the nunnery, and his rejection of self-centered secular poetry for edifying religious verse, had actually saved them from the deleterious effects of "the sacred serpents of song." Through this process of vehement con-

---

[27] For an interesting analysis of the German concept "moldy changeling" ("Wechselbalg") which occurs in this passage and its relationship to the problem of poetic fantasy, see Klaus Wille, *Die Signatur der Melancholie im Werk Clemens Brentanos* (Bern: Herbert Lang, 1970), p. 56.

demnation the author may have succeeded in erasing some of the doubts that plagued the Orphean singer, but he lost sight of the fact that one of the most appealing facets of the *Romanzen* was the very human quandary in which he had embroiled his heroine.

Biondette's Orphean dilemma comes to the fore at the outset of the work, when, for instance, Meliore describes the hypnotic effects of her evensong on nature's most exalted singers, the nightingales (W I 670). They are so enthralled with Biondette's singing, that they emulate it in their own fashion. Her performance in the theater achieves even more striking results, since the opera, as a kind of total work of art, or "Gesamtkunstwerk," makes the maximum appeal to the aesthetic faculties of the audience. Under the tutelage of "Sirene" Biondette had learned that the aim of art was to transfix the senses in order to transfigure the spirit:

> Und sie [Sirene] lehrt die junge Seele
> Sich erschwingen im Gesange,
> Und mit Engeln auf der Töne
> Himmelsleiter freudig tanzen.
>
> . . . .
>
> Alle Herzen sollen beben
> In dem Klange deiner Harfe!
> Bannen sollst du alle Seelen
> In die Kreise deines Tanzes!
>
> Mit der Künste heil'gem Zepter
> Schlage an das Herz der Sklaven,
> Die du in den Sinnen fesselst,
> Um im Geist sie zu entlassen![28]

(W I 734)

In order to illustrate the full scope of this artistic process, Biondette performs two contrasting operatic excerpts, both of which are derived from biblical sources (the first apocryphal, the second canonical): Judith's triumphant exit from the tent in which she has slain Holofernes, and the portrayal of Jephthah's daughter, who, in contrite obedience to paternal authority, submits herself to the sacrificial altar.

---

[28] "And she [Sirene] teaches the young fledgling / To soar upward while singing, / To join the notes of joyous angels / On the ladder of heaven dancing. // Every heart should now be quaking / With each resounding of your harp! / Every soul you should be charming / To the circles of your dance! // With art's sacred, mighty scepter / Strike upon the heart of slaves, / Whom you fetter in their senses / That their spirits may go free!"

Hubris on the part of the victor, humility on the side of the victim. The musical background for the respective tableaus not only captures the contrasting mood of the protagonists, but in addition illustrates Sirene's contention that art fetters the senses in order to free the spirit.

The Judith scene, for example, marshals every musical means available: a torrent of tones engulfs the listener and echoes the frenzy of the heroine. Judith initially appears "Tonumflutet vom Orchester" (W I 735),[29] and the musical crescendo grows in intensity: "es stieg hoch überschwellend / Melodie aus allen Schranken" (W I 735); "Jauchzend durcheinander wehten / Alle Töne" (W I 736).[30] In sharp contrast to this lush, almost Wagnerian orchestration (which is compared with a "wilden Flamme, / Die sich wieder selbst verzehrte" [W I 736])[31] stands the austere accompaniment for the scene depicting the plight of Jephthah's daughter. All we hear are the tones of Biondette's harp ("Als die zarten Finger beben / Durch der Saiten goldnen Garten" [W I 737])[32] and the pastoral melodies of shepherds' flutes. The self-consuming flame that characterized the previous selection has dwindled to a "heil'ge Opferflamme" (W I 737).[33] Finally, even the sotto voce sounds of the harp give way to complete silence, or perhaps one should say: to a more ethereal form of musical expression:

> Da der Wald im Glanze stehet,
> Schweigen rings die Flöten alle,
> Und ein Chor von Hörnern schwebet
> Klagend auf im Widerhalle.
>
> Und das Volk lauscht tief beweget,
> Denn die Sonne widerstrahlend
> Spielet, die nicht auszusprechen,
> Lieder durch die goldne Harfe.[34]
>   (W I 739)

Under such conditions, the prophecy of "Sirene" is fulfilled:

[29] "Inundated with tones from the orchestra."
[30] "It grew louder, ever louder / Its melody was uncontrolled." "All notes / Reverberated in exultant confusion."
[31] "Wild flame / That consumed itself again."
[32] "As the tender fingers quiver / Through the golden garden of strings."
[33] "Holy sacrificial flame."
[34] "As the forest stands in splendor, / The flutes are silent all around, / And a brass choir rises up, / Echoing its complaint. // The people listen, deeply moved, / For the sun's reflected light / Is playing songs that can't be spoken / Through the golden harp."

> Also waren alle Schmerzen
> In Biondettens Lied entschlafen,
> Scheiden kann sie von den Herzen,
> Die in Wunderträumen wandeln.[35]
>
> (W I 740)

However, Brentano's world view is too multifaceted to permit such unmitigated success. Misfortune intervenes in the form of a conflagration that breaks out in the theater. This event had been prepared for on the figurative level by the fire imagery used in conjunction with Biondette's performance of the tableaux depicting Judith and Jephthah's daughter. The actual instigator of the blaze is Biondette's uncle, the perverse scholar-philosopher-necromancer Apo; the roaring inferno reflects not only his illicit (and incestuous) passion for the songstress, but also serves as reminder of the ever-present danger posed by the sensual nature of man, a force that can thwart even the loftiest manifestation of art.

With the intervention of Apo in the world of Biondette's music through his henchman Moles, the Orphean aspects of her art become enmeshed with both the sublime and the satanical elements of Christian mythology. One indication of this development is the correlation of the figure of the Greek poet-singer Arion and his dolphins with the biblical motif of the spirit hovering over the waters (or perhaps with the New Testament scene of Christ walking on the storm-tossed waves). Note, for instance, the following lines portraying the effects of Biondette's playing on the theater audience:

> In den weißen Arm gelehnet
> Schimmerte die goldne Harfe.
>
> Schweigend glich das Volk dem Meere,
> Über dem ein Gott hinwandelt;
> Also ruht und wogt die Menge,
> In Biondettens Sang und Harfe.[36]
>
> (W I 729-730)

Following the conflagration in the theater the fear arises that Biondette may have perished in the flames. The possible loss of the songstress

[35] "Thus all pains were made to sleep / In the song of Biondette, / She can depart from those hearts / That walk in dreams of wonder."

[36] "Nestled in her snow-white arm / The golden harp was shimmering. / The people, in their silence, resembled the waters, / Upon which a god was walking; / Likewise reposed and swayed the thousands / To Biondette's harp and singing."

and her music is mourned on the cosmic level by the constellations—until they catch sight of her gliding, Arion-like, across the waters of the sea:

> Und was schimmert dort so golden,
> Rauschend durch die Wasserbahnen,
> Zieht gleich einem Arione
> Ruhig durch die Meere, harfend?
>
> Heil! Es ist die schöne Tochter;
> . . . .
> Und die Sterne freudig horchen,
> Denn es zieht durch ihre Harfe
> Äolus mit süßem Tone,
> Daß die Ufer rings entschlafen:[37]
>
> (W I 836)

The resurrection of the Orphean singer restores—if only temporarily—the harmony of the universe. But again, Brentano has so manipulated the course of events that Biondette's physical deliverance is inevitably linked to her spiritual downfall. The reader has had a clear premonition of the path this development will take from Apo's instructions to Moles just prior to the latter's incendiary tactics in the theater:

> Bringe mir Biondetten ruhend
> In dem Schoße süßer Moose,
> Singend, von Gewürzen duftend,
> Wie das Lied des Salomone.[38]
>
> (W I 762)

The Song of Solomon (or Canticle of Canticles, as it is sometimes called) has proven to be one of the most controversial documents of Christian liturgy because of its precarious amalgamation of mystical longing, religious symbolism, and sensual love, set in a rich, musico-poetic idiom. Apo, of course, is primarily concerned with the sensuous elements (hence the stress on sweetness and fragrance).

The connecting link between the Orphean conquest of death and

[37] "And what is shimmering there so golden, / Rushing through the waterways, / Moving Arion-like and tranquil / Over the oceans, playing the harp? // Hail! It is the lovely daughter; / ... // And the stars, ecstatic, harken, / For there scatters from her harp / Sweet aeolian intonations, / That the shores about must sleep."

[38] "Bring me Biondette resting / In the lap of sweet moss, and singing, / Fragrant with the best of spices, / As the Song of Solomon."

the Christian Song of Songs is furnished by Meliore. When Apo casts aspersions on Biondette's moral character, Meliore counters these slurs by comparing her virtue with a sacred shrine, an impregnable citadel, which shall one day arise from the rubble of the charred ruins of the theater through the might of her music:

> Freudig auf die Pfeiler steigen;
> Hörst du, wie Biondette singt?
> Wie nach ihrer Harfe Reigen
> Stein auf Stein zum Himmel dringt?
>
> Wie nach ihren Melodeien
> Kuppel sich an Kuppel ringt,
> Und die Säule ihre Reihen
> Mit dem Palmenknauf verschlingt?
>
> Der Kapellen Einsamkeiten
> Ordnen sich in Harmonie;
> Wo die Töne sich durchschneiden,
> Wölbt des Chores Halle sie.
>
> Wo die Töne höher steigen,
> Heben sich die Türme spitz,
> Die zum Firmamente reichen
> Mit der Kreuze goldnem Blitz.[39]
>
> (W I 878)

A fusion of Greek legend and Christian lore is attempted by linking an Orpheus-Amphion motif with the construction of a Romanesque church or a Gothic cathedral. Musical architecture connects the world of ancient Greece with the universe of medieval Christendom.

The next stage in this process entails the incorporation of Solomon's "Hohes Lied" into Orpheus' conquest of Hades. In the context of Brentano's *Romanzen*, the dangers posed by a descent into the heathen underworld no longer stem from the perils of that nether region per se, but rather from the very means employed to vanquish the realm of death: the "Song of Songs" itself. Biondette intones her "Hohes Lied" in order to rescue Meliore, her beloved, from certain

---

[39] "Pillars rise with loud rejoicing; / Hear you Biondette's song? / How to the round of her harp / Stone on stone throngs to heaven? // How to her melodies / Dome joins with dome, / And the posts entwine their rows / With capital of palm? // The loneliness of chapels / Set themselves in harmony; / Where the notes traverse one another, / She arches the hall of the choir. // As the tones are higher sent, / There arise the pointed towers, / Reaching to heaven's firmament, / With golden flashes of the cross."

death. A poisoned wound inflicted by Apo threatens his life. However, because of Brentano's unique conception of this medieval world, the success of her venture would have had even more catastrophic results than her failure. Since Meliore is her half-brother (a fact that is unknown to Biondette), the danger of incest constantly lurks on the periphery of their relationship. The author assures us from the start of this episode, however, that her bold attempt to defy death is predestined to fail:

> Und die Harfe nimmt die Süße,
> Läßt die Saiten wild erbeben;
> Ach, die heißen Liebesgrüße
> Können nicht sein Aug' erheben!
>
> Keuscher Tod, du drückst sie nieder,
> Solche Raserei zu sehen,
> In dem Klang der gift'gen Lieder
> Soll er sie nicht wiedersehen.[40]
>
> (W I 888)

The metaphor of the 'variegated serpent" with which Meliore had previously characterized Biondette's singing, and the concept of the "sacred serpents" that Biondette herself once used to describe the essence of the songs she learned from "Sirene," are now subsumed under the designation "venomous songs." This is a subtle admonition that even the loftiest Orphean accomplishment can be disastrous in a world so constituted that brother and sister become unwillingly and inextricably involved in a dangerous liaison. Nevertheless, Brentano's subsequent portrayal of Biondette's daring venture almost belies his claim that the attempt to overcome "chaste death" was destined to failure from the beginning.

Just as Orpheus at the gates of the underworld sang to the guards and then to Hades and Persephone about his beloved Eurydice, so, too, does Biondette intone the praises of Meliore to the watchmen of the city of Bologna. All the lush sweetness and aromatic fragrance which Apo had anticipated enjoying from Biondette's "Song of Songs" ("von Gewürzen duftend," "süßer Moose") are lavished upon the expiring Meliore instead:

---

[40] "And the sweet one takes the harp, / As her strings cavort with sound; / Oh, the ardent greetings of love / Cannot lift up his eye! // Death, chaste death, you so depress her, / To have to see such wayward madness; / With the sound of venemous songs, / He shall not see her again."

Wie Gewürze duftend, grüßen
Seiner Wangen Blumenzellen,
Süße Myrtenöle gießen
Seiner Lippen Rosenquellen.

. . . .

Wie mein Saitenspiel, erklinget
Süß und lieblich seine Kehle,
Und zu seinen Lippen dringet
Lustberauschet meine Seele.

(W I 889)

. . . .

Und es tönet meine Stimme
Süß, o süß ist meine Kehle,
Bis wetteifernd süß ergrimme
Und verglimme Philomele.

Und ich singe zu dir nieder:
Mein bist du und mir gegeben,
Und es sehn dich meine Lieder
Unter Rosen weidend schweben![41]

(W I 891)

At this point, Biondette's impassioned plea reaches the pitch of a magical incantation. Yet the numerous repetitions of the adjective "süß" throughout these verses have an ambivalent and markedly ironic overtone. This situation culminates in the stanzas in which success seems to crown Biondette's efforts and to belie the author's promise:

Aber traurend sitzt die Süße,
Läßt die Harfe leis erbeben,
Daß ihn schön das Leben grüße,
Das die Liebe ihm gegeben.

Wie die Töne sich ergießen,
Fühlt die Jungfrau in dem Herzen
Wunderbaren Zauber fließen,
Und so süße, wilde Schmerzen.

Höher sie die Saiten schwinget,
Denket nicht mehr des Gesellen;

[41] "With the fragrance of spices, shine / The blossoms of his cheeks; / The rose wells of his lips / Pour out sweet myrtle oil. // As my harp song, there resounds / Sweet and lovely his voice, / And to his lips rushes / My soul, drunk with joy. // And my sound is heard, / Sweet, so sweet is my voice, / Until in sweet competition / Philomela would grow angry and die away. // And I sing down to you: / You are mine and given me, / And my songs will see you, / Hovering with delight in roses!"

Wie der Schwan im Tode singet,
Glühend ihre Töne schwellen.

Tausend Töne, die sonst schliefen,
Aus der Harfe lebend brechen,
Und in allen Herzenstiefen
Hört sie laut das Echo sprechen.

In dem Tode hallt es wider;
Schüchtern zu des Lebens Schwelle
Rufen ihn die Zauberlieder,
Seine Blicke werden helle.[42]

(W I 894)

The seductive force of Biondette's music stems from two sources:
the sensual (subsumed under "süß") and the magical (expressed by
"wunderbaren Zauber," "Zauberlieder"). The sweeter Biondette's melodies become, however, the more bitter will be the aftertaste. The
erstwhile "saintly songstress" and "pious dancer," who was prepared
to abandon the operatic footlights for the cloister cell, and the contrite
daughter of Jephthah have vanished; in their place stands an agitated
Judith, who has come not to slay her Holofernes, but to save him.
There are elements of the sorceress or "shaman" in her incantation.
The sounds that emanate from Biondette's lips and harp are totally
alien to her previous music ("Tausend Töne, die sonst schliefen"); the
singer is literally "beside herself"—stressed by the repetition of the
term "frenzy" (W I 888; W I 893)—so much so that she becomes oblivious of her avowed purpose ("Denket nicht mehr des Gesellen").
Engrossed in the autonomous and hermetically sealed world of artistic
magic, Biondette loses touch with the actual circumstances. It was such
a self-contained, self-centered aesthetic universe, a realm of "art for
art's sake" without religious or metaphysical ties, which Brentano
eventually rejected as untenable: "For a long time I have had a certain
aversion to all poetry that mirrors itself and not God" (S II 165);
"therefore every mirror of art which mirrors anything other than the

---

[42] "But saddened sits the maiden sweet, / Gently plays her vibrant harp
/ That life might greet him in beauty, / Life, which love had granted him. // As
the notes are poured out, / The virgin feels in her heart / A wonderous type of
magic flowing / And such sweet, wild pains. // Swinging higher aloft the harp-
strings, / She thinks no more of her dear friend; / As the swan who sings in
death, / Her notes rise up glowing. // A thousand tones, that otherwise slept,
/ From her harp now break to life, / And in all depths of the heart / She hears
the echo speak loudly. // It echoes in death; / Shyly to the threshold of life / The
magic songs call him, / His view becomes bright."

way, the light, and the truth must also be a mirror of darkness. And everything that is not this, that leads astray, retards, teases away from Him, in art as in life generally, be far from me, . . . for it is temptation of the devil" (S II 237). However, the fact that this potential for narcissistic preoccupation manifests itself in a performer who had been as pious and "theocentric" as Biondette, was a prospect that both frightened and fascinated the poet.

The manner in which Brentano attempts to extricate Biondette from this compromising situation reveals that the Orphean "crisis of conscience" sometimes lay more with the author than with his fictional counterparts. In order to insure that Meliore would not "see" Biondette in the "sound of venomous songs" Brentano has to resort to a sleight of hand tactic. When Meliore returns from the shadow of death to the threshold of life ("des Lebens Schwelle") under the influence of Biondette's "Zauberlieder," Brentano employs a *deus ex machina* device to avoid the tragedy of incest: Biondette is afflicted with temporary blindness, and Meliore experiences blurred vision. The trance-like state in Biondette is so profound that she neither recognizes Meliore when their eyes meet nor hears the term he uses to address her: "my sister" (W I 891). Meliore, on the other hand, regards his recall from death merely as a momentary hiatus during his pilgrimage to heaven:

> "Süßer Tod, den ich erlitte!
> Goldne Töne zu mir gehen,
> Selig in des Himmels Mitte
> Soll ich wieder auferstehen"[43]
> (W I 894)

The Christian framework of the epic thus makes possible a resolution of the Orpheus-Eurydice myth which the Greeks could not have foreseen: the "threshold of life" on which Meliore stands does not lead from Hades back to earth, but rather bypasses the world as the individual journeys from the shadow of death to the light of heaven. When Biondette endeavors to sustain the magic spell, however, it is Meliore who experiences a malfunctioning of the senses: he imagines her to be the Virgin Mother (W I 894). Whereas Orpheus lost his Eurydice forever because of his attempt to see whether she was following him, Biondette and Meliore gain eternal salvation because a benign

---

[43] " 'Death, sweet death, yet to be endured! / Golden tones come to me, / In the midst of heaven, gloriously / I shall again be resurrected!' "

Christian deity prevents them from "seeing." The use of the term
"evil" to designate those forces which thwart Biondette's efforts to
revive Meliore has the same ironically tinged ambivalence as the forms
of "sweet" found elsewhere in the romance: "Weh! es walten böse
Künste" (W I 896).[44]

In spite of the somewhat contrived resolution for this emotionally
charged episode, in which Brentano combines the greatest musical
feats of the pagan world of the Greeks with the high point of musical
lore in the Christian tradition, there are several deft motivic touches
throughout this scene which bind together certain loose ends in the
cycle. For instance, the bandage that Biondette twice applies to Meliore's
wound recalls his opening comment concerning the "wounds of love"
that her music had inflicted on him. During the course of her "Song of
Songs," the serious nature of this "wound" comes to the fore:

> Als sie diesen Frevel singet,
> Springt sein Blut ihr neu entgegen;
> Den Verband, der Hilfe bringet,
> Kann die Raserei nicht legen.[45]
>
> (W I 893)

The term "Verband" (derived from "binden") could be explained with
reference to that interpretation of "re-ligion" which regards the term
as stemming from a form of "binden."[46] The binding force that will
save Meliore at this point is to be found not in autonomous ("bin-
dungslos") art, but rather in a medium that will restore the severed
connection with the godhead. We are given a hint at the close of the
romance that the breach has been closed, at least to some extent. As
Meliore is wafted away from her, he notices her bandage ("Binde")
covering his wound (W I 896). The wound, inflicted by Biondette's
sacred song and reopened by her "Song of Songs," has been closed
forever by a power that transcends human comprehension and control.
However, the destiny of the Orphean singer is ultimately entrusted to
her own hands—just as the Greek bard determined his own mode of
existence following the disappearance of Eurydice.

Subsequent to her "Hohes Lied," Biondette ceases to be referred

---

[44] "Woe! Evil arts are here in power."

[45] "As she sings this heresy, / Leaps his blood at her anew; / The band that
brings all help / Cannot be bound in madness."

[46] According to *Webster's Third International Dictionary*, p. 1918, the word
"religion" probably stems from the Latin verb "religare" meaning "to tie back,"
"tie up," or "tie fast."

to as the "holy singer" and "reverent dancer." In addition to losing these epithets, she also forfeits the instrument with which she expressed her pious devotion. During the course of her scuffle with Apo's cohorts, her harp is demolished (W I 915), after which she takes her own life in order to avoid the necromancer's lecherous designs. But even though the harp with which Biondette had held so many listeners spellbound, and through which the rays of sunlight played their symbolic, silent song, lies broken, the power of music is reaffirmed—this time in a distinctly minor key and diabolical mode. Just as Michaly's performance had been mocked by a satanical double (the cat Mores), so Biondette's tones echo in the playing of her distorted counterpart, Älia Lälia Crispis. On this occasion, the relationship between protagonist and double is more intimate, in so far as Älia Lälia Crispis is actually an evil spirit that has been infused into Biondette's lifeless body. Whereas Biondette intoned her "Hohes Lied" in order to rescue a loved-one from the throes of death, Älia Lälia Crispis performs her "Song of Songs" in commemoration of the spiritual demise of mankind through original sin. One might draw the following analogy between the respective performers: Älia Lälia Crispis' ethic and aesthetic are related to those of Biondette much as a photographic negative is related to the positive print. One point to be borne in mind, however, if this analogy is pursued to its logical conclusion: the print is dependent upon the negative for its essence and its existence. The physical similarity of the demonic singer-dancer-harpist Älia Lälia Crispis to her Orphean predecessor Biondette, together with their contrastive but nevertheless complementary musical magic, underscores once more that dangerous liaison between the divine and the diabolic, between the sublime and the sordid—if not the ridiculous—which frustrates every attempt at categorization or at making black-and-white distinctions. It was, in the final analysis, the gray areas of life and art which provided the fertile breeding ground for Brentano's doubts with regard to his craft and the dilemmas which racked his conscience.

The very name Älia Lälia Crispis with its succession of parallel assonantal and alliterating sounds (ä-ä, ia-ia, l-l, is-is) has a parodistic or mocking character in keeping with the figure who bears it. Her initial musical offering is also imitative, in this case not so much of Biondette as of another woman who, in the course of human history, played a major part in inducing man to sin: Eve. According to the account of Creation provided by Apo's Mephistophelian companion,

Moles, Eve first adorned herself with fine vestments and then danced
toward Adam (W I 788), accompanied by a cosmic chorus:

> Tausend Engel, sie zu preisen,
> Vor dem klaren Weibe gehn,
> Singend, spielend sie umkreisen
> Rings mit himmlischem Getön.
>
> Und es tanzten rings den Reigen
> Sonne, Mond und Sterne fern,
> Nach der Engel Harf' und Geigen,
> Vor der Braut des Erdenherrn.[47]
>
> (W I 789)

In a similar encircling or "ensnaring" maneuver, Älia Lälia Crispis—
a "second" wife to Apo following the loss of his "bride" Biondette—
pays a musical tribute to her prospective spouse:

> Wie die Kranken zu zerstreuen
> Mein Gesang dir diene oft.
>
> . . . .
>
> Ob ich dir zur kurzen Weile
> Buhlerliedlein singen soll?[48]
>
> (W I 959)

Apo responds to her suggestion with characteristic libidinousness:

> Lüstern die beseßne Leiche
> Küsset nun der alte Tor,
> Moles spielet auf der Geige
> Ein vermaledeites Chor.
>
> Und in buhlerischem Eifer
> Tanzet, wie der trunkne Lot,
> Mit der Braut er einen Schleifer
> In fatalem Teufelstrott.[49]
>
> (W I 960–961)

---

[47] "A thousand angels, to praise her, / Go before the serene woman; / Singing, playing they encircle her / Round about with heavenly tones. // And now
there join in dancing rounds / Sun, moon and distant stars, / To the angel's harps
and fiddles, / Before the earth-lord's bride."

[48] "Thus the sick ones to distract, / May my song oft serve you well. / ... /
If I should sing for your enjoyment / Songs about a sweet amour?"

[49] "Lasciviously now, the old fool covers / The possessed corpse with kisses;
/ On the fiddle Moles plays / A chorus accursed. // And in an amorous rush,
/ Like the drunken Lot he dances / A waltz with the bride / In a devastating
devil's trot."

The image of Moles performing execrable tunes on the violin is reminiscent of Michaly's feline counterpart Mores (in addition, there is an acoustical kinship in the names Moles-Mores owing to their assonance and alliteration), while Apo's reactions resemble the wild gyrations of the tomcats in response to their leader's wretched tones.

The description of Älia Lälia Crispis' singing includes a final—and appropriate—variation of the constellation "bunte Schlange," "gift'ge Lieder," and "Lieder heil'ge Schlange":

> Älia Lälia Crispis schreiet
> Mit verruchtem, gift'gem Ton,
> Und Biondettens Kehl' entweihet
> Eines frechen Liedes Hohn.[50]
>
> (W I 961)

But since Apo had anticipated hearing nothing less than "the Song of Solomon" from Biondette's lips, he is offended by these harsh sounds and demands a change in tune: Älia Lälia Crispis must sing the wedding song with Biondette's voice (W I 961). One prerequisite for such an "imitatio" is the procurement of a suitable instrument, since Biondette's harp has been demolished. Älia Lälia Crispis prescribes the appearance and purpose of this instrument in terms that suggest a repetition of original sin:

> Mit gedrehten Schlangenhäuten
> Lasse mir vom Apfelholz
> Eine Harfe bald besaiten,
> Ich bin auf dergleichen stolz.
>
> Ich will die Akkorde greifen,
> Daß du mich gewißlich lobst,
> Daß der Weiber Augen greifen
> Rings nach dem verbotnen Obst.[51]
>
> (W I 961–962)

Älia Lälia Crispis is unmasked as counter-Orpheus insofar as her music will serve not as an antidote to death, but rather as a means of depriving all mankind of the promise of eternal life. She herself states this succinctly: they will eat their own death (W I 962).

---

[50] "Älia Lälia Crispis shrieks / With notes of vile and venom, / And profanes Biondettes voice / With mockery of an insolent song."

[51] "With the twisted skins of serpent, / String for me of apple-wood / A harp now quickly, / For of such I am proud. // I will grasp the chords, / That you shall certainly praise me, / That the eyes of women shall grasp / About for the forbidden fruit."

In this capacity as an anti-Biondette, Älia Lälia Crispis nevertheless exploits that very ambivalence of art which proved so disturbing
in Rosadora's case. Pious melodies are made to revile rather than
revere the deity:

> Und die Jungfrau spricht: "So sei es!
> Lieb' ich gleich nicht jenen Ton,
> Freut sich gleich des frechen Schreies
> Mehr ein freier Musensohn.
>
> Lieb' ich lügend doch zu gleißen,
> Und zweideutig will ich Gott
> Dir in schiefen Weisen preisen,
> Mir zum Lobe, ihm zum Spott!"[52]
>
> (W I 961)

The discrepancy between the essence and the appearance afforded by
the innate ambiguity ("zweideutig") is manifest both in the content
of these lines and in their tonal pattern. The discerning ear can detect,
in the sound strata throughout the stanzas devoted to Älia Lälia Crispis,
a tendency toward impure rhyme (here, for example, "Schlangenhäu-
ten—besaiten"; "gleißen—preisen") as well as the frequent appearance of composite rhyme schemes ("der trunkne Lot—Teufelstrott";
"So sei es—Schreies"), which alerts the reader to the fact that the intention of the singer is not in accord with the execution of her art. The
same technique is employed when Moles describes the stringed instrument he has procured for her:

> "Eine Harfe ist besorgt,
> Der galanteste der Geister
> Hat die seine mir geborgt.
>
> Ist sie gleich ein bißchen heischer,
> Ist sie doch vom besten Ton,
> Wird die Sängerin erst keuscher,
> Wird sie besser stimmen schon"[53]
>
> (W I 962)

[52] "And the virgin speaks: 'So be it! / If I find that note ungracious, / A
candid son of the Muses finds / That cry audacious gladdening. // Telling lies,
I love to sparkle; / I will praise this God ambiguously, / Praise him to you in
oblique ways / To my glory, to his scorn!' "
[53] ' "A harp has been provided me; / The most gallant of all spirits / Has
lent to me his own. // Should it seem strained, / It's yet a harp of finest sounds;
/ If the songstress becomes more chaste, / It will be more euphonic.' "

If the requisite for purity of tone is chastity on the part of the performer, then the delineation of this condition in terms of impure rhyme ("heischer—keuscher") hints at the futility of such a hope in the case of Älia Lälia Crispis. Her subsequent performance affirms this prognosis: "Und sie singet Schändlichkeiten / Ihnen vor im frechen Ton" (W I 964).[54]

However, the fact that the listeners are elated by the singing of this "Babylonian whore" (W I 964), and react to her performance in a manner comparable to those Orphean tones of her physical double, Biondette ("Wer sie sieht, steht wie versteinert" [W I 965]),[55] leads to such a conflict in the mind of the author that he finds it necessary to express his consternation both contextually and visually by omitting— for the first and only time in the cycle—the closing line of that quatrain in which the account of her performance culminates:

> Also frech ist ihr Bezeigen
> Jedem Buben scheint sie eigen,
> Ich erschrecke und muß schweigen.[56]

The missing line speaks more eloquently for Brentano's "crisis of conscience" than any verses he might have written to portray a situation which must have been so reminiscent of his own.

Whereas the tolling of church bells had once put an abrupt end to Mores' musical spell and had sounded the death knell for Biondette's dangerous "Song of Songs" by arousing Meliore (W I 896), a similar sound in the midst of Älia Lälia Crispis' performance merely serves as an impetus for further blasphemy. The cause for the tolling of the sacred bell (W I 964) is, on this occasion, the funeral procession of Biondette's sister Rosarosa. It is in the midst of this solemn cortege that we also catch a glimpse of Meliore for the final time. Judging from his deportment on this occasion, it seems that his resurrection from the shadow of death through Biondette's "Song of Songs" has led not only to his physical revitalization but also to his spiritual regeneration. Towering above the throng, the former love-struck student becomes a hero among the herd, an artist whose feet are firmly planted on the ground, but whose prophetic glance remains transfixed on the heights:

[54] "And she sings to them disgraceful tones / On a bold and insolent note."
[55] "Whoever sees her stands as if transfixed."
[56] "So insolent is her behavior, / She seems to belong to every scamp, / I am shocked and must be silent."

Er hat selbst das Lied gesungen,
Das der Feind jetzt um ihn singt.

Aber der ist unbesieget,
Der ein Dichter und ein Held,
Weil er in dem Himmel wieget
Seines Schmerzes gift'ge Welt.

Und es steigt an seinem Leiden
Heilend Sonn' und Mond empor,
Unter Sklaven kann er schreiten
Wie ein Sänger in dem Chor.

Er ist einsam im Getümmel,
Und er geht in sel'gem Traum,
Und sein Auge steigt zum Himmel
Ewig von dem ird'schen Saum.[57]

(W I 982–983)

Here is a poet-singer of both Orphean and Christian commitment, a Tasso-like figure to whom the power has been given by the gods (or better, by God), to transmute his suffering into verses that speak to all men at all times, to celebrate in song the divinely ordained "musicalization of life" which Biondette, the "Golden Rose," had proclaimed before her own downfall precluded its realization:

Und es sang nun Rosadore
Zu dem Klang der goldnen Harfe.

Solch ein Lied, so sel'gen Tones,
Hat nur da die Luft getragen,
Als der Heiland ward geboren
Und die Engel Gloria sangen.

Also sang des Lichtes Bogen,
Da den Lustkreis aller Farben
Gott durch seinen Raum hinrollte
In dem Glanz des ersten Tages;

---

[57] "He himself has sung the song, / That the foe now sings around him. // But he remains unvanquished, / A poet and a hero, / Because he lulls to sleep in heaven / The venomous world of his pain. // And with his sorrows / Moon and sun ascend, healing wounds, / Among the slaves he can stride / Like a singer amidst the choir. // He is lonesome in the turmoil, / And he walks with blissful dreams, / And his eye is raised to heaven. / Eternally looking away from earthly toil."

Also tönt' des Wassers Woge,
Mit dem Rund des Erdenballes
Selig spielend in der Sonne,
Jauchzend an dem ersten Tage.

In so süßen Tones Strome
War die Luft aus Gottes Atem
Um die junge Welt ergossen,
In der Lust des ersten Tages.

Und die neue Erde rollte
Unter also freud'gem Klange
In den Kreis von Mond und Sonne,
Jubelnd an dem ersten Tage.

Also sang das Blut, ergossen
Durch des neuen Menschen Adern,
Also sang der Mensch voll Wonne,
Da er zu der Welt erwachte.

Doch annoch viel höhern Tones
Wird das Lied der Sel'gen schallen,
Wenn sie aus dem Haus des Todes
Zu dem Antlitz Gottes wandeln.[58]

(W I 862–863)

Critics have frequently suggested that Meliore represents a self-portrait of Brentano. Although there are admittedly elements of similarity between poet and protagonist with regard to physical appearance and temperament, it becomes evident after reading the final description of Meliore that he embodies an idealized portrait of the artist as a young man, a singer not as Brentano was but as he would like to have been.[59] Such an Orphean figure might have served as the focal point

[58] "And now Rosadore sang / To the tones of her golden harp. // Such a song, such blessed tones / But once before were borne on air, / As the Lord was sent to earth / And the angels sang their Glorias. // Thus sang the arches of light, / As God rolled out through space / The joyous circle of colors / In gleaming luster on earth's first day. // Thus resounded waves of water / On the globe of earth, / Peacefully playing with the sunlight, / Exulting on our earth's first day. // In such streams of sweetest tone, / The air of God's breath / Was poured out over the young world / In the joy of earth's first day. // And the new earth rolled / Into the circuit of moon and sun / With such joyful sound, / Jubilant on our earth's first day. // Through the veins of newborn man / Sang the blood thus while flowing; / When man to the world awoke, / Sang he thus with rejoicing. // Yet the songs of the blessed will sound / With a much higher tone / When they leave the house of death, / And rise up to God's countenance."

[59] The name Meliore is, of course, derived from the Latin comparative "melior" and found in such English words as "ameliorate."

for that "new mythology" which Friedrich Schlegel propounded in theory,[60] for that "romanticization of the world" which Novalis sought in practice,[61] for that "musicalization of life" which Brentano—in spite of his grandiose attempt in the *Romanzen vom Rosenkranz* to synthesize the musico-poetic heritage of Graeco-Roman antiquity, the legacy of the Judaeo-Christian tradition, and the lore of the medieval-modern epoch—never found.

[60] See Schlegel's "Rede über die Mythologie" in his *Kritische Schriften*, ed. Wolfdietrich Rasch (Munich: Hanser, 1964), pp. 496–503.

[61] Novalis, *Werke, Briefe, Dokumente*, ed. Ewald Wasmuth (Heidelberg: Lambert Schneider, 1957), II, 53, speaks about the need for and the process of romanticizing the world.

3. The Musicalization of Life

T HE preceding chapter presented a survey of the leading Orphean singers in Brentano's literary repertoire together with an analysis of the "crisis of conscience" which plagued them or their creator. The following excerpt from Walther Rehm's study *Orpheus: Der Dichter und die Toten* recapitulates the essential facets of the legend treated thus far and at the same time touches upon a number of related thematic fragments and motifs that merit closer attention insofar as they illustrate the "musicalization of life," which so many Romantic poets strove to realize and which underwent a great number of variations in Brentano's works:

> According to Bachofen, Orpheus, son of Apollo, descends from the lineage of those mighty prophets who proclaimed the reality of the invisible with powerful expletives ... : Orpheus, in seeking out the mysterious constantly and thereby elevating the spirits, enchanted everything and subjugated everything to himself. Not the actual lyre, nor any actual music at all was for him the crux of the matter [1], but rather that harmony of the worlds which he imitated in the seven-string lyre [2]. That Orpheus descends to the dead and there obtains his beloved's release through song [3], that through his song he calls inanimate nature to order and tames the wild beasts, that after his death he sings forth and resounds from the whole of nature [4]: these aspects of the myth are symbols for the unparalleled, magically transfiguring power of music [5], for the magical power of poetry, for its ethos and pathos, its nomothetic station [6].[1]

The numbers inserted in the above passage indicate those areas which will be examined in detail in the present chapter under the respective headings: [1] The Legacy of Orpheus' Lyre: Instrumental Symbolism; [2] The Ethos of Harmony; [3] The Pathos of Love and Death; [4] Musica Naturata—Musica Naturans; [5] The Cosmos and Chaos of the Dance; [6] Metamorphosis and Catharsis: "Singen-Lobsingen" (to sing-to sing hymns of praise).

[1] Walther Rehm, *Orpheus: Der Dichter und die Toten* (Düsseldorf: L. Schwann, 1950), p. 9.

The Legacy of Orpheus' Lyre: Instrumental Symbolism

The range of instruments at the disposal of Brentano for the purpose of his "literary orchestration" was much more comprehensive
than what was available to the Greeks at the time the Orpheus myth
took shape. The string family, for instance, had been expanded far
beyond the lyre and the "cithara" to include the harp, the lute, the
guitar, the violin, the viola, the violoncello, and the double bass, while
the winds encompassed two distinct branches; the woods (which enriched the pipes and the flutes by the tones of the oboe, the clarinet,
and the bassoon) and the brass (including trumpets, trombones, French
horns, and so forth). To the above generic groups (strings and winds)
could be added the enlarged percussion family with its various modes
of drum, the triangle, the cymbals, and other means of producing
rhythmic noise. Finally, one might also consider the sonority achieved
by the entire orchestral ensemble in the concert hall, together with its
liturgical counterpart, the organ (a composite instrument with the
capacity of emulating most of the orchestral timbres).

With regard to the effects produced on the listener by the strings
and winds, Brentano, for the most part, adheres to the views expounded
in the speculative writings of thinkers such as Plato and Aristotle.[2]
The strings found approval, since the performer could direct or control
the emotional and intellectual responses of his audience by reciting a
poetic text to the musical accompaniment. However, when one performed on a wind instrument, this was not possible, and consequently,
the musings of the listener might run rampant owing to the suggestive
powers of the unrestricted musical stimuli. It was not simply a matter
of coincidence, therefore, that in Greek mythology the lyre became
the instrument sacred to Phoebus Apollo, the god of light, the epitome
of form and order, while the pipes or flutes could be heard in the retinue
of Dionysus, the wine deity celebrated in wild orgiastic rites reflecting
man's innate drive to revel in unrestricted freedom and uninhibited
sensual intoxication. These contrastive functions were previously ob-

---

[2] John Hollander, *The Untuning of the Sky: Ideas of Music in English Poetry
1500–1700* (Princeton: Princeton University Press, 1961), pp. 35–36. A contemporary of Brentano's, Christian Friedrich Daniel Schubart, formulated in his
treatise *Ideen zu einer Ästhetik der Tonkunst* of 1806 (reprinted Leipzig, 1924),
pp. 198–211, a system of emotional coefficients for the timbre quality of various
musical instruments.

served with regard to Biondette's harp and Radlauf's fife respectively—except that the distinctions were, on both cases, by no means as unequivocal as the original premises would indicate. For instance, Biondette's purest harp tones could unintentionally induce a state of emotional euphoria in the listener, while the harp of Älia Lälia Crispis was specifically intended for that purpose. And whereas the force of Radlauf's fife music initially serves to secure justice and reestablish order, the same instrument in the hands of Mausohr becomes a means to inflict terrible punishment on the innocent victims of royal machinations. There is, one must conclude, an element of ambivalence in the particular function and the symbolic implication of each of these instruments, and so the original Platonic and Aristotelean attitude with regard to the strings as a harbinger of "cosmos" and the winds as the instigator of "chaos" should be modified. Before investigating the symbolism of these instrumental families as well as that of the percussion group and the orchestra-organ complex, it would be advisable to examine briefly Brentano's concept of the "symbol" in general.

Two passages—one from an early fictional context (1800) and the other from a piece of expository prose (1812)—will help clarify the poet's attitude toward the complicated issue of the form and function of the literary symbol. In a previously cited excerpt from *Der Sänger* the statement was made that "many things become well-known concepts to us only when clothed in symbols" (W II 484). This succinct formulation implies that the symbol may convey what is otherwise inexpressible or what at best can be grasped indirectly and intuitively. The second elucidation comes from the *Erklärung der Sinnbilder* quoted in connection with the Orpheus figure. Here Brentano's conjectures go a bit deeper when he declares: "The symbol should be only a hint, which coincidentally reinterprets itself; it is to a certain extent a metamorphosis, taking place before our eyes, of matter into an image of its meaning. Within the symbol there is movement, transformation, no mimicry, no intent to portray, no active mirroring . . . also the symbol must evolve from the ideal . . . , but not be contrived from the real" (W II 1051–1052).

The process of metamorphosis and idealization noted in these lines could be traced with reference to the lyre as it appears in Brentano's works. Brentano generally employs the term "Leier" (and its counterpart "Lyra") to refer to the most exalted form of mundane song. For instance, in the solemn prologue to *Die Gründung Prags* (1814)

the poet, regarding the task before him as a kind of religious calling, summons the full power of his creative talents in order to transmit adequately these scenes from the mythical past of the Czech people:

> O sende freudig feierlich nun, meine Leier!
> Die Klänge durch des Domes ernste Hallen,
> Wo ich der Zukunft Seheraug gesehen
> Fromm sinnend durch der Vorzeit Tiefe spähen.[3]

(W IV 554)

However, following his return to the fold of Catholicism, Brentano began to formulate a different scale of aesthetic values, and the lyre became a means of suggesting the type of secular song which he now rejected: "I could . . . ," he declares categorically in 1831, "sing a tune of lamentation and torment, and of the utter lack of what, where, how, and why if I were not now, in a more rational moment, hanging up my mistuned lyre on the willows of Babylon" (GS IX 258).[4] Trying to persuade his conscience that salvation for him lay in the confines of a heavenly Jerusalem rather than within the walls of a sinful Babylon (the habitat of Älia Lälia Crispis), Brentano characterized himself rather derogatorily in 1837 as a "faded, discharged Arion without lyre and dolphin" (S II 359).

Frequently, Brentano exploits the dual symbolic potential inherent in the terms "Leier-Lyra" (referring either to the musical instrument or to the northern constellation into which Orpheus' lyre was transformed.) In such a context, "Lyra" functions as a means of suggesting the intervention of a benign, transcendental force in the course of human affairs. Already in *Godwi* the interplay between the instrumental "Leier" and the astrological "Lyra" can be observed in the monument erected by the protagonist in memory of the reluctant prostitute, Violette. The monument consists of two parts: the pedestal, containing on its four sides allegorical bas-reliefs, which depict the titanic struggle for Violette's soul waged by a Dionysian satyr and a benevolent spirit ("Genius"), the latter embodying the force of Apollinian order in the universe; a statue above the pedestal, portraying Violette's apotheosis in the form of her death and transfiguration. The bas-reliefs show the

---

[3] "Oh, send joyfully, solemnly now, my lyre! / The tones through the staid halls of the cathedral, / Where I saw the seer eye of the future / Searching piously, pensively through the depths of prehistory."

[4] The same image with reference to a fellow poet who had just "reverently hung his lyre on the willows of Babylon in order to serve more sublimely" occurs in the prologue to *Die Gründung Prags* (W IV 546).

apparently successful temptation by the satyr, who offers Violette a tambourine filled with luscious fruit, at which the benevolent spirit expresses his dismay by strumming frenzied tones on the lyre: "Es bricht in seines Liedes Lieb und Leiden / Der Genius der Lyra goldne Saiten" (W II 299).[5] The image of an instrument with torn strings became for Brentano emblematic of a passion that had run its course, of the remorse which is the aftermath of an overindulgence in sensual pleasure.[6] On the fourth of the bas-reliefs at the base of the statuary, however, the satyr's instrument is crushed underfoot and Violette is seen striving for a higher plane of existence: "Streckt sie die Hand, die Lyra zu erlangen, / Die hoch erhebt" (W II 299).[7] On the embossed surface of the bas-relief it was possible to portray the "Lyra" as either the musical instrument or the constellation of stars; for the statue towering above the pedestal the latter mode of presentation was no longer feasible. Consequently, the intervention of supramundane forces on behalf of beleagured humanity was concentrated in this instance in the lyre held aloft triumphantly by the "Genius":

> Das ganze Bild, in Einigkeit verbunden,
> Gleicht rührendem Gesange,
> Wie heilige Gebete aufwärts dringen.
>
> . . . .
>
> Mit schmerzenvollem Drange
> Muß es nach Lieb und süßen Tönen ringen,
> Zu Ruhe sich zu schwingen.
> So hebt es sich, so strebt es nach der Leier.[8]
>
> (W II 301)

Whereas the "Leier-Lyra" complex in *Godwi* signified the transfiguring power of pure love and its victory over base sensuality, the same configuration in the *Romanzen vom Rosenkranz* becomes another expression of Apo's ubiquitous libido—he transforms the music of the spheres into a bit of erotic astrology:

[5] "In the love and suffering of his song, / The Genius breaks the golden strings of his lyre."

[6] Rosadora-Biondette spoke of her own demise in terms of the time "When the strings of my harp / Have been torn apart in this world" (W I 689).

[7] "She stretches out her hand to reach the lyre, / That elevates to the heights."

[8] "The entire scene, bound in unity, / Is as a touching song, / As holy prayers directed upward.... Under painful stress / It has to battle for love and sweet tones, / In order to come to rest. / Thus it elevates itself, thus it strives for the lyre."

Frei strömt, wie zur Hochzeitsfeier,
Berenicens Locke hin,
Und im Klang von Orpheus' Leier
Schaukelt trunken der Delphin.[9]

(W I 871)

The same spirit of a "topsy-turvy cosmos" embodied in the once exalted lyre concept can be seen in Brentano's radically disillusioned assessment of the aesthetic scene in 1824: "Cozy smoke-stacks," he comments, "are the true thoroughfares of art over which the nine witches of Parnassus travel, in old German style, upon the broomstick of criticism to the Blocksberg, where the lyre appears to the clairvoyant as the skull of a horse's carrion (Pegasus)" (GS IX 51).

Another member of the string family, the harp, had enjoyed, ever since biblical times, the reputation of exerting a purely edifying or soothing effect upon the listener.[10] In Brentano's hands, however, this instrument and its symbolic overtones assume a new dimension of meaning when he writes:

> I was a golden harp, drawn with animal strings; all types of weather put me out of tune, and the wind played me, and the sun stretched me. And love played forte so passionately that the strings ripped, ripped in such a stupid way that I can scarcely string a spinning wheel with what remains. . . . Now I have purged the harp in fire and strung it with metal and play it myself; or my friends or a mouse run across it, tinkling, or a fly—but the latter I consider prophetic and I then . . . array myself with trust. (S II 157–158)

This image traces a development exactly the reverse of Biondette's—the gravitation away from the dangers of "animal" passion to a well-tempered, even-honed emotional balance. The allusion to torn strings might, in this case, be a veiled reference to his two tragic marriages—the first terminating in death (which not even the harmonies of Orpheus-Brentano could stay), the other in discord and divorce.

Brentano's determination to master his fate instead of responding like an Aeolian harp to every capricious breeze, and his confidence that some benign force will henceforth guide his destiny, are based, however, on a fallacious premise. What the writer postulated in the above letter

---

[9] "Freely stream Bernice's locks, / As to a marriage feast, / And to the sound of Orpheus' lyre / Dolphin staggers drunkenly."

[10] One might note in this context, for example, the soothing effects exerted by David's harp music on Saul's tormented spirit.

to Fouqúe (1811) as a chronological sequence for both his life and his art was and remained a temporal coincidence ("I *was* a golden harp, drawn with *animal* strings. . . . *Now* I have strung the harp with *metal*"). Biondette had sought—and failed—to put her golden harp exclusively in the service of the godhead; this very instrument later became the means to embroil her in a precarious situation that might have had devastating consequences. It would have been as erroneous to separate the two aspects of art as to isolate Werdo Senne from his instrument after he resolved to sing no more out of grief; his musical "alter ego" continued to function in the capacity of an Aeolian harp. In a letter of 1818, Brentano came to acknowledge—if only grudgingly —the fact that his art occupied an intermediary position between conflicting (but not mutually exclusive) forces: "Pray," he urges," that art might become good, it teaches us to sing and to praise, and it lies, as life itself, between heaven and earth, opening the gateway to both; but the animal skin must be tanned that it might bear the letters and the word" (GS VIII 330). What had previously been designated "animal strings" in the realm of human passion now becomes a tanned animal hide in the sphere of art. But whereas in the harp image of 1811 Brentano hoped to replace the animalistic component with tempered metal, he implies in the passage from 1818 that the element of animal vitalism must, indeed, be restrained, but by all means retained.

A third member of the string family which assumes a leading role in the musicalization of life is the bass viol. This instrument is, in a unique fashion, consistent with the traditional function of the strings as the means of establishing (or maintaining) order when chaos or confusion threatens. The "Baßgeige," namely, prevents false hopes or delusions from gaining the upper hand. In such a capacity, the bass viol functions as the "spoiler," the voice of reason, which squelches idle revelries. There is a clear presentiment of this trend in an early letter to Bettina when Clemens complains how experiences in the "real" world undermine the illusions that fantasy constructs: "Whenever one is awake," he remarks, "one sits in the midst of the vacuous aggravations of daily life, and all the prophetic sounds of experience in the hollow bass viol greet one with the odious: Didn't I tell you so?" (F 311). A very vivid demonstration of the manner in which reality may send man's fragile hopes tumbling to the ground like a house of cards is found in the comedy *Ponce de Leon*. While cleaning the deserted ballroom after the festivities of the previous night, a weary

servant discovers the string bass leaning against the wall and decides
to make it his bed: "I fit right in with the bass viol—with music there
is always a comfortable sleep" (W IV 164). A short time later, however,
Ponce enters the hall and, apparently envious of the snoring servant,
whose untroubled conscience allows him to rest so peacefully, inaugu-
rates a bit of musical mischief:

> PONCE: The snorer is like an alarm on the clock. (He goes toward the
> servant, takes the viol-bow.) He's snoring *adagio* in F minor, I'll
> transpose him to *allegro* in the major key. . . .
> He who lies thus in the arms of lovely music, him music should
> awaken. (He plays.)
> SERVANT (drunk with sleep): Leave me, comrade,—damned box, the
> whole night you allow someone to fiddle on you, and now you
> won't let me rest with you.
> PONCE: He's getting ill-mannered, insulting the ear of music with am-
> biguities, it's losing its temper. (Playing livelier.)
> SERVANT (jumping up): Unfriendly being, dumb vessel. (W IV 169)

By illustrating the dual potential of the lyre and harp, by alloting
to the double bass the task of signaling the intrusion of harsh reality
into the escapist world of dreams and quixotic ideals, Brentano both
adheres to and alters the "classical" view of the strings as the guarantors
of Apollinian order as opposed to the Dionysian forces unleashed by
the flutes and pipes. The interplay of tradition and innovation is embodied in the figure of Georg, the consumptive servant in *Godwi*,
whose flute playing proves so detrimental to his health:

> "Why must the poor man play precisely the flute with his consumptive
> illness, and why must he love music just as much as his ailment detests
> his instrument; if he is incurable, he should be allowed to die sooner
> from this lovely passion, rather than from his loathsome disease."
> (W II 306)

These observations of Maria, which anticipate the link between art
and disease (a theme that was to be developed by German authors from
E. T. A. Hoffmann to Thomas Mann), are substantiated by Godwi when
he suggests a stringed instrument—lute or zither—(W II 306) as a
possible remedy for Georg's plight. A lute is eventually found, and the
description of its exterior (decorated with angelic cherubs), together
with the music Maria performs on it while testing its tone quality (the
hymn "Ave Maris Stella"), bears witness to the fact that a more propitious future may be in store for Georg:

It was a large, beautiful instrument, and the Gothic scrolls which surrounded the sound-hole were finely worked in gold and ivory. A very agreeable idea was that through this portal all the tones peeked out in the form of cherubic angels' heads, as if they were locked in like heavenly children, and were singing lovely songs through the opening. They began to sing in succession, the first forcefully and then more and more subdued, just as the height or depth of the tone were expressed in the age of their faces. The bridge represented an aeolian harp, behind which an attentive maiden, propped upon her arm, was lying in a sleeping position.

I [Maria] brought the strings into harmony with pleasure, and I took delight in the peaceful, rich tone of the instrument. (W II 323)

Although Maria cautions Georg against overexertion, ultimately it is the strain brought on by his singing to the lute which contributes to the deterioration of the latter's health. The entire episode ends on a highly ironic note, when Maria himself dies while playing this instrument. Since Maria had been prevented from singing because of "an inflammation of the tongue," we must assume that the lute alone had a share in his demise: "Suddenly the pain gripped him very strongly, he dropped the lute, and it broke on the ground." (W II 445). Broken instrument and broken singer: this was a situation which, in the *Romanzen*, marked an event of considerable magnitude. The same constellation in *Godwi*, however, is deprived of any such aura of significance; instead, the "broken lute" becomes a convenient *deus ex machina* device with which to unravel some of the riddles surrounding the identity of certain mysterious figures in the novel (it contained a number of letters).

The flute, abandoned by Georg because of its possible deleterious effects on the well-being of the performer, together with the pipes, bag-pipe (Mores) and shawm ("Schalmei," a type of medieval oboe) constitute the principal woodwind instruments in Brentano's writings. From the context of the Mores episode, it is evident that the "classical" attitude toward this family still persists. Under these circumstances, it is understandable that the woodwinds should provide the accompaniment for Biondette's tableau portraying Judith in her agitation ("Freudig Flöt' und Zimbeln klangen" [W I 736]);[11] and yet, in the scene in which Jephthah's daughter appears, similar sounds are heard: "Rings die Hirtenflöten flehen" (W I 738).[12] Like the strings, the winds have

[11] "Joyfully flutes and cymbals resound."
[12] "Round about the shepherds' flutes implore."

acquired a dual potential, a multidimensional range of effects. The refrain from one of Brentano's most famous poems, "Die lustigen Musikanten," for instance, reads in part: "Schweifen die Pfeifen, und greifen / Ans Herz, / Mit Freud und mit Schmerz" (W II 396).[13] The tones of the shawm also evoke a mood of bucolic tranquility associated with the pastoral milieu or they function in a manner akin to the bass viol—they disturb and disrupt the serene but illusory worlds that fantasy creates. In the *Tagebuch der Ahnfrau*, for example, there is a poem which begins by telling of dreamlands in which the handicaps of real life are overcome; however, the poem concludes on a harsh note and is "orchestrated" accordingly:

> Kömmt dann Wahrheit mutternackt gelaufen,
> Führt der hellen Töne Glanzgefunkel
> Und der grellen Lichter Tanz durchs Dunkel,
> Rennt den Traum sie schmerzlich übern Haufen,
> Horch! die Fackel lacht, horch! Schmerz-Schalmeien
> Der erwachten Nacht ins Herz all schreien.[14]
>
> (W III 866–867)

The symbolic significance of that branch of the wind family represented by the brass (the horn, the trombone, the trumpet) can also be regarded as dualistic in nature. For instance, the hunting horn or French horn usually signals the Romantic desire to move out beyond the borders of one's physical or intellectual horizon. Thus the protagonist in the novel *Godwi* remarks that "loudly before me the merry horn of the coachman calls out its enticing tones through the bushes brilliantly, tones that summon us to distant lands" (W II 17–18); yet the "antagonists" in this work, the philistines and other men of mediocrity, are only attuned to domestic music—the "song of bourgeois righteousness" (W II 39)—and become unnerved by what they call the "wailing of the postilion's horn" (W II 39). Whereas the horn retained overtones of joyous prospect for those of sensitivity,[15] the "Posaune"

---

[13] "The pipes ramble and seize / The heart / With joy and with pain."

[14] "When truth then comes marching stark naked, / Leading the glitter of bright tones / And the dance of glaring lights through the dark, / It painfully overthrows the dream, / Hark! The torches laugh, hark! Pain-shawms / Of the awakened night all scream at the heart."

[15] Toward the end of Brentano's life (1841), when the Romantic hunting horn had long ceased to be a meaningful poetic symbol, the author could still infuse fresh vigor into the concept by alluding to the ephemeral goal of German political unity as "the sacred hour for Germany, when all German postilions blow in unison the same melody" (S II 406–407). .

(trombone or, in some cases, trumpet)[16] warned of imminent death and destruction, perhaps deriving from the biblical reference to the "trumpet of Gideon," which helped conquer the Midianites, that of Joshua, which leveled the walls of Jericho, or to the "last trump," which announces the Day of Judgment. In the pageant *Viktoria*, for example, one soldier upon hearing the tones of Wellington's "Posaunen" (the pun in German is based on "Ton" and "Wellington"), predicts that the army of Gideon (that is, Napoleon's forces) will soon collapse. Aside from the many occasions on which the sounds of this instrument are associated with military maneuvers and battlefields, there are several instances when the "Posaune" is allied with the Last Judgment. For instance, the guilt-ridden progenitor of the three rose-sisters, Kosme, is continually plagued by the "trumpet of wrath" ("Zornposaune," W I 720), which apparently he alone perceives. Whether it serves as a prelude to military conflict or to a day of great spiritual turmoil, the "Posaune" in Brentano's works invariably evokes an ominous atmosphere, the feeling of impending disaster.

The most prominent member of the brass family, the modern trumpet (German "Trompete"), opens symbolic perspectives in two different directions, a situation that becomes apparent in its role of announcing the arrival of personages of royalty. The trumpet fanfare and the roll of drums which precede the appearance of socially prominent individuals frequently contain a humorous aside that deflates the pomposity of the occasion—as, for instance, when the court musicians of the rival factions in the *Rheinmärchen* engage in a kind of bellicose water-music—or an ironic overtone, as when the hypocritical King Hatto enters the church in Mainz after one of his more insidious deeds, and is welcomed by trumpet fanfares and drum rolls (W III 44).

The general aura of dialectic ambivalence surrounding the symbolic function of the individual instruments in the scoring of Brentano's works also persists with regard to their aggregate ensemble: the orchestra. On the one hand, Brentano admires the coordination that can be achieved with such an amorphous contingent. In his first major work, the fantastic satire *Gustav Wasa*, "the tuning of the orchestra" even appears as a character and, pertaining to one of the interludes prescribed for the orchestra in the farce, the following stage direction

---

[16] In its literal sense, the German word "Posaune" may be translated as "trombone"; in more figurative contexts, the English rendering is "trump" or "trumpet" (as in the biblical phrase "die letzte Posaune").

occurs: "In the orchestra the tones touch each other; individual ones break forth one by one, seek each other with wonderment, find each other with love" (W IV 55). In contrast to such smooth coordination and rapport, an undisciplined orchestral group can serve as the embodiment of chaos and confusion. For example, in the preface to the revised *Gockel* fairy tale, Brentano compares the eclectic and erratic mind of his erstwhile mentor, Herr Schwab, with a motley ensemble performing a wild, melodic potpourri:

> Then . . . Don Quixote sang: "Joy, lovely spark of the gods," and finally —here the crinoline with the *chemise grecque* danced the cotillion at the marriage of Sir Roger [an English country dance] to the accompaniment of an all-encompassing orchestra consisting of Scheidler's old lute, the glass harmonica and the harp of the blind virgin, Paradise [Marie Therese von Paradies, 1759–1824, a well-known blind virtuoso], several Jew's harps, Papageno's pan pipes and modern guitars. (W III 625)

This mélange of literary satire, political allusion, aesthetic aperçu, and musical parody reflects, both in its obscurity of allusion as well as in the incompatibility of the performing instruments, the extremely complex orchestral (intellectual) world into which Herr Schwab had introduced the author and in which each tarried for the remainder of his life.

If there were any brief moments during his career in which Brentano felt himself a part of, rather than apart from, the world around him, these occurred when he experienced a sense of communion with the Church. The musical instrument that best exemplified the spirit of unity and community in the realm of religion was the organ. The overwhelming sense of religious awe that fills the heart of the listener as he enters a baroque church to the tones of an organ fugue is expressed by Julie in *Der Sänger* when she speaks of the inability of even a master craftsman to paint murals in an edifice in which such organ tones resound: "The song swells up in mighty waves, the glowing stream of holy organ tones flows through high arches and carries away with it his individual creation to the wonderment of all—he drops the brush, his hands intertwine, . . . he . . . prays" (W II 494). However, it is evident from the fate of Rosarosa and Jacopone in the *Romanzen vom Rosenkranz* that the organ's edifying tones, just as the harp with its sublime melodies, could embroil the performer or the unsuspecting listener in spiritual dilemmas and, as had been the case with Meliore and Biondette, even endanger the well-being of his soul.

Biondette's sister Rosarosa (Brentano also spells the name Rosarose) is an accomplished organist whose pious melodies awaken in the heart of Jacapone (the erstwhile bookworm and recently appointed doctor of law) an erotic longing akin to the "wounds of love" inflicted upon the university student Meliore by the "devout singer." There are, as a matter of fact, several striking parallels in the respective romances of the two sisters and their ultimate resolution. For instance, Rosarosa's organ music captivates the realm of nature in a manner analogous to that in which Biondette's harp enthralled the nightingales:

> Längs den still beblumten Feldern
> Wiegen sich die vollen Rosen,
> Von den Tönen tief beweget
> Einer süß gerührten Orgel.[17]
>
> (W I 800)

These same sounds strike at the innermost being of Jacapone and, in a sense, restore him to emotional life after years of self-imposed seclusion:

> So fand er sich tief beweget
> Und dem Bücherstaub entronnen,
> Neue Liebe in dem Herzen.[18]
>
> (W I 801)

The scene portraying Jacapone standing on the threshold of the tiny chapel in which Rosarosa performs is reminiscent of Eurydice following Orpheus' song to the gateway of life:

> Und er wurzelt auf der Schwelle;
> Rosarose schlägt die Orgel
> Singend, ohne ihn zu sehen,
> Zwischen Engelbildern golden.
>
> Auf dem kleinen Orgelwerke
> Steht das Bild der Mutter Gottes;[19]
>
> (W I 801)

[17] "Along the quietly flowered fields / The full roses gently sway, / Deeply moved by the tones / Of a sweetly-touched organ."

[18] "So he found himself deeply moved / And released from the dust of books, / New love in his heart."

[19] "And he is rooted at the threshold; / Rosarosa strikes the organ / Singing, without seeing him, / Between golden angel figures. // Upon the small organ / Stands an image of the Mother of God."

The modifications of the Orphean situation, however, are significant.
The "pagan" Greek lyre has become a Christian organ; the threshold
to a "new" life is not the boundary between the upper and lower worlds
but a religious shrine; the Orphean performer, in this case, does not
turn around nor is she even aware of her "feat"; she simply keeps her
glance fixed on the object of religious devotion, the Madonna.

The ambivalent aspect of music, however, comes into play with
regard to the erotic message that Jacapone reads into these essentially
religious melodies. In order for this to happen, Jacapone must experience a strange malfunctioning of the senses similar to that which
afflicted Meliore and Biondette. Jacapone is deluded into believing for
a moment that Amor, rather than the divine child Agnus Castus, provides the generating power for these tones:

> Und die leichten Bälge tretend
> Sieht er [Jacapone] einen goldumlockten,
> Schönen Knaben freudig schweben.
> Ach! er glich dem Liebesgotte,
>
> Wäre nicht so fromm sein Wesen;[20]
>
> (W I 802)

In order to dispel all doubts concerning his identity, the boy makes the
purpose of his actions clear:

> "Ich will singen, ich will beten;
> Schlag auch meinem Lied die Orgel!"
>
> . . . .
>
> Und er singt, die Bälge tretend,
> Wie ein Engel klar aus Wolken:[21]
>
> (W I 804)

This clarification, together with the absence of any allusion to the
"sacred serpents of song," confirms the impression that Rosarosa and
Jacapone will not be endangered by incest to the same degree as that
which threatened Biondette and Meliore. Jacapone, too, is fully cognizant of the spiritual "death" from which this music rescued him:

> "Ach, wie auf so sel'ge Wege
> Hast du, Jungfrau, mich gelocket!

---

[20] "And treading the light bellows, / He [Jacapone] sees a handsome lad,
/ Golden-tressed, joyously soaring. / Alas! He would resemble the Love-god,
// Were not his bearing so devout."
[21] "'I would sing, I would pray; / Play the organ for my song too!' // . . .
And he sings, treading the bellows, / Like an angel from the radiant clouds."

Aus dem dunklen Bücherkerker
In den Blumensaal der Sonne,
Zu der heimlichen Kapelle,
In den sel'gen Klang der Orgel!"[22]
(W I 805)

The repetition of the adjective "selig" in this context has a counterpart in the duplication of the adverb "freudig" in the following passages describing the mood and mode of Rosarosa's music after she and Jacapone subsequently become man and wife but live in a "chaste" conjugal relationship:

Sie setzt freudig sich zur Orgel,
Läßt ein Requiem erschwellen
Recht in freudig vollem Tone.[23]
(W I 819)

A "joyous requiem"—almost a contradiction in terms—is possible because Rosarosa knows that her marriage with Jacapone (her half-brother) represents a probationary period during which the hereditary guilt weighing heavily upon their family can be expiated—at least in part—by an act of abstention. Under such circumstances, Thanatos, which comes in the wake of Melos and Eros, is actually a welcome release. Consequently, Rosarosa's plea to Biondette after sustaining fatal injuries in the theater blaze:

"Singe mir ein Lied zur Harfe,
Daß die Seele vor dem Tode
Auf dem Klang vorüber wandle!"[24]
(W I 845)

Her sister eagerly complies:

Da ergreifet Rosadore
Geistberauschet ihre Harfe,
... süße Töne lockend.[25]
(W I 845)

---

[22] " 'Oh, how you did entice me, / Virgin, onto such blissful paths. // From the dark dungeon of books / Into the flower-hall of the sun, / To the secret chapel, / Into the blissful organ tone!' "

[23] "She sits down joyously at the organ, / Lets a requiem swell / In a full and joyous tone."

[24] " 'Sing me a song to the harp, / So that my soul before death / Might journey across upon the sound!' "

[25] "Then Rosadora, / Spiritually enraptured, seizes her harp, / ... calling forth sweet tones."

In contrast to Biondette's frantic attempt to thwart Meliore's death by intoning music which is "lustberauschet" (intoxicated with desire), the sounds she produces here are "geistberauschet" (intoxicated with spirituality), still in keeping with the ethereal plane of spiritual trans-figuration to which this Eurydice is to be elevated. The quandary that plagued Biondette and Meliore never seems to have touched Rosarosa's life; her ties with the transcendental remain unbroken. This situation is also reflected in the organ symbol, especially in the scene in which Rosarosa describes that magnificent cathedral to be erected in her memory, an edifice that is to rise from the charred ruins of the opera house. She requests that this shrine be filled with angelic sounds and, as we learn from a subsequent passage, the choirs of heaven do join in antiphonal interplay with the tones of the organ:

"Und Gesang und Klang der Orgel
Durch die Säulenwälder wachsen."
(W I 859)

"Durch der Kirche hohe Bogen
Himmelschöre nieder drangen!"[26]
(W I 860)

The Ethos of Harmony

According to the analysis of the Orpheus myth by Walther Rehm, it was not the actual harmonies of the singer's lyre that were of para-mount importance, but rather the "harmony of the worlds," which these tones represented. With regard to Brentano's application of the harmony concept (together with its converse—discord, dissonance, or cacophony), four such "worlds" or areas of applicability might be dis-tinguished: the aesthetic, the personal, the social (or political), and the transcendental. Whereas the first classification (aesthetic harmony and discord) can be fairly well isolated for purposes of discussion, the other three categories are closely interwoven, so that in any attempt to treat them as separate entities some overlap will result.

The aesthetic harmony experienced in conjunction with a work of art is, according to Brentano's formulations, the result of several fac-tors: the harmony which the observer, listener, or reader imparts to an

---

[26] " 'And song and sound of the organ / Soar through the pillar-forest.' 'Through the high arches of the cathedral / Heavenly choirs downward thronged!' ' "

artifact; the contribution made by the performer as intermediary between artistic conception and audience reception; the intrinsic qualities
of balance, proportion, and symmetry in the work. To illustrate the
first of these conditions, one might cite a remark of Godwi's friend
Römer, when he comments on the harmonic potential of an Arcadian
landscape portrayed in a tapestry "that always harmonizes well with
me [Römer] whenever, falling into slumber, I let the ritardando, dec-
rescendo, and diminuendo of my present life resound" (W II 53). The
function of the performer in establishing a harmonious atmosphere is
underscored by Brentano when he lauds the singing of his sister Sophie,
commenting especially on her "slender ivory neck, from which emerge
nightingale melodies, while her dainty marble hand . . . draws golden-
toned harmony from the zither" (U 37). This bit of preciosity is then
augmented by several lines of verse:

> Ihr Füßchen hebt im Tanz sich schön,
> Ihr Leib trägt dann das Haupt empor.
> Voll Anmut weiß sie sich zu drehn,
> Zu folgen Takt und Musikchor. u.s.w.[27]
>
> (U 38)

The Schillerian grace and controlled mastery of the aesthetic media is
a trait shared by the fictitious actress Psyche in the *Briefe über das
neue Theater* (1818): her nightingale tones and imposing demeanor
represent "the resounding figure of the most magnificent, most harmonious soul" (W II 1164).

Balanced structure, symmetry, and proportion in a work of art
is, of course, a prime factor in evoking a sense of harmony. In *Gustav
Wasa*, for example, the theater (which as "the total edifice" becomes
an actual stage figure in the farce) declares that all its component parts
are "harmoniously bound" (W IV 56), even though the chaotic impression produced by this parodistic piece belies any claim to such an
attribute. Amidst the apparent confusion of another of Brentano's
youthful productions, *Godwi* (designated by the author as "an in-
tractable novel"), Römer functions as a spokesman of aesthetic harmony. For instance, following a disturbing personal experience, he
tells of his intention to attend a concert "in order to see if harmony
could call my sweet raptures to life again" (W II 64). As in the *Roman-*

---

[27] "Her dainty foot is lifted artfully in dance, / She holds her head high.
/ Full of grace she knows how to twirl, / How to follow the beat and the chorus,
etc."

zen vom Rosenkranz, however, Brentano so manipulates the threads of the plot that the music which Römer hears in the concert hall stems from the very source—Lady Molly Hodefield—which had caused his spiritual discord in the first place. In the same novel, the pictorial arts are likewise examined from the point of view of their inherently harmonious and harmonizing features: thus it is maintained of Francesco Firmenti's paintings and arabesques that they contain "much harmony and music" (W II 168–169).

What is disturbing about the above passages dealing with aesthetic harmony is the fact that Brentano refrains from any explanation or analysis of the phenomenon. And even when he attempted to clarify the concept on later occasions—as in the *Erklärung der Sinnbilder*—the results are far from conclusive: "Whereas the level rests there," he notes in conjunction with Orpheus, "the shepherd's flute rests here, for nature builds only according to the laws of harmony" (W II 1050). We do gain some insight into the nature of artistic harmony, however, from an occasional poem (1816) written in honor of the architect Karl Schinkel, which speaks of structural design in terms that recall the towering cathedral erected by Biondette's melodies:

> Ich weiß, Grundtöne führen Dir den Plan
> Und Harmonieen wiegen Dir ihn aus
> Und Melodieen treiben bis zum Strauß
> Des Gipfels Dir die Linien hinan,
> Kein Zug läuft eigenwillig seine Bahn,
> Und macht auf eigne Hand sich blumenkraus,
> Du pflanzest nicht auf tolles Formgebraus,
> Nein auf organ'sche Gipfel nur den Hahn.[28]
>
> (W I 342)

A key concept here with reference to aesthetic harmony is the stress placed on that principle of organic development which coordinates each facet of the work with the other components and prevents the arbitrary domination of a single aspect to the detriment of the whole. Similar attributes are stressed in the following section of a letter of 1816 in which Brentano discusses "a tiny booklet" sent to him by Arnim: "But on no book does such a blessing lie as upon Kempis. It is

---

[28] "I know, fundamental tones guide your ground-plan / And harmonies calibrate it for you / And melodies drive the lines onward / To the crest of the peak, / No stroke goes its own self-willed way, / Making itself flowery and frilly in its own right, / You did not place the pinnacle on a wild, unruly structure, / But rather only on organically evolving peaks."

again proof to me that beauty, peace, harmony are the result of a balanced development of the entire inner substance and its external appearance: these are always the hallmark of perfection, also in spiritual life. Kempis is eternal, and a Christian work of art" (S II 148). From this passage it is difficult to ascertain whether the "Harmonie" in question applies to a book *by* Thomas à Kempis or to a work *about* him. No matter which of these possibilities is intended, however, it is evident that Brentano, at this stage in his career, found in the coincidence of outer appearance and inner essence a prime requisite of harmonious Christian art.

In view of the above hypothesis, it is somewhat surprising to find that the poet was more inclined to comment on the aesthetic discord which he found in various religious works than on their concordant features. But instead of employing the specific terms "Mißton," "Dissonanz," or "Disharmonie" to describe such conditions, Brentano prefers to draw attention to this discord indirectly by pointing to discrepancies between the artistic quality of the work in question and the expectations of the discriminating church-goer. The implication of this form of comment might be this: if the artistic facets of church life are characterized by disharmony, does this perhaps indicate that the spirit of religious devotion from which they spring could also be "out of tune" with the requirements of faith? For example, when recording his impressions of a baroque church in Dülmen in a letter of 1818, Brentano decries the presence of paraphernalia from the Lutheran service in this originally Catholic edifice; such alien elements disrupt the "inner unity and harmonious opulence" (GS VIII 277) of the building. In a tongue-in-cheek aside he adds: "They have already exchanged the painted organ for an elegant commode" (GS VIII 277). Because of the symbolic significance which the harmonies of the organ assumed in an ecclesiastical milieu, Brentano appears to have been particularly disturbed when the music performed on this instrument fell short of the highest artistic standards. Thus he complains in 1826: "The services and church singing are totally chaotic, and the organists are as posessed by the evil one" (GS IX 132) and laments in another passage about the decline of liturgical practices with reference to the inferior quality of organ music:

> Oh, if God would but for one-half year give the organ human voice and words, or make all Christian ears *clairouiants*, what experiences would be had in the services! For never have such heresies, debasements,

blasphemies, obscenities . . . been conceived, *as are daily ground out
in barrel-organ fashion (georgelt) in many places, particularly in the
German churches!*[29]

Concerning religious pictorial art—especially that practiced by the
group of painters known as the Nazarenes—Brentano detects certain
discrepancies in their mode of presentation, and he remarks near the
end of his life (1839): "Then, I never was a patron of those curiously
wide-open Overbeck angels' 'chops' either, which could just as easily
be eating macaroni as singing, etc." (S II 370). The avoidance of specific terms denoting discord and disharmony with reference to religious
art also carries over into Brentano's observations on the dissonances
in his own religiously oriented writings. For instance, when character-
izing the *Tagebuch der Ahnfrau* of 1835 and comparing it with the
Chronika eines fahrenden Schülers (original 1802, revised version
1818), Brentano admits that the former represents a work "which I
had not yet brought into harmonious bearing with the tone of the
same" [*Chronika*] (W III 628). The tendency either to paraphrase
the discordant features of art or to circumvent them by means of litotes
and other rhetorical devices did not persist, however, when Brentano
approached the problem of harmony or its negative counterpart in
either the personal, the sociopolitical, or the transcendental spheres.

Harmony on the level of the individual personality can be found
in two principal modes throughout Brentano's writings: the harmonious condition that results when the emotional and intellectual faculties
of the individual operate in balanced proportion with no single component tending toward excess; and the harmony stemming from the
congruence of inner essence and outer appearance. This latter condition prevails when the surface image is not simply a façade or mask
("Schein," or appearance) but rather the true reflection of the inner
self ("Sein," essence or true being). The following discussion will
demonstrate that whereas Brentano prescribed both of these facets of
personal harmony for others and praised those individuals in whom he
found them exemplified, neither of them proved to be a permanent
feature of his own spiritual constitution.

The metaphor of the "harmonious" soul or personality has been
a standard *topos* in the poetic repertoire long before Brentano began

[29] Johannes B. Diel and Wilhelm Kreiten, *Clemens Brentano: Ein Lebensbild
nach gedruckten und ungedruckten Quellen.* 2 vols. (Freiburg im Breisgau:
Herder'sche Verlagshandlung, 1877–1878), II, 347–348.

writing.[30] He frequently drew upon the conventional frame of reference before making his own distinctive contribution to the traditional concept. Shortly after meeting Sophie Mereau, for instance, he alludes to her as a "harmonious soul" (U 111), more in the spirit of flattery than in an effort to give an honest appraisal of her character. Consequently he later speaks of the necessity of inculcating the virtue of "harmony" in her and writes with Kleistian pedagogical zeal: "Only . . . in a constituent union of harmonious forces is there permanence" (SB II 53). He advises an equally strong-willed woman—his sister Bettina— that she combat the disorder of the world by fostering "the complete harmony of feelings" (F 11). To another sister, Cunigunde, he suggests cultivating a talent for dispassionate, objective judgment, an attribute possessed by either "the person harmoniously formed by God" (U 293)—Brentano cites Arnim as an example—or "the detached, methodical individual" (U 293)— for which Savigny serves as a model. Brentano's line of argumentation must have been persuasive, for Bettina subsequently married Arnim, and Cunigunde later became Savigny's wife. Nevertheless, the personal harmony cited in connection with these respective suitors is not without negative under- and overtones.

Whereas Brentano frequently referred to Savigny in such terms as "You just and harmonious one" (U 457) and constantly sought the companionship of the budding jurist in the belief "that the proximity of a imperturbable, ever harmonious person" (U 378) would impart stability and permanence to his own career, he also suspected that the "Harmonie" attained by his brother-in-law had been acquired at too high a price: namely, at the cost of creative fantasy and the imaginative faculty. This was a compromise which Brentano was neither prepared nor able to make. The dubious nature of such a state of enforced "harmony" can be seen in the figure of "die Brünette" from the "bureau d'esprit" in Godwi. The milieu in which she resides serves as an "objective correlative" of her well-ordered, intellectual household: "The exceedingly simple . . . harmonious, yet colorful furnishings of the chamber show at once that a woman lives here who holds the world and its substance within herself" (W II 209). The wordplay (the German reads: "ihren Inhalt in sich hält") with which the above

---

[30] See, for instance, Margaret Ives' article "Musical Elements in Schiller's Concept of Harmony," *German Life and Letters*, 18 (1964–1965): 111–116, or her more extensive treatment of the subject in *The Analogue of Harmony: Some Reflections on Schiller's Philosophical Essays* (Pittsburgh: Duquesne University Press, 1970).

passage concludes, however, warns the reader that there may be questionable aspects to a mastery of life acquired in this fashion. This suspicion is undergirded by a later characterization in which what initially appeared to be a very positive attribute is unmasked in its spiritual limitations:

> She is a perfect being that resounds eternally in all the strings that are stretched over the tone-breadth of her resonant existence, and wherever she is, she is so totally interwoven into being there that she echoes in all points of "somewhere."
>
> What rules her and what surrounds her is the variation of her own theme, unfortunately more the song of society than divine poetry. (W II 209)

The negative inferences of the above lines are recapitulated by Römer in his final assessment of her overall personality:

> And if I could ... set her to music, then she would have to play the whole picture with her very artificial resignation on her small piano with her small fingers, she would have to sing with her fine voice, so that it would not sound ever-lovingly boring. (W II 209)

In spite of the somewhat critical stance taken by Brentano with reference to those who—in fact or in fiction—acquired a state of emotional equilibrium by suppressing certain potentially disruptive forces in their makeup, he eventually came to regard a balanced temperament as the *non plus ultra* of human personality. While serving as the recording secretary for Anna K. Emmerich, for example, he informed Luise Hensel that the stigmatic visionary prayed daily "that you [Luise] might develop harmoniously in every respect" (GS VIII 411). He went on to define "harmonisch" as "without tension and struggle," "childlike," "uncomplicated" (GS VIII 411)—in short, in terms of a host of attributes which he felt were lacking in himself. It was also during and after his contact with the Dülmen nun that Brentano discovered the sense of spiritual concord that prevailed in the lives of his Catholic friends. Apollonia Diepenbrock, for instance, is characterized as "the . . . extraordinarily harmonious Appel,"[31] while Brentano finds in her brother, Melchior, "more that is splendid and harmonious than in any contemporary known to me [Brentano]" (GS IX 48). Undoubtedly, the "beautiful Christian tone and melody of character" (S II 248)

---

[31] *Clemens Brentano und Apollonia Diepenbrock: Eine Seelenfreundschaft in Briefen,* ed. Ewald Reinhard (Munich: Parcus, 1924), p. 27.

which he found in certain Catholic acquaintances aided in their attaining a harmonious equilibrium. During the 1830s Brentano was still applying this term of approval to those devoted to the task of caritas or other community service. For example, the deaconess of a Catholic school for girls is lauded for having led a life that fused "understanding and fullness of heart in more beautiful harmony" (GS IX 284) than most others. Such a condition stands in sharp contrast to the author's own career, which, in spite of his return to the Catholic Church, remained under the sway of the unruly, imaginative faculty. There is more truth than poetry in his famous confessional statement of 1842: "We had nurtured nothing but fantasy, and it had partly eaten us up again" (GS IX 423), in spite of both the temporal ("had . . . eaten us up") and modal ("partly") qualifications.

The second facet of personalized harmony—that involving a coincidence of physical appearance and spiritual essence—is not necessarily depicted in every case with reference to the term "Harmonie" or its derivatives, but rather assumes a variety of diverse forms and is represented by various life situations. Note, for instance, the following remark of the poet from the year 1800: "Each day is different in my world, and if I could follow this change, then, I would live in a lovely but inconsistent harmony. But I am unfortunately always too much the same . . . always so much the same, that my inner being often stands in the most peculiar contrast to my outward appearance. There is never any change in me at all, only simplicity or duplicity" (S I 48–49). Axiomatically—and yet paradoxically—Brentano maintains that the only stable factor in his life is the persistence of a discordant clash between outward representation and inner constitution. And yet in the very same year in which this perceptive statement was made, Brentano created a fictional character—the "Sänger"—whose appearance was indeed a hieroglyphic of his innermost soul. Therefore, Julie, for whom "every disharmony . . . is terrible" (W II 496), lauds him as one of those individuals "in whom the inner harmony is still recognized with the eyes and without comparison, where all halftones still appear throughout the entire being and where the most secret relationship is visible" (W II 502). Of course, the fortuitous coincidence of "Schein" and "Sein" in this case does not reflect the kind of inner serenity that Brentano postulated for Thomas à Kempis; instead, the "Sänger" reveals by his unruly demeanor the restlessness and existential malaise that torments his soul. However, in another fictional hero from the same period—Godwi—the converse of this situation holds true. Godwi, like Julie, is easily disturbed "by a small discord" (W II 162), and he registers his dismay at the fact that inner feelings and the outer forms of life so frequently are at odds with one another:

> O Römer! so much joy dwells about us and languishes unrecognized, but we go proudly by and our boisterous conduct makes the tender daughter of heaven so shy. In the harmonious chord of our outer and inner life she comes to embrace us. Only a few chosen ones achieve the return of a self-created, beautiful world of art into themselves, into loving, living nature, and all those who lamented were not able to reach the octave higher and are too proud to return from the few tones they have achieved into the echo of the pure fundamental. (W II 118)

Throughout Brentano's works, discrepancies which exist between "Appearance" and "Being" are associated with a literary symbol that subsumes both elements: the mask. Since the present analysis is primarily concerned with musical traits in literature, the discussion will be confined to examples of the "mask of music" (even though the masquerade, the masked ball, the concept of "role playing," and to a certain extent, even the modern facet of "games people play" might also be included).[32]

A standard feature of Brentano's musical masks is the fact that his masqueraders are invariably poor players who, in strutting their hour upon the stage, allow the reader—either willingly or unwittingly—to penetrate their disguise, to perceive a discord that belies the merry tunes they sing. The most frequent manifestation of this condition is found in the motif of "singing-weeping" (singen-weinen). As with many of the musico-poetic variations of Orphean themes treated thus far, there are several forms which the "singen-weinen" components can take. For example, there are those occasions when the artist actually seeks to bring his audience to the brink of tears; thus Valerio, in *Ponce de Leon*, declares: "I shall sing you a tune such that you will weep" (W IV 140). More often, however, the listener misses or misinterprets the deep-seated tragedy in the heart of the singer owing to the veneer of gaiety under which such a performer hides his sorrows. It was against this very form of aesthetic disguise that Kierkegaard inveighed in his well-known polemic directed specifically at the Romantic poet: "What is a poet? An unhappy man who bears burning

---

[32] See the chapter "Das Spiel der Maskierten: Brentanos 'Ponce de Leon'" in *Die ernste Komödie* by Helmut Arntzen (Munich: Nymphenburger Verlagshandlung, 1968), pp. 156–168.

pains in his heart, but whose lips utter loud sighs which sound to the uninitiated ear like beautiful music."[33] Since this latter possibility intrigued Brentano, the manner in which a performer conceals or reveals his inner sorrow through a mask of boisterous melody in an attempt to delude either his audience or himself will serve as the focal point for the following analysis of harmony.

In a letter of 1801 to Savigny, Brentano tries to make it clear to this "Harmonischen" that not all individuals are able to experience the same degree of concord in life which the budding jurist enjoys. To illustrate his point, Brentano tells of an occasion when he was compelled to feign happiness, quite contrary to his mental disposition at the moment:

> Now I am to ... express noble feelings and am so sad, so joyless. In Frankfurt there was a band of musicians at the last fair, you know them, the gayest of the lot, everybody danced when they played; they blew on satyr-flutes which they held aloft; there was a poor devil among them who had a fever and who had to blow on and on. I don't know anything more terrible—that is the way I feel now. (U 213)

The fictional *locus classicus* of the above dilemma is the novel *Godwi*. In the dedication of the work to the Reichenbach sisters, Brentano speaks of his bizarre appearance and adds that this is "shattered" and "unharmonious" (W II 14). On the other hand, the principal spokesman for musico-poetic-existential ties in the novel, Lady Hodefield, hides the discord in her present *modus vivendi* beneath a "harmonious exterior" (W II 20), even though there is little hope that the true harmony of her being can ever be restored: "They have taken so much from me, that in the harmony of my existence they have crushed whatever still belongs to me" (W II 61). The condition enunciated here by Lady Hodefield is amplified by her son, Römer, and experienced vicariously and existentially by the "author," Maria.

One evening, as Römer sits alone in his room, "a groaning, broken tone" (W II 200) emanates from the street beneath his window. Having ascertained that the singer in question performs religious music in order to eke out a livelihood, Römer comments: "Alas, how sad it is that this man must sing because of poverty, and that all notes that might become sighs and laments are forced to take on the manner of joyful tones and of exultation, by which means the touching veneer

---

[33] Søren Kierkegaard, *Gesammelte Werke*, I (Jena: Eugen Diederichs, 1911), 17.

of such songs arises" (W II 200). Subsequent to this, it is Maria who dons the mask of music; although mortally ill and completely removed from the sphere of sensual pleasure, the frustrated poet must relate Godwi's amorous adventures on the Rhine in order to earn enough money to cover his [Maria's] funeral expenses. Maria's appraisal of his task is unequivocal: "Dear reader, if you knew how sad it is to sing, to sing merry songs and be scarcely able to move one's lips, much less the heart" (W II 395). Whereas the motivation for singing joyously through a veil of tears was in both the above instances poverty, the basis for the music of the morose merry minstrels themselves is either spiritual turmoil or physical torment:

> Ich habe meinen Freund verloren,
> Und meinen Vater schoß man tot,
> Mein Sang ergötzet eure Ohren,
> Und schweigend wein ich auf mein Brot.
>
> . . . .
>
> Die hellen Becken muß ich schlagen
> Und ward von vielem Weinen blind.
>
> . . . .
>
> Ich muß die lustgen Triller greifen,
> Und Fieber bebt durch Mark und Bein,
> Euch muß ich frohe Weisen pfeifen,
> Und möchte gern begraben sein.
>
> . . . .
>
> Ich habe früh das Bein gebrochen,
> Die Schwester trägt mich auf dem Arm,
> Aufs Tambourin muß rasch ich pochen—
> *Sind wir nicht froh? daß Gott erbarm!*[34]
>
>   (W II 399–400)

Crippled in both mind and body, these minstrels stress the compulsion to sing (four of the troupe explicitly use the verb "müssen"; in the other case, necessity is implied). And yet not even the mask of music (represented here by the boisterous refrain that resounds after each

[34] "I have lost my friend / And they shot my father dead, / My song delights your ears, / And silently I weep upon my bread. // ...I must strike the bright cymbals / Although blind from much weeping.... // ...I must strum merry trills / And fever quivers through marrow and bone, / I must pipe merry tunes for you / And would like to be buried. // ...I injured my leg when I was young, / My sister carries me on her arm, / I must pound the tambourine briskly— / Aren't we gay? may God have mercy!"

stanza) is in itself adequate to conceal their anguish, but must be supplemented by the cover of darkness:

> Doch sind wir gleich den Nachtigallen,
> Sie singen nur bei Nacht ihr Lied,
> Bei uns kann es nur lustig schallen,
> Wenn uns kein menschlich Auge sieht.[35]
>
> (W II 398)

The protective shield of night prevents the wretched plight of the singers from becoming apparent to the audience, while, on the other hand, their incessant refrain allows the private grief that each has voiced in his "monologue" to find musical—that is, implicit rather than explicit—expression:

> Um Kling und um Klang,
> Um Sing und um Sang
> Schweifen die Pfeifen, und greifen
> Ans Herz,
> Mit Freud und mit Schmerz.[36]
>
> (W II 396)

The discriminating listener will recognize the tragic roots of this joyful song. In order to make certain that the reader would always remain aware of the element of dissonance between the beautiful aesthetic format and the ugly existential form from which it so often sprang, Brentano deliberately had his poetic counterparts alert their audience to such discrepancies.[37]

All aspects of harmony treated up to this point presuppose two divergent concepts of musical harmony, each of which has a distinct historical background. The term "harmonia" in music from the ancient Greek world through the medieval period implied a form of monody in which individual phrases and tonal intervals were balanced and proportioned in accordance with the structure of the entire phrase (to describe this principle, one might borrow Lessing's words from *Laokoön*: "Nacheinander in der Zeit," succession in time). The "har-

---

[35] "Yet we are as the nightingales, / They sing their song only by night; / We can only resound merrily / When no human eye sees us."

[36] "With tinkling and tone, / With singing and song / The pipes ramble and seize / The heart / With joy and with pain."

[37] For representative samplings of examples ranging from 1802 to 1834, see: W I 131, W I 385, W I 567, and W IV 662.

monia" of post-Renaissance music, on the other hand, signified the simultaneous sounding and euphonious blending of two or more tones ("Nebeneinander," or "simultaneity," to borrow another term from Lessing's essay). Both modes of harmony came into play and interplay when Brentano expressed his views on different forms of social intercourse by means of musical metaphors of harmony.[38]

That personal harmony was a necessary prerequisite for any type of social interaction can be inferred from a comment made by the poet to Bettina in 1801, when he compared the world in which they lived to a "woven fabric, in which the harmonious development of each human being must be a necessary and durable thread" (F 15). The initial stage of progression from intra- to interpersonal harmony entails the establishment of rapport with specific individuals. Once this has been accomplished, then integration into, or accommodation with, larger social units can be undertaken.

A sense of spiritual accord was essential to the most intimate of human relationship—the love of one person for another. In *Godwi*, the resolution of what Brentano termed the "harmony of love" (W IV 35) ran the gamut from ethereal concord to jarring discord. Lady Molly Hodefield, for instance, is only able to find a harmonious resolution to the dissonance of her amorous affairs in an entirely unexpected source: her illegitimate son, Römer, about whom she says: "Oh, if everyone who struck a dissonant chord in love could save himself with this harmony" (W II 104). Since Godwi's glance is directed toward the "eternal feminine," no finite particular can sustain a harmonious relationship with him for more than a brief span—not even Otilie, who seems to embody "a series of lovely feminine forms in harmonious waves" (W II 141) and who appears to transform time into eternity for him:

> Oh, what a quiet change in me; in measured rhythm the moments stride along, like the notes for a beautiful melody of life, and if my spirit wanders through all the chords on harmonic paths linking the one to the other, then it attains not uncommonly . . . a peak where all measured time gives way and the song peers freely and unfettered into eternity. (W II 130–131)

In the final analysis, not even Otilie is equal to the task of supplying more than an occasional harmonic interval in the discordant melody of the protagonist's life.

[38] For a detailed historical discussion of these concepts of harmony, see Hollander (n. 2 above), pp. 26–31.

With reference to the role of "harmony" between the individual and the social strata on a more comprehensive level, Brentano formulated the following key ideas in a letter of 1802 to Bettina:

> However, that consistency which is worth something, which indeed alone determines the worth of man, is a musical one; it is harmony in the broadest sense, and it will only modulate in harmonic transitions, inasmuch as an individual is more or less contiguous with all of life, encompassing more or fewer keys and modulations. Now to the extent that he is simply the theme of the entire piece of music, his movement is out of himself and he can have character; but to the extent that he contributes to the total harmony, he has only the character of his instrument; but his life is without character, only a part of the total harmony. But we can only speak of this consistency of harmony with people of broader scope, for in order to become harmonious, one must already encompass a certain number of tones. (F 134)

By means of this extended musical analogy, Brentano expresses the fundamental existential dilemma of man as a creature who is both "independent of" and "dependent upon" the other echelons of society. In his "thematic" capacity, the individual possesses a distinctive timbre and performs a unique sequence of tones ("Nacheinander," in succession), a harmoniously proportioned solo melody which, by means of its variety, reflects many facets of experience (through key changes, modulations, rhythmic alterations, and so forth). Concomitant with this, however, is the obligation to contribute to the harmony of society as a whole by blending one's timbres and directing one's tones in such a manner that they complete the general chordal design and complement the tone quality and dynamic level of the entire social organism ("Nebeneinander").

The emotional upheavals of the hectic decade following this hypothesis of personal and social harmony (1802–1812), however, convinced Brentano that the dominant "melody of his life" (which he had incisively labeled no "adolescent tone in the minor key" shortly before the above letter) (S I 25) was simply not to be harmonized with the music of society as it was then constituted. Consequently, in 1813 he could write that poignant passage to Rahel Varnhagen cited in the first chapter of this study, revealing him as a soloist deserted by the orchestra, but defiantly carrying on with his melody until the tension becomes too overbearing.

It was not within the superstructure of the secular world that

Brentano would discover what he felt was the "harmony of communal life, in which all discordant tones are resolved" (U 496), but rather in the corporate body of the Catholic Church: "In the church, seen as a body which is to unite men who are of different opinion, divided, and bellicose into one loving, harmonic whole" (GS IV 367). Yet in the final analysis, even this projected harmonious resolution of the problems of individuation proved—at least in Brentano's case—to be a "deceptive cadence." Before this last phase of his development is traced, however, the wide range of social harmony in his works—extending from the idealistic dreams of youth to the "gentle harmonies" between man and beast (postulated in the late fairy tales)—will be outlined.

As he had revealed in his correspondence with Bettina, Brentano grappled with the problem of a harmonious integration of the individual into the social complex most extensively in those works written at the outset of his career. The poem "Phantasie," for instance, not only has stanzas "orchestrated" for various solo instruments (in Tieck's manner), but also contains two strophes marked "tutti" in which the thematic substance of the passage on "the consistency of harmony" is presented in verse form. The bassoon cautions in its solo: "Wer den eignen Ton nicht hört, / Lausche, bis er wiederkehrt" (W I 28).[39] This act of self-cognition becomes a preliminary step on the path from individual isolation to social integration:

> Es eilet jed Leben die eigene Bahn;
>
> . . . .
> Und reißet vom Ganzen nicht einer sich los;
> Doch blüht einem jeden das Ganze im Schoß.[40]
>
> (W I 29)

The early work which serves as a veritable compendium for all gradations of social harmony is, once again, *Godwi*. The titular hero appears to refute the premises of the poem "Phantasie" when he declares his aloofness from the "throng" as follows:

> I gladly lend my ear to the harmonies of others, gladly give away my tones to them; whether they please them or not, the great harmony does come forth. If such as myself were not present, this harmony (Einklang) would become a monotony (Einerleiklang); and who gives

---

[39] "He who hears not his own tone, / Let him listen, till it comes again."

[40] "Each life rushes its own way; / ... And not one tears itself loose from the whole; / In the heart of each individual blooms the totality."

the concert anyway, he who plays the solo, or those who provide the accompaniment? Without such as myself the general public would fall asleep out of boredom at the old *adagio* that you play eternally for the entertainment of all. (W II 42–43)

In spite of such arrogant claims, Godwi's air of flippant indifference is only sham, merely a façade concealing behind a blasé exterior the pressing need for social ties:

My heart beats so monotonously, so alone in my breast. Everything is harmony and melody, and everything sees itself as kindred in the arms of another, given life a second time, given a soul a second time.... Nature did not tune me so that every artist could unite my tones into a chord with the great general din. (W II 76)

In essence, the novel concentrates on the frustrations of those who, like the central figure, are unable to live for any extended period in harmony with others. Nevertheless, it does articulate the properties of such cherished relationships. Friendship, for instance, is seen as "the parallel flow of harmonious tones" (W II 361), an accord in which neither partner dominates, but in which each complements the musicality of the other "for the sake of the grand harmony of their undertaking" (W II 241). Love, on the other hand, is regarded as pure melody and contrasts with friendship in the following manner: "Love gives tone and music, friendship is just the juxtaposition of tones to melody, which is itself a product of love. Friendship dwells in love, but within itself there is no love, but only harmony, tone-relationship" (W II 241).

Admittedly, one aim of these complex musico-sociological excursions is to *épater le bourgeois*—the latter represented by Maria's companion, the pedestrian translator, Haber, on whom such subtle imagery is wasted. Yet these analogies do afford insight into the kind of social hierarchy envisioned by the poet during this age of change and transition. Maria evolves an even more complicated theory of harmonious group dynamics, which he combines with a syntactical analysis of language and grammatical principles. The musical portion of this involved passage reads:

The stages of growth, the station of individual friends, stands in the same relationship as ... tone, chord, phrase.... I carry about in my head the ideal of one who understands his fellow-man, who could categorize types of men into ... individual tone variations and who could really ... produce a thorough-bass of social life. By means of his thorough-bass alone, one could . . . find true friendship, which is rooted in laws just as secretive as the relationship of tones. One could then play entire national histories on the piano and chant them in verses, and life would have become art. (W II 241)

The concept of a "thorough-bass of social life" is reminiscent of the *topos* of the "body politic," a standard form of harmonic representation in the emblem literature of the seventeenth century.[41] Brentano revives this baroque configuration in a poem which is itself an "imitatio" of the work of a seventeenth-century writer, Martin Opitz: "Lied von eines Studenten Ankunft in Heidelberg und seinem Traum auf der Brücke" (1806). After the wandering student has surveyed the mirror image of Heidelberg in the waters of the Neckar, he finds his daydreams suddenly interrupted by a musical interlude; "Da hebt sich aber ein froher Klang, / In allen Türmen die Glocken schwanken, / Beginnen ein hell harmonisch Zanken" (W I 175).[42] The "harmonious quibbling" of the church bells is an introduction to the boisterous music that celebrates the restoration of the equilibrium in the state through the recovery of its ruler from serious illness. At the same time, these sounds and their antiphonal response suggest the continuity and perpetuation of this new-found harmony through the imminent marriage of the monarch's son and heir (W I 176–177). Ironically, during the same year in which these lines celebrating the restoration of political harmony in a provincial state were printed (1806) the German dream of national unity was abruptly terminated by the defeat of the Prussian forces at Jena. During his subsequent years in Berlin (1810), Brentano was ever alert to detect signs of political accord in the Prussian capital. He cited an instance of musical cooperation to underscore his hopes for the future: "Even the music academy is a splendid thing, where all classes that know something about music—housewives and noblemen—perform magnificent music in serious, proper union just as in church they kneel next to one another" (U 423). From this period until the fall of Napoleon, Brentano championed a harmonious alliance of European forces against the common enemy. He was particularly disturbed by any defection from this united front, as, for example, "when German fops sang the Marseillaise while sipping tea" (GS VII 345). His patriotic pageant "Am Rhein, Am Rhein" hails the restora-

---

[41] Hollander, pp. 47–48.
[42] "There arises then a joyful sound, / In all towers the bells are swaying, / They begin a brilliant, harmonious quibbling."

tion of harmony among the German states in allegorical form: "O freudige Gestalt, / Der Eintracht Becher stützt Concordia" (GS VII 497).[43]

The transition from sociopolitical concord to transcendental harmony is marked by a passage in the story *Die Schachtel mit der Friedenspuppe* (1814–1815). At one point in the narrative a chorus of children celebrates the favorable outcome of the Battle of Nations at Leipzig (1813), and their singing seems to receive divine approval when a meteor illuminates the horizon. All who witness this moving spectacle embrace, whereupon the author interjects the comment: "In true elation all chance ceases, this elation is infinite harmony" (W II 735). Many of Brentano's later poems contain hints of a harmony linking heaven and earth; an allegorical "Bildgedicht" (poem based on a painting) of 1832, for example, entitled "Transitus Apostolorum," represents what might be considered the literary counterpart to the painting of the Nazarene school and incorporates the view that divine harmony was manifest on earth in the concord of the apostles: "Der Lehre Saiten Gottes Engel stimmt, / In Eintracht sicher Petri Schifflein schwimmt" (GS I 180).[44] Finally, even the love he experienced toward Emilie Linder during the waning years of his life became immersed in a religiously transfigured light and was expressed in terms of harmonious music: "Thus we do not stand distant from each other and our tones resound up to God in the same chords" (EL 30).

The existence of a harmony in the universe, which transcended earthly life and linked man with the divine godhead, was a conviction which Brentano had expressed early in life. Those partaking of this experience seem to stand in an enviable light: "Nothing can disturb them," Brentano writes in 1802, "nothing can gladden them; they stand there in peaceful contemplation, for they know that pain and suffering in life are nothing but different modulations of tones that all come together again in the one great harmony in which the order of things exists and whose composer is God himself" (S I 152). Taken out of context, the above lines seem to denote an enviable group of individuals; however, this attitude changes when we read that the same faction is referred to as "inquisitive anatomists" (S I 152) and "deep thinking machines that dissect everything with their wheels ac-

---

[43] "O joyous sight, / Concordia supporting the beaker of harmony."

[44] "God's angel tunes the strings of doctrine, / Peter's ship floats securely in harmony."

cording to eternal laws" (S I 153). Such qualifications equivocate the positive impression the reader gains from this divinely ordained group, just as the epithets of Savigny, "you just and harmonious individual," had negative qualities that affected their affirmative value adversely. Brentano emphatically divorced himself from such a clique that is cognizant of the heavenly rewards in store for them; he casts his lot with those for whom presentiment replaces absolute certainty:

> No, . . . I am not the type, I am not so great and powerful as to reduce everything down to its basic parts, . . . to tear the resonant tongue out of tones in order . . . to trace everything back to the wave-lengths of some gut-strings through which the secret spirits of music are conjured up; and I will explain to you why I am sad . . . here I sit, and my yearning lies on the other side. . . . Thus man is separated from all divinity by a foreign element, and there only shines and resounds toward him a reflection of the splendor from the distance. (S I 153)

This passage brings to mind several well-known concepts. First of all, it is reminiscent of the quotation cited at the end of chapter 1 to illustrate Brentano's antianalytical approach to the art of music. Secondly, it anticipates the famous proclamation of Faust in Part II of the tragedy: "In mirrored hues we have our life and being." Finally, it reiterates the Orphean "threshold" condition in terms of a dichotomy between the world of God, the "divine composer," and the realm of man from which we can perceive only the reflected glory of His handiwork. And yet, during the most turbulent years of his life, Brentano was granted sudden insight into the nature of that music which God composed for mankind: in a letter of 1813 to Rahel Varnhagen, the recipient of many a personal confession, Brentano declared:

> Why am I not irreproachable, calm, modest, mild, industrious, chaste, pure, noble, clear-thinking, and discreet! Do I not have all the means in my hands, do I not stand in the midst of sacred Nature's harmony, which I am only allowed to resemble? But that is the deviltry: that the devil is even in nature, and that even dissonances are assimilated into the great harmony, and if one listens then with his intellect and with his wretched omniscience, then one thinks that people have always played correctly because the whole thing does come out in the end. . . . But man is even God himself and is free and has a knowledge of good and evil, and he should not play what the devil, who frequently distributes the notes, sets before him; he should fiddle from his own inner full score, and this is revealed to all in conscience, in religion, in all that is beautiful and sacred. (BP 100)

This personalized view of the Christian theodicy also reflects the crises inherent in the Orphean odyssey. Brentano is well aware that the Christian should not "fiddle with" the devil and that the latter's discords are not the dominant key but rather passing tones in the grandiose score which the deity has composed for mankind. Implicit in this critique is also an aesthetic principle—the realization that unadulterated harmony is dull, that the tensions introduced by tones and chords alien to the fundamental triad instill in the listener the desire to return to the tonic, that modulations to remote but related keys do not destroy the feeling for the original but actually reinforce the need to affirm it once more.

The Pathos of Love and Death

Brentano was certainly not unique in expressing the emotion of love (and, not infrequently as a complementary factor, death) in terms of musical imagery. The most familiar literary formulation of the triadic constellation of music, love, and death (for which one could employ the Greek concepts of Melos, Eros, and Thanatos) was that of Shakespeare in the opening lines of *Twelfth Night, or What You Will*: "If music be the food of love, play on! / Give me excess of it, that surfeiting, / The appetite may sicken and so die" (act 1, scene 1). The alliance of music and love pervades both Brentano's personal documents and his poetic writings in a variety of modes, some quite explicit, others more subtle, but all illustrative of a condition which Sidney Lanier articulated aphoristically a generation later: "Music is Love in search of a word."[45]

The link between music and love may exploit the ambivalence between maternal affection and erotic attraction, as in the poem of 1800:

> Du reichst mit deiner Liebe im Akkorde
> Ein Lebenslied, das sich zu dir gesellt;
> Erstorben ist die Sprache, wenige Worte
> Durchirren, sich verspätend, meine Welt;
> Da öffnest du in stiller Nacht die Pforte,
> Willkommen sind sie dir, und wohlbestellt
> Ist deine Hütte, meine Töne klingen
> Zu deinen gut ein sanftes Lied zu singen.

[45] From the poem "The Symphony" of 1877.

Ein zartes Lied, es kann es keiner lehren,
Es schaffet sich im inneren Gemüt,
Wo Sehnsucht, Lieb' und himmlisches Verkehren
Beisammen sind. In Liedes Busen glüht
Ein leises Bitten und ein still Gewähren.[46]

(W I 59)

The casual reader would hardly suspect that the bond referred to in
the above lines was that between mother and child. The poem "Gesang
der Liebe als sie geboren war" (better known as: "O Mutter halte
dein Kindlein warm") alludes to the security and intimacy of the
womb in the prenatal state, and closes with the mother-beloved's con-
soling words: "Und hab' dir kindisch Sorg' und Harm / In Liedern
weggesungen" (W I 169).[47] The act of maternal consolation through
song is reversed in an occasional poem of 1814 marking the death of
Baroness von Hügel: the latter's normally taciturn daughter communicates with her deceased mother in "Tönen, die allein unschuldig /
Sagen, was die Lieb' der Liebe schuldig" (W I 317).[48]

For Brentano, whose own mother had passed away so early in his
life, the quest for maternal affection expressed in terms of musical
image and metaphor became inextricably allied with his search for
love from those women who only too often served as surrogates for
the lost mother figure. The reactions he elicited from the various
women he encountered ranged from passive acquiescence to silent
indifference. One of his earliest attempts to strike a "related tone"
(U 137), for instance, resulted from his contact with Amalia Welsch
in 1797 (they were taking violin lessons together). Instead of develop-
ing into the "splendid duet" which Brentano originally envisioned,
however, their relationship deteriorated into a "wretched solo."[49]
The operatic—and somewhat melodramatic—framework erected here
was expanded by the poet in conjunction with another acquaintance:
Minchen Günderode, for whom Brentano harbored a passing infatua-

---

[46] "In accord with your love, you present / A song of life that allies itself
with you; / Language is dead, few words / Tardily stray through my world; /
Then, in the quiet of night you open the gate, / They are welcome to you, and
well-ordered / Is your hut, my tones sound / Well with yours in singing a gentle
song. // A tender song, no one can teach it, / It creates itself in the inner soul,
/ Where longing, love and heavenly communication / Are together. There glows
in the bosom of song / A gentle pleading and a tacit granting."

[47] "And have sung away your childish care and grief / In songs."

[48] "Tones which alone innocently / Tell, what love owes to love."

[49] Clemens Brentano: Briefwechsel mit Heinrich Remigius Sauerländer, ed.
Anton Krättli (Zurich: Artemis, 1962), p. 68.

tion rather than a deep-seated passion. Minchen is dubbed by him the "heroine of my opera," and she will, he predicts, fall into his arms at the conclusion of a long aria (F 228). This prima donna of his affections came to life a short while later in the music that Peter Ritter composed for *Die lustigen Musikanten*:

> My heroine . . . has enticed me into writing this opera, each day the conductor, Ritter, makes her grace resound in the loveliest melodies, and often I must tell it to her myself in tones. Even late at night I compose melodies for my verses, which Ritter assimilates into the opera with gracious acknowledgment. To me this all sounds very beautiful, even overpowering. But it cannot keep me from doubly serenading her, with melody and words. (F 263)

To several other women who caught Brentano's fancy during the period of his acquaintance with and growing alienation from Sophie Mereau (1798–1803) he addressed similar arguments. Even though he assured Minna Reichenbach that he spoke to her in an idiom which, like music, represented "communication with a higher world," and which could only be comprehended "from heart to heart,"[50] as it were, the response he received was stunned silence. A more favorable reaction, however, seems to have come from Gretchen (or Gritha) Hundhausen and her circle of friends (including Benedikte Korbach and Hannchen Kraus—the latter referred to often as "mein neuer Arnim," my new Arnim). Brentano complains that ever since Gritha and the others returned his guitar filled with rose petals he has resisted playing the instrument lest the resulting song (which now slumbers in the strings like a child in its cradle) disturb this tacit spokesman of their feelings:

> My guitar lies full of rose petals and does not sound. . . . As I saw the guitar being brought, my heart was throbbing; I scarcely dared to open it, for I would have wept and torn the strings had it not borne a sign from you. And how could you speak more pleasantly than with rose-lips! So pleasantly, as the music speaks, which utters no words that first have been borrowed from language, no, that takes, I should like to say, from the innermost heart of nature, from the secret workshop of God, the simple, eternal tones, understandable to all, and expresses their will. . . . The roses . . . do not speak; but the music also

[50] *Clemens Brentano und Minna Reichenbach: Ungedruckte Briefe des Dichters*, ed. W. Limburger (Leipzig: Insel, 1921), p. 42. Henceforth: L (page given in text). For examples of use of musical terminology with reference to his feelings toward Minna, see pp. 25, 80–81.

does not speak, and yet I understand it. . . . He who does not understand what music and spring say does not know what the new Arnim's
eyes say either. (S I 121–122)

Although he understands the mute language of the flowers only too
well, Brentano is not certain which of the women in question is responsible for this encouraging sign: "Alas, who tossed the rose petals
into the cradle of my songs, of my love" (S I 123). The metaphoric
equating of the guitar with both his music and his love indicates how
closely allied Melos and Eros were in his mind. From a later reference
it becomes clear that Hannchen Kraus placed the flowers in the instrument (S I 157), and when her interest in the poet apparently waned, he
threatened her—albeit in lighthearted fashion—with musical revenge:
"And I shall write all my songs to you, and have them set to music and
distribute them to all the ladies, so that you will encounter them on all
pianos. . . . Bettina will also visit you and sing . . . the songs about you
that I wrote to you."[51]

The rose-laden guitar speaking eloquently in silence, the operatic
scenario as the libretto of love, jocular threats of musical revenge for
unrequited affection—such was the tone Brentano used toward those
women who temporarily filled the void in his life caused by the estrangement from Sophie Mereau. In spite of an occasional melancholy
undertone, these musico-erotic allusions are distinctly "major" in
mood and "allegretto" in mode. The somber tone in the Melos-Eros
format of the letters to Sophie, on the other hand, is apparent even before their separation. For instance, he confides to a friend during his
courtship: "My S. M. is a faithful individual, and I gladly forgive her
when she does not understand how much I suffer, and when a beautiful, pure sound dies away without an echo" (S I 93). Only in himself
does he find a constant and consistent "theme and variations," which
is the refrain "Ich liebe Dich" (SB II 20). One of the best examples of
Brentano's "variations" is the following passage in which he implores
Sophie to become the "instrument" of his passion:

> Alas, all posthumous fame is indeed a funeral dirge, and all joy, all
> spring is to be found in God's presence. My beloved, string everything
> that is resonant in you like the strings of a lute, may your love become
> an ear, for my love will become a great musician, you shall hear songs

[51] Clemens Brentanos Liebesleben, ed. Lujo Brentano (Frankfurt am Main:
Frankfurter Verlags-Anstalt, 1921), pp. 89–90. Henceforth: LB (page given in
text).

resound in you, over you and from you, songs which you yourself will become; and finally, when I become an even greater artist of love, then I will find the scale for every discord and will also be able to sing on a single string to you how much I love you. (SB I 135–136)

A religiously tinged *unio mystica* is proposed here, an intimacy that applies on both the musical and the physical plane.

One striking feature of Brentano's correspondence with Sophie is the fact that the intensity and frequency of his musico-erotic images stands in inverse proportion to the geographical proximity of the partners. For example, during his journey to Berlin in 1804, Brentano received a note from his wife which closed, not with the customary "Ich liebe Dich," but rather with the jaunty quatrain from a popular song. This ambiguous message induced Brentano to reply: "I despair completely when I hear such words that sound like music to me, for they come from beloved lips, from your sweet, kissable lips, but I do not know how things stand in your heart" (SB II 130). Yet in a letter written before his departure for Berlin, Brentano complains to Arnim of the domestic squabbles in which he and Sophie are embroiled and hints at the need to break the chains that bind him: "All the locks of my chains say go! and that is sad; she does not love me, and when I dally with her she responds unmelodically, and when she is resting, then it is quiet and desolate in the dungeon, no sound" (S I 243).

The unmelodic chains of matrimony that bound Brentano to Sophie in the silent prison of domesticity were, however, "music to his ears" when compared with the clanking fetters with which Auguste Bußmann held him incarcerated. The marked absence of any musical allusions in his letters to her bear ample testimony to the fact that their relationship was also devoid of Melos and Eros. Even though Auguste was reputedly a guitarist of no mean skill, she abandoned this instrument, perhaps because of such comments of her spouse as the following: "Madame did not experience any maladies the following day except for a very violent singing with her guitar" (S I 362).

There is, however, a strange paradox that manifests itself with regard to Auguste Bußmann and the other women (principally Luise Hensel and Emilie Linder) who dominated Brentano's later life. Although the correspondence addressed to these respective ladies is, for the most part, barren of musico-erotic metaphor, the poetry written during the period of his acquaintance with each of them contains some of his most significant contributions to—and variations of—the

Melos-Eros-Thanatos theme. Aside from an occasional exception such as when he addresses Luise as a "pure, sonorous jewel"—"Du kluges, klares, klangvolles Kleinod" (S II 205)—Brentano appears to have refrained from incorporating musical imagery in these all too personal documents, preferring instead to weave them into a poetic context where the curtain of anonymity and noncommitment could be more tightly drawn.

Illustrative of the above situation are two poems which appeared in the *Zeitung für Einsiedler* (1808) and which can be correlated with the poet's precipitous courtship of Auguste (1807) and with his attempts to salvage their ill-fated marriage by demonstrating in poetry how the spirit of music fosters love. The first of these lyrics, "Die Einsiedlerin," is a dialogue between the recluse and her erstwhile lover in which the latter vows to divert her from an eccentric way of life through the power of his song of love echoing through the forest. Aided by the forces of nature, the singer succeeds in this undertaking. A similar fairy tale "happy ending" combines with modified Orphean motifs in the companion poem, "Auf einen grünen Zweig." Wandering through an enchanted forest, the singer discovers an artificial garden inhabited by a bird unable to move or sing owing to the toxic atmosphere of the environment.[52] The frantic attempts of the minstrel—who had previously renounced song as an effective means of transfiguring the hostile world around him—to revive the avian songstress by musical means eventually succeed, and the latter, upon awakening from a state of suspended animation, rewards its benefactor in kind: "Das Vöglein weiß so süß zu singen, / Es singt den armen Knaben reich" (W I 202).[53] In this poetic world of wish-fulfillment and make-believe, Brentano wrought more miracles through the transforming power of music than are dreamed of in real life, where only disappointment and disillusion proved to be his reward. Nevertheless, he never completely abandoned his naïve faith in the mysterious forces linking music and love.

In contrast to the fairy-tale aura and never-never-land atmosphere which characterizes these poems from the Auguste Bußmann period,

[52] For an analysis of the importance of the enchanted garden in Brentano's works, see Werner Vordtriede's article "Clemens Brentano's Novalis Experience," *Modern Language Quarterly*, 11 (1950): 73–78.

[53] "The little bird knows how to sing so sweetly, / It sings the poor boy to riches."

the Melos-Eros framework of the poetry written during his alliances (or misalliances) with Luise Hensel (1816–1819) and Emilie Linder (1833–1834) is religious and mythological respectively. In conjunction with the former, the principal musical allusion is angelic or seraphic song;[54] with regard to the latter, the classical figure of the Siren predominates.[55] Whereas the force of attraction in the song of the angel is uplifting and edifying, in that of the Siren it becomes degrading and destructive. To illustrate the first of the above frames of reference, the poem entitled "Ich bin durch die Wüste gezogen" (1816) may be cited. In the barren, sterile "desert" of life, the pilgrim—Brentano's poetic counterpart—finds comfort and consolation in angelic singing;

[54] There are, to be sure, sporadic allusions to angelic singing in Brentano's works before his encounter with Luise Hensel (about whom, however, the concept seems to cluster). For instance, in *Aloys und Imelde* the singing of the heroine is frequently compared with that of angels. Examples can be found in Clemens Brentano, *Sämtliche Werke*, ed. Carl Schüddekopf et al., 10 vols. (Munich and Leipzig: Georg Müller, 1909–1917), IX:2, 327. Henceforth: SW (directly in text).

[55] Biondette's foster-mother was known as "Sirene," and the latter's music —even her devotional hymns—had an aura of lush sensuality about them: "Siren / ... Sings on the moonlit threshold / To the tones of crystalline harps" (W I 730). The transition from the positive to the negative side of the siren figure in the *Romanzen* is marked by the use of the generic term "die Sirene" in place of the specific referent "Sirene." Kosme, the guilt-laden father of the half-siblings, hears the siren "singing again / Her venomous songs" and feels "the hearts sinking / Into the shallow, sweet delusion" (W I 723). Eventually, the term "siren" becomes associated with Biondette (W I 697; 883) and her Song of Songs did have the potential to drag Meliore down to the depths of incest. Later in his life, Brentano came to realize that the devastating effects of the siren's song were only possible with the overt or covert compliance of the listener. Thus an element of *amor fati* pervades the lines of "Gärtnerlied im Liedergarten der Liebe" (date uncertain) when the speaker portrays his acquiescence in hypothetical terms: "I would perish with rapture / Upon these crags / If, so fervently, / So fervently and sensuously, / The blossoming lips / Of the Siren of Song / Had joined me in singing" (GS II 276). In the numerous confessional statements of the 1820s condemning secular art, the term "Sirenentöne" (W I 454) or some variant of it paraphrases the target of attack. A journey to Paris in 1826 elicits a "fire and brimstone" denunciation of the city of sin, this place where "each one can hear the siren-song of seduction in his favorite melody, in his dialect, indeed, in the very beat of his own pulse" (GS IV 355). The Church became the firm "rock" to which he hoped to cling whenever the siren exercised her fatal allure (GS I 548). One of the more modern aspects of the siren motif introduced by Brentano is found in his dramatic fragment *Die stumme Engländerin* (one of many previously unpublished manuscripts held by the *Freies Deutsches Hochstift* for publication in the complete, critical edition) when the once vaunted songstresses reach the nadir of their art in the apex of ineffectiveness: "Sirens—yes, sing now—but they are completely silent—the crew namely is too stupid for love...." For a perceptive analysis of this problem see Heinz Politzer, "Das Schweigen der Sirenen," *Deutsche Vierteljahrsschrift für Literaturwissenschaft und Geistesgeschichte*, 41 (1967): 444–467.

note the progression in the following three stanzas from silent isolation to song-filled communion, from a burning wasteland to an oasis-like, paradisical garden:

> Da hört' ich ein Flügelpaar klingen
> Da hört' ich ein Schwanenlied singen,
> Und fühlte ein kühlendes Wehn
> Und sah mit tauschweren Schwingen
> Einen Engel in der Wüste gehn.
>
> . . . .
>
> Und vor ihm kniete ich nieder,
> Er legte sein tauicht Gefieder
> Mir kühl um das glühende Haupt,
> Und sang mir die Pilgerlieder
> Da hab' ich geliebt und geglaubt.
>
> . . . .
>
> So haben wir da wohl gesungen,
> Und Hand in Hand da geschlungen
> Und Flügel in Flügelpaar
> Uns über die Wüste geschwungen,
> Die ein Garten voll Segen war.[56]
>
> (W I 356–357)

The poem "O Schweig nur Herz!" contained in a letter to Luise of 1817, offers, as a counterbalance to the agitation caused by its jagged rhythms, the assuaging promise of seraphic sounds:

> O schweig nur Herz! Horch! Klang von Engelschwingen
> Was zuckst du so, du mußt fein leise tun,
> Wo man dir singet, wie so sanft sie ruhn,
> Die Seligen, dahin wird man dich bringen,
> Sei still, was schreist du, einsam ist kein Leben,
> Kein Grab, schlaf süß, die Liebste träumt daneben.[57]
>
> (W I 362)

[56] "Then I heard a pair of wings / Then I heard a swan song, / And I felt a cooling breeze, / And saw an angel soaring in the desert, / His wings heavy with dew // And I knelt down before him, / He laid his dewy plumage / Coolly about my fevered brow, / And sang me the pilgrim songs / Then I loved and believed. // So then we sang together / And hand in hand intertwined there / Wing in wing / We were transported across the desert, / Which was a garden full of blessings."

[57] "O heart, be still! Hear, sounds of angel's pinions / Why do you quiver so, you must be nice and quiet, / When they sing to you how they rest so gently, / Those blessed ones, to that place they will take you, / Be still, why do you cry out, no life is lonely, / No grave, sleep sweetly, your beloved one dreams beside you."

Even in poems such as "Einer Jungfrau bei dem Geschenk der Sakontala" (1817), where Luise serves as the recipient and Brentano becomes the donor of Kalidasa's dramatic works, the spirit of an uplifting religious charisma prevails, even though there is no specific reference to angelic music:

> Doch klingt ein Griff verwandter Töne,
> Den Gott in unsre Harfen tut,
> Von je und jetzt in gleicher Schöne,
> Denn alles ist in ihm ja gut![58]
>
> (W I 348)

Whereas the poems to Luise Hensel from this early period (1816–1819) incorporate the concept of angelic song into a religiously tinged atmosphere of romance,[59] the epilogue to one of these—the "Frühlingsschrei eines Knechtes aus der Tiefe" (1816)—written after Brentano had accidentally met her in 1838 at the home of Joseph Görres in Munich, projects the tonal quality of her voice into a diametrically opposed framework:

> Stimme nachtigallenfarben,
> Ätzend Liederpulver streuend,
> Daß zu Wunden werden Narben
> Leid und Lied und Schmerz erneuend.
>
> Torenstimme einer Weisen
> Weise Stimme einer Törin,
> Stimme aus den Zaubergleisen
> Der Frau Venus, Klang der Möhrin.
>
> Weh, wie diese den Tannhäuser
> Lockte mit der Zauberflöte,
> Lockt den Pilger heiser, leiser
> Jetzt von Linum die Tralöte![60]
>
> (W I 623)

[58] "Yet there echoes the touch of kindred tones, / That God put in our harps, / Through all eternity in equal beauty, / For everything in him is indeed good."

[59] For a full analysis of this form of sublimation, see the "Nachwort" to Wolfgang Frühwald's edition Clemens Brentano: Briefe an Emilie Linder (EL), pp. 301–317.

[60] "Nightingale-colored voice, / Strewing corrosive dust of song, / So that scars become wounds, / Suffering and song and pain renewing. // Foolish voice of a wise woman, / Wise voice of a foolish woman, / Voice from the paths of magic / Of Lady Venus, of that Moorish woman. // Woe, as she enticed Tannhäuser / With her magic flute, / Now from Linum the raucous horn (Tralöte) / Thus entices the pilgrim, coarser, softer."

Luise's voice, once foolish in its advice (to renounce love for religion) but still fascinating in its allure, reopens wounds in the heart
of the pilgrim, who long ago, under the influence of these "nightingale-colored" tones, had forsaken love and sought redemption in the
Church.[61] The analogy with Tannhäuser, however, suggests that the
speaker, like the medieval Minnesänger, passed through the castle of
Venus as well as the cathedral of the Virgin. The major difference, however, stems from the fact that for Brentano the very same woman
served in both capacities.

A similar development can be observed in conjunction with Emilie
Linder. At the outset of their relationship in 1834—at which point he
wrote the "Text zum Oratorium von Ett"—he finds the Melos-Eros
bond full of optimistic promise:

> Sie haben allerlei gesungen,
> Und alles war ein einzig Lied,
> Vom Zauberknoten süß verschlungen
> Aus Huld und Reiz von Glied zu Glied.
>
> . . . .
>
> Was süß sich in den Tönen wieget
> Was sehnet, seufzet, ringt und schwingt,
> Ist all süß Lindi, die sich schmieget,
> Wenn sie der Augenblick umschlingt.
>
> Es weben all die Wundertöne
> Nur einen einzigen Akkord,
> Süß ist süß Lieb, sie ist das schöne,
> Das linde, liebe, wahre Wort.[62]
>
> (W I 560–561)

The predominance of "süß" in these stanzas to Emilie may have the
same inference as was indicated previously in conjunction with Biondette's singing: latent danger concealed behind a sweet, appealing ex-

---

[61] New light has been shed on the Hensel-Brentano relationship by two
recent publications: Hans-Joachim Schoeps, "Clemens Brentano nach Ludwig
von Gerlachs Tagebüchern und Briefwechsel," *Jahrbuch des Freien Deutschen
Hochstifts* (1970), pp. 281–303, and Jürg Mathes, "Ein Tagebuch Clemens Brentanos für Luise Hensel," *Jahrbuch des Freien Deutschen Hochstifts* (1971), 198–
310.

[62] "They sang of all sorts of things, / And everything was a single song,
/ Sweetly tied with a magic knot / Of grace and charm from link to link. //
Whatever sweetly sways in the tones, / Whatever longs, sighs, struggles and
soars / Is sweet Lindi, who nestles close, / Whenever the moment embraces her. //
All the miraculous tones weave / But a single chord, / Sweet is sweet love, it is
the lovely, / The soothing, dear, true word."

terior. The following stanza from another poem of 1834 indicates that this is not merely idle speculation:

> Süß Syrene auf der Hüfte
> Wiegst du dich am Felsenriff
> Selig, wer vorüberschiffte,
> Wen der Zauber nicht ergriff.[63]
> (W I 543)

Happy is he who, like wise Odysseus, by clever ruse or calculated reason, never falls victim to such fatal allure. Yet the seafarer in another poem from the same period discovers a mysterious affinity between the songstress and himself:

> Da ward mein Herz so schwer, so schwer,
> Ich schiffte einsam auf den Wogen,
> Da hat dein Lied vom Felsen her
> Mich in die Brandung hingezogen
> Sirenenkind, ich mußt' an deinen Klippen stranden
> Mich lockten Flammen, die auf deinen Lippen brannten.
>
> Ich drang zu dir, ich rang zu dir
> Der Unerkannten, Tiefverwandten,
> Du wichst vor mir, du schlichst zu mir
> Und legtest mich gebannt in deine Banden.[64]
> (W I 549)

The unfathomable and yet undeniable link ("unerkannt . . . tiefverwandt") between speaker and siren is reinforced by a preponderance of internal rime which underscores the force of attraction, even when the literal meaning of the lines seems to say the opposite: "du wichst vor mir" becomes, in the final analysis, "du schlichst zu mir." The closing remarks of the boatsman suggest on this occasion, however, that he can remain impervious to her persuasive and seductive song: "Laß dich durch mich nicht stören, / Mich singt dein Lied zur ew'gen Ruh" (W I 550).[65] Even though the "eternal rest" might be a euphe-

---

[63] "Sweet siren, you sway / Upon your rocky crag; / Happy is he whose ship passed by, / He whom your magic did not seize."

[64] "Then my heart grew so heavy, so heavy, / I set sail alone on the waves, / Then your song from the rocky crag / Dragged me down into the surf / Siren-child, I had to run aground on your cliffs / Those flames enticed me, which burned upon your lips. // I pressed toward you, I struggled toward you, / You unrecognized but deeply kindred spirit, / You withdrew from me, you drew toward me / And laid me charmed in your fetters."

[65] "Do not let me disturb you, / Your song sings me to eternal rest."

mistic paraphrase for death by drowning, the casual and confident
tone in which he speaks leave the impression that the final triumph lies
with him rather than the siren. That such a victory was purely Pyrrhic,
however, may be inferred from the penultimate stanza of another siren
poem from the Linder period ("Den ersten Tropfen dieser Leidensflut"), in which the lady has the last word:

> Und als sie so gesungen
> Ein bißchen süß gegaukelt,
> Und sich herum geschwungen
> Geschlungen und geschaukelt
> Rief sie: "Gut' Nacht mein Brüderchen
> Addio! schreib, mach Liederchen."[66]

(W I 553)

The taunting diminutives with their impure rhyme indicate that the
siren experienced nothing deeper than a mere flirtation. Her patronizing advice ("schreib, mach Liederchen") represents the reductio ad
absurdum of all poetry of the "great confession" school and mocks the
poignancy of Tasso's sublime calling: "Und wenn der Mensch in seiner
Qual verstummt, / Gab mir ein Gott, zu sagen, wie ich leide" (V,v).[67]
Thus the closing couplet of the above poem reveals the siren at the
apex of her ambivalent art, as the embodiment of a form of Melos-
Eros which was both charming and alarming.

Following this brief outline of the manner in which Brentano
incorporated musico-erotic allusions in his correspondence and his
lyrics with a marked autobiographical stamp, the discussion will now
focus on three major works—*Ponce de Leon, Aloys und Imelde*, and
Godwi—in order to examine the Melos-Eros-Thanatos theory in literary practice,[68] bearing in mind the basic concepts of music as the

[66] "And as she sang thusly, / Sweetly flitted about a bit, / And swung herself around, / Writhed and rocked to and fro, / She called: 'Good night, my little
brother / Adieu! Write, compose little songs.' "

[67] "And when man in his mortal anguish grows silent, / A God has granted
me the power to tell how I suffer."

[68] This triadic complex has been analyzed at length with reference to the
Romanzen vom Rosenkranz from a different perspective in the preceding chapter.
The only other work in which the three components play a significant role is in
the fragmentary tale *Der Sänger* in which such key lines as the following occur:
"You know how we like to find in every variation, in every tone . . . a lofty, meaningful word, a tender hieroglyphic of our love" (W II 486–487); "that love can
more easily be sung than said . . . music and poetry can and do express our most
secret and sacred feelings" (W II 502). For some preliminary remarks on the subject, see my article "Clemens Brentano's *Godwi*: Variations on the Melos-Eros
Theme," *Germanic Review*, 42 (1967): 108–123.

food of love, as love in search of a word, and as the death of love when song grows silent or elicits no response nor echo.

In the comedy *Ponce de Leon* the bond between music and love supplies the framework for the verbal fireworks and etymological pyrotechnics on which the play depends for its humor. At the outset of the piece, Ponce appears almost as an anti–Don Juan, boasting of the numerous ways in which he has not loved during his lifetime. Disguising himself as a musician, Ponce sets out with his friend Aquilar in search of the girl with whose portrait he has become infatuated. The masquerade in which the companions indulge is mirrored by the duplicity and double perspective of the language they employ. For example, upon hearing lute music and a lady's singing from a distant castle, Ponce and Aquilar experience divergent reactions to these stimuli—each in accord with his spiritual predisposition:

> PONCE: Oh, listen, how that breaks the heart!
> AQUILAR: I find that it refreshes ear and heart; I don't hear any false tone.
> PONCE: How could such sweet lips sing false tones? Yet I say that *that* man's heart is false, whom these plaintive tones accuse, and false is he who hears them, for alas! I am not the true one. (W IV 211)

The paradox of Ponce and Aquilar as Flemish musicians who refuse to play a single note because they are suffering from internal and external wounds respectively becomes the source of many a Shakespearean pun based on the homonyms "Seite-Saite" (side-string) and double meaning of "verstimmt" (musically "out of tune" and mentally "out of sorts"). For Aquilar, being such a poor musician automatically precludes amorous success: "As it now stands, we have little hope for the quartet; the girls are playing in major and we in minor" (W IV 221).

It is Ponce's idealized lady, Isidore, who puts her finger upon what is perhaps the basic reason why the reluctant minstrels do not perform: "Beautiful music," she declares, "and dancing, all that would put in too good a word for them" (W IV 241). Rather than masking or generalizing emotions to the point of anonymity, music might become too explicit. Having overheard this comment, Ponce immediately responds with a variation on the theme: "Love only whispers . . . it doesn't need the resounding, treacherous word; only lonesome love resounds" (W IV 241). An example of Ponce's fear that the musical tone also might make the implicit message too obvious is found somewhat later in the play in his objection to Aquilar's attempt to silence Eros with its own weapon—a musical instrument:

> AQUILAR: And there lie the pipes also on which to disparage love; pay attention, my friend, I shall perform a death march for your love.
>
> PONCE: Oh, let these pipes be, for they rule this world. You can never decry love, for every tone is love, love which decries man.
>
> AQUILAR: These pipes rule the world? Well, then I finally have the world under my thumb; I will avenge myself and make them despair with false tones. (Taking his pipe.)
>
> PONCE: Let it be, I pray you; he who loves not does not understand the tones—Oh, don't play! (Aquilar laments on the pipe.) Oh cease, give no words to our mute dissonance! . . . let the ogres of my displeasure slumber. . . .
>
> AQUILAR: Thus I have indeed found the means—well, I am curious to see that—your malady is then nothing else than slumbering disharmony? (W IV 259–260)

When Ponce, in his agitation, draws his sword and challenges his friend to a duel in order to silence this taunting music, Aquilar obliges by "holding the pipe in his mouth and fencing while playing" (W IV 260); at this point in the action, the threat of "Thanatos" as a complement to Melos-Eros framework clearly comes to the fore. However, in a comedy of language, even such a scene as this—laden with tragic potential—death is averted by a bit of linguistic virtuosity:

> PONCE: Fine, here I stand with sword-blade (Klinge) bared.
>
> LUCILLA: That sounds (klingt) so terrible in the presence of a girl.
>
> PONCE: Only in the presence of a woman does it sound at all, in woman alone is love, love alone is sound (Klang), and without it everything is silent, even Ponce will grow silent soon. (W IV 263)

The denouement of the comic fantasy reveals that the reverse of the above is the case. Ponce does not "grow silent" in either the literal or the figurative sense of the term. Instead, he sings for his prospective bride a stanza from a poem that he had once recited to the tones of Valeria's lute. The veil of silence is dropped, and all other "masks" fall as each of the lovers finds a proper marriage partner and the piece concludes with a festive round-dance on stage.

Whereas in the comedy *Ponce de Leon* the ingredients for a genuine music of love had to be painstakingly brought to the surface, the Romeo-and-Juliet-like tragedy *Aloys und Imelde* makes the ties be-

tween Melos and Eros apparent from the outset.[69] Music in both the
background and the foreground of the play functions as a catalytic
agent linking the children of two hostile families. Aloys is captivated
by Imelde's music long before he learns the identity of the singer, and
he analyzes her song in a "song" of his own:

"Dein Lied erklang, es war kein Ton vergebens,
Der ganze Frühling, der von Liebe haucht,
Hat, als du sangest, nieder sich getaucht
Im sehnsuchtsvollen Strome meines Lebens,
Im Sonnenuntergang,
Als mir dein Lied erklang!"[70]

(SW IX:2 367–368)

The device of singing about song—which one might characterize as
"telescoping"—is carried a step further by Imelde when she, in turn,
notes how her original love song, after being filtered through Aloys'
response, was then communicated to her by the birds: "Mich lockt die
Sonne und der Vögel Lied / Ich lausche gern dem Sang, seit ihm mein
Lied erklang!" (SW IX:2 369).[71]

Amidst the ubiquitous music of love there is, however, a somber
tone in the world of family rivalries and chicaneries inhabited by Aloys
and Imelde. For example, the girl Zinga, who is infatuated with Aloys,
sees her hopes dashed by the overwhelming effect which the music of
her unknown rival—Imelde—exerts on him: "Listening to him, I heard
him praise a voice that yesterday sang him into sweet delirium; Oh,
dear God, the voice came from above, my fate descended upon me with
the sound of that voice" (W IV 340). The act of "falling" inferred by
this comment parallels the ominous portent of "sunset" and "submer-
gence" found in Aloys' reaction to Imelde's music. The overwhelming
odds against finding happiness in such a game of love and intrigue are
expressed in musical metaphor by another frustrated victim of love in

[69] This play exists in two forms. The original prose version, which Brentano
completed, was stolen—in manuscript form—by his acquaintance Varnhagen von
Ense for personal reasons. This original text is found in W IV 321–523. After losing the manuscript to Varnhagen, Brentano rewrote the first two acts from
memory and put them into iambic verse. This adaptation can be found in SW
IX:2, 275–472. In the remainder of this study, pertinent passages from both
versions will be incorporated.

[70] " 'Your song rang out, no note was in vain, / All of spring, with its breath
of love, / Immersed itself as you sang / In the yearning stream of my life, / In
the sunset, / As your song rang out to me!' "

[71] "The sun and the song of the birds entice me, / I listen gladly to their
song, ever since my song rang out to him!"

the drama, Orthon: "That is like playing a double-sonata for four hands with one finger" (W IV 368).

This prediction of insurmountable difficulty is borne out in the case of Aloys in his competition with the Spanish grand seigneur, Benevides, for Imelde's hand in marriage. On the latter's instructions, Aloys arranges for a group of musicians to perform a serenade during which the lovers can converse. This plan is thwarted, however, by the appearance of Benavides with a musical contingent of his own: "Hey, quiet there, don't pollute the embroidery of heaven with the hackneyed tune of a street song!" the rival gibes, and then instructs his performers: "Now, dear notes, wander about more sonorously, so that the moon of my lady might shine down on us, since that other one is leaving in shame" (W IV 397). The plight of Aloys is further worsened by the arrival of his father, Comingo, who is determined to prevent the union of his son with the daughter of a hated foe: mistaking Benavides for Aloys ("it seems as if hell were making music at my downfall" [W IV 397]), Comingo becomes so enraged when he hears his "offspring" (actually Benavides) declare his love ("I am overjoyed that you lend an ear to my tones; had I but a voice that I might sing! But like a noble swan, my heart remains silent" [W IV 398]), that he threatens to transform this into an actual swansong: "You scamp, I'll beat you to death, swan, so that you can really sing" (W IV 398). In the ensuing melee, father, son, and rival engage in hand-to-hand combat, at which point one of the combatants bitterly invokes the Orphean power of music to restore order and sanity: "Ho, musicians, play and let the trumpets blare, music has often enough cured the insane, yea, yea!" (W IV 398). In the course of the remainder of the drama, the irony in this allusion to the curative powers of music acquires tragic proportions. Following Benavides' marriage to Imelde, the jealous husband admonishes his wife that his physical infirmity—blindness—by no means dulls his awareness of deceit: "Do not deceive me, I am kind, like the tiger hearing the sound of a harp; but do not play any false notes, don't sing me any song meant for the ears of someone else!" (W IV 469). The love triangle does indeed end tragically when the raging Benavides stabs Imelde only to be mortally wounded by Aloys.

It is in keeping with the dimension of "universality" which characterized the Romantic novel that Brentano's only completed work in this genre, *Godwi oder Das steinerne Bild der Mutter*, should serve as a virtual compendium for the Melos-Eros-Thanatos complex in all its manifold variety. The personalities of both the major and the minor female figures in the novel are delineated in terms of musical imagery and analogy. The blonde girl from the "bureau d'esprit," for instance, is more flexible and flighty than her sister, the brunette; whereas the latter had a passion for order and regularity, the former exhibits spontaneity and variety: "the blonde disconnects and dissolves, and lapses into an Italian aria, which she immediately sings at the piano" (W II 189); "she cannot sing a sustained note without falling into a trill" (W II 191). Römer's summarizing assessment of both possibilities makes use of an image which suggests that neither woman could supply the necessary musical complement for his emotional needs: "These women all have something of the siren about them which resolves into a fish-tail" (W II 189). The juxtaposition of "siren" and "fish-tail" expresses Römer's conviction that disenchantment invariably follows in the wake of physical attraction; the enticing female form above the water singing seductive melodies is a powerful stimulus, until the inevitable moment of disaster strikes and the destructive force of this composite creature makes itself manifest.

Römer becomes acquainted with the women of the "bureau d'esprit" after his encounter with the most eloquent spokesman for the alliance between art (music) and love as well as the art of love: Lady Molly Hodefield. When comparing his experience with Molly with his subsequent liaisons, Römer does so in terms of contrastive performers: "The beginning of my dream was a grand concert and the omnipotent voice of an omnipotent woman; and my awakening is the sweet voice of a charming girl who plays upon a Parisian guitar with her dainty little fingers" (W II 50). The all-powerful Molly expounds her aesthetic-erotic credo to a fellow artist, Werdo Senne, in terms ranging from passionate response to abject silence. Love, she maintains, is originally a synthesis of which the individual arts are merely isolated and fragmented forms: "Now music, painting, and sculpture and poetry stand for me as a relic of the whole, which is love" (W II 94). Molly illustrates the disintegration of the primordial totality with the image of an ancient temple now standing in scattered and silent ruins, an edifice in which once her prayer "resounded rhythmically through the chambers of the exalted array of columns and embraced, at the crowns of these columns, lovely melodies" (W II 94). There remains, however, one means to evoke—if only imperfectly—reminiscences of that majestic and unified structure:

> Whenever I make music, then every individual part is as sad as a letter
> to a distant, intimate world which misunderstands me because it does
> not perceive the beat of my heart, my glance, the concept of what I
> performed in my fantasy, or the impotence of the machine and the
> tyranny of the lever which my physical self places so clumsily between
> me and my outer manifestation. (W II 94–95)

Molly does not merely decry the resultant discrepancy between conception and execution; she actively seeks to terminate the fragmenta-
tion of her once integrated universe of love through the potentially
binding force of music:

> When my friend accompanied me, I found in the accord of his flute with
> my harmonies at least the apparently unrestricted creativity of love in
> similar and reciprocal pleasures. . . . I indulged in fantasy and expressed
> myself completely, but soon I became inhibited by the strange feeling
> that I myself was growing into a wild, formless song which constantly
> projects outwardly but never returns to itself. . . . I had sung, and no-
> body had heard me. The note that is not heard is not there. I no longer
> heard myself, for I sang myself.
>
> I sang at public concerts and was enraptured with the general silence.
> (W II 95)

These lines touch upon the dangers inherent in the exclusive preoccupation with one facet of an entity that consists of several components
in equilibrium. If love is a kind of "Gesamtkunstwerk," as Molly indicated at the outset, then her *pars pro toto* approach had to lead to a
distortion of perspective. And distortion, if allowed to persist or, as
in this case, run rampant, culminates in the dissolution of every form,
aesthetic as well as ethical. When love and art lose all sense of proportion and become "a wild, formless song," there can be no more appropriate response than silence; this reaction, however, should not be
confused with the unfeeling indifference to the music of love—a trait
that characterizes the shrewish Laura in the German translation of an
Italian poem which Brentano incorporated into the novel:

> Ein Felsen bin ich, der sein Lieb nicht höret;
> Er sing, doch packe er sich bald und wandre.
>
> . . . .
>
> Geht, Simpelchen, steht nicht die ganze Nacht hier;
> Die Dinger, die ich brauch, kann man nicht singen.[72]
> (W II 327)

[72] "I am a rock, which does not hear his love; / Let him sing, but then he

Lady Hodefield, like Goethe's "Zauberlehrling," has unleashed forces that she is no longer able to control:

> The apparent contour of music, its eternal change and yet at the same time the slavery of certain relationships, fetters from which one never escapes and yet which, because of their latitude offer such an attractive freedom, its imageless abundance, which I can mold into a thousand images, this indefatigable mass which can never achieve that of which it is only a part—all love and mine—which I nevertheless so completely encompass, at last alarmed me as if I had a force in my hands that elevates itself above its master and toys with him. (W II 96)

Molly's statement taps the roots of both Romantic irony and Romantic agony. The musico-erotic artist is apparently born free, but finds himself everywhere in chains. One would do well at this point to recall the dual social commitment outlined for man by Brentano in the passage on the consequences of harmony cited earlier. Life and love—in addition to art—require a precarious balance between dynamic forces; if a single component seeks to usurp the functions of the others, then this poses a threat to the welfare of the entire organism. For Molly Hodefield, however, exclusive reliance upon music and the rigors of her virtuoso role in the "Gesamtkunstwerk" of love resulted in a loss of equilibrium ("Gleichgewicht") (W II 100). This was not, however, the shallow form of harmony and balance achieved by Savigny's machine men or automata. Rather than suppressing his weaknesses or fostering only certain modes of expression, the superior artist is able to compensate for his shortcomings in a manner which eludes Molly in her one-sidedness:

> Just as for me the only talent of creation lies in sexual love, so has many a singer been silenced no doubt by muteness even as the greatest painter may have remained blind and the greatest musician deaf. But for these men there remains a way out: poetry is and remains the soul of their drive, and they become painters, singers or musicians through the greater power of one single organ in them. So then there can evolve from the paintings of a blind man music or a poem, and from the music of a deaf man can come a painting. (W II 100)

The ideal of "Poesie" transforms the heterogeneous into the homogeneous, it makes possible a total work of art of which the total impres-

---

should pack up and leave. // Go, you simpleton, don't stand here all night; / What I need cannot be rendered in song."

sion is far greater than the sum of its individual parts: it represents that elusive spiritual landscape which Brentano and his contemporaries could not paint, but merely surrounded with arabesques and framed with the fantasy of the poetic symbol.

Like Molly Hodefield, the titular hero of the novel runs the gamut of musico-erotic adventures without achieving—for more than a fleeting moment—an awareness of the complex range of emotions involved in any single experience or the complementary interplay of forces which, on the surface, seem mutually exclusive. At the extreme poles stand opposed a kind of Apollinian clarity and order and a Dionysian obscurity and chaos. The first of these has already been discussed in conjunction with the beneficial effects of Otilie Senne's harmonious personality on the protagonist. However, this idyllic interlude was too much out of character to contain or content Godwi for any extended period. His dynamic and nervous temperament could not tolerate such an environment of unadulterated Apollinian order, and consequently the second part of the novel introduces Godwi to a milieu in which the Dionysian idiom in music clearly dominates. We find him wandering along the Rhine during the grape harvest—a season congenial to the ancient deity of the vines—and participating in the festivities of the boisterous throng in order to overcome the feeling of isolation that has always plagued him: "It was a splendid life, a single love was not possible, a person could not be attracted by a single individual, everything was as in a golden age again, one loved everyone and was loved by everyone" (W II 389). Godwi's Rhine journey is marked by several modes of musical accompaniment. As he quaffs wine with a group of monks, for example, he sings for them "gay Italian arias to the accompaniment of the organ" (W II 389). Hearing the boisterous songs of the vineyard workers, "happy-go-lucky people whom the festival of that joyous deity had brought together" (W II 390), Godwi unceremoniously dismisses the entire Apollinian world of Part I of the novel from his mind: "With his second glass of wine he forgot Otilie and . . . goodness knows what all the names of the eccentric, noble souls were" (W II 390).

After having followed a mysterious, unidentified rider, who was singing a folk song of amorous intrigue, to a chateau on the Rhine, Godwi makes his way into a darkened chamber and stumbles upon the statue of a naked Venus. His path then leads to an unlit bedroom where he finds all sorts of feminine attire strewn about and hears someone breathing heavily. At this point in the narrative the musico-erotic imagery becomes painfully obvious:

> His foot touched something resonant, he reached down, it was a guitar leaning against the chair; he strummed on it, but now the breathing in his proximity intensified.... As he grasped for it with his hands, as with feelers in total darkness, he winced markedly, his fingers touched someone ... who quivered, laughed and fled. (W II 394)

Even though the unseen lady suddenly vanishes from the room, Godwi's great expectations are sustained by a bit of sensual background music:

> The wide Rhine murmured on as music in the distance, from the villages and the nearby town the merry waltz-melodies blared, in disordered fashion and as if tumbling and whirling about. The sweet smell of new wine penetrated to his window from the vineyard below, the nearby forest rustled and in the marvelous, intoxicated landscape squibs and rockets shot boisterously into the heights and exploded, joyous even in death. (W II 394–395)

However, Brentano is an astute enough prose stylist not to allow such a series of scenes to build an unbroken climax. Instead of a uniformly rising crescendo, he creates by means of interjections on the part of the narrator—the poet Maria—a counterbalance to temper the unmitigated triumph of the hero with a note of tragedy. To the musico-erotic escapades of the protagonist reported by Maria, the latter juxtaposes an experience from his own drab life filled with disease, disappointment, and the prospect of death, as the following excerpts will show.

> Maria's report of Godwi's adventures (and Maria's interjections): "His foot touched something resonant, he reached down, it was a guitar" ("... but upon awakening I do not nudge against a resonant guitar, my foot strikes the bottom of the inert bed") "... he strummed on it" ("... my fingers do not strum on strings, they play about on the bed-spread"). (W II 395–396)

For virtually every phase of Godwi's amorous adventures which Maria records in order to defray his own funeral expenses, there is a corresponding element of disillusionment in his life. This macabre situation culminates in the fact that when Godwi was forsaken by his female companion in the Rhine castle, he opened the shutters and was greeted by a rousing form of love music; at this juncture Maria also discovers music emanating from the street below his own window. However, the tunes which he hears are not a stimulating serenade but rather the tones of the morose, "merry" minstrels lamenting the plight which he shares: the compulsion to feign happiness through a veil of tears.

Godwi's affair with the mysterious female inhabitants of the castle on the Rhine concludes on a very off-key Orphean note. The Countess, whose ultraliberal (and even libertine) views on love and matrimony may be couched in a unique verbal idiom ("consistories, where there is no longer any love to sustain marriage—divorces set to music to be sung" [W II 413]), proves to be only a temporary diversion. Godwi's final rendezvous with her ends more with a "whimper" than a "bang." Just prior to his departure, Godwi recalls the refrain from a song sung by the grape harvesters before his initial contact with the Countess: "My autumn neither rings nor sings, but I wouldn't trade it for yours" (W II 390). The passionate music that had ushered in Godwi's meeting with this woman (and her daughter, Violette) peters out on a note of silence, just as Lady Hodefield's ardent but formless song found no response in the crowded concert hall.

Brentano appends a "coda" to the episode with the Countess. After leaving her, Godwi again rides along the Rhine and chances upon a rococo "pleasure castle" in the forest. The artificial symmetry of this secluded structure, contrasting as it does with the "architecture of nature" and its "harmonic disorder" (W II 432), recalls the familiar eighteenth-century juxtaposition of the stylized French garden and the English park allowed to grow in an uninhibited fashion. The highly ornate and artificially decorative building might be regarded as the embodiment of the world represented by the Countess herself (she was French), while the natural surroundings could serve as the correlative of her daughter, Violette, a young girl whose spiritual integrity and natural wholesomeness had been undermined by her mother's compelling her to lead a life of prostitution. In his mind's eye Godwi envisions the pleasure castle in its heyday, filled with sensual enticements including "Singspiele" (operettas) composed for an aristocratic assemblage, which delighted in masked games and dallied in mirrored chambers with "a bevy of naked girls, full of joy, jesting, dancing and singing" (W II 433). Forsaking this world of powdered wigs and porcelain figurines, of masks and minuets, Godwi turns to the realm of nature, where he perceives "the flowing of the Rhine," the "simmering of flaming spirits . . . , which dart flittingly, performing a mysteriously fiery dance, across the dark forest and gorges" (W II 436). Appropriately, it is at this point that he discovers Violette, the embodiment of natural emotions rendered unnatural by the wiles of her mother. Unlike Orpheus of old, however, Godwi does not risk a descent into the "underworld" represented by Violette's spiritual death. Instead he flees from the scene, only to learn later of her demise; in partial atonement for his failure to intervene previously, Godwi has the tale of Violette's wayward life, her unmediated death and ultimate transfiguration by forces of divine love immortalized in stone—an all too vivid reminder of an Orpheus who failed his Eurydice by the author who, at the conclusion of the novel, is invoked to restore the myth of Melos-Eros-Thanatos for the benefit of future generations.

Musica Naturata—Musica Naturans

According to Walther Rehm's interpretation of the Orpheus legend, the Greek singer served as the mediating voice between man and the realm of nature, both during his lifetime ("through his song he calls inanimate nature to order and tames wild beasts") and after his death ("after his death he sings forth and resounds from the whole of nature"). To be sure, nature had its own unique musical idiom, the tones of which might be described as "musica naturata" (a term which, in analogy to "natura naturata," or "nature created,"[73] signified a finished product, or "nature's music" as perceived by man). However, of far greater significance poetically was the other aspect of the problem, "musica naturans" (in analogy to "natura naturans," or nature *creating*, this concept suggests a process rather than a product; it connotes a kind of mysterious affinity between the pristine musicality of nature, which is sui generis, and the corresponding creative faculties of the human mind). Whereas writers such as Herder had alluded to this kinship in theory,[74] it was the German Romantic generation that

[73] For a discussion of the concepts "natura naturata" and "naturans" see the article by Wolfgang Preisendanz entitled "Zur Poetik der deutschen Romantik I: Die Abkehr vom Grundsatz der Naturnachahmung," pp. 56–57 in: *Die deutsche Romantik*, ed. Hans Steffen (Göttingen: Vandenhoeck & Ruprecht, 1967), and the essay entitled "Romanticism" by Raymond Immerwahr, pp. 204 ff. in: *The Challenge of German Literature*, ed. Horst S. Daemmrich and Diether H. Haenicke (Detroit: Wayne State University Press, 1971).

[74] In his essay "Vom Erkennen und Empfinden in der menschlichen Seele," *Sämtliche Werke*, ed. Bernhard Suphan, VIII (Berlin: Weidmannsche Buchhandlung, 1892), 240, Herder notes: "In all of nature there are euphonious sounds with which we should practice incessantly. Around us resounds a great, eternal concert of movement and rest. The storm, the murmuring of the breeze, the music

put postulates such as the following (by Novalis) into actual practice: "Nature is an aeolian harp—a musical instrument—whose notes themselves are the keys to higher strings in us."[75] The attempt of the artist to fashion his music (or his poetic rendition of music) after that of nature gives rise in the history of intellectual thought to the view that only when "musica naturata" and "musica naturans" have been tempered by the aestheticizing powers of man can their full potential be realized. Rehm considers Orpheus the indispensable link between the ubiquitous music of nature and the apotheosis of it in the man-made artifact:

> Orpheus knows the "inner poetics of nature," he tarries as the primeval singer and poet within its orbit, he becomes the voice and song of the universe and of its music. In his song the spirit of nature becomes perceptible. In his proximity, inanimate objects begin to dance, they break out in song, truly harmonious, "synthetic poetry" resounds, conjured from the spirit and from the perceptible love of the universe . . .
>
> Orpheus is the powerful organizer and appeaser, the lofty master and bringer of salvation who hears the harmony and music that live in nature (though disturbed), and makes their voice, their rhythm mysteriously resound again in his own song.[76]

The attainment of an artistic correlation between "musica naturata" and "musica naturans" was generally felt to have been an accomplishment of a remote "golden age" long since past. By evoking the memory of this ideal condition, however, the poet tacitly expressed the hope that paradise lost might, at some distantly envisioned time, be regained. Paul Böckmann articulates this situation most tellingly: "The images and sounds of language testify by their musical relationships to man's participation in the life of nature. . . . In the process music becomes a unifying medium between man and nature."[77] The following discussion—confined in scope because of the vast panoply of nature music in Brentano's oeuvre—will concentrate on three rep-

---

which must lie in every physical tone from its inception to its extinction in every degree of vibration, all this gives our soul for all times a task of dissolution, foresight, and enjoyment of itself in every tone."

[75] Novalis, *Werke, Briefe, Dokumente,* ed. Ewald Wasmuth (Heidelberg: Lambert-Schneider, 1957), II, 126–127.

[76] Rehm, pp. 62 and 65.

[77] "Klang und Bild in der Stimmungslyrik der Romantik" in: *Formensprache: Studien zur Literaturästhetik und Dichtungsinterpretation* (Hamburg: Hoffmann and Campe, 1966), p. 430.

resentative areas of interplay: the literary rendition of the music of inanimate nature, animal and insect performers, and avian singers.

When considering the contribution of the inanimate forces of nature to her grandiose symphony of sound, one might single out in Brentano's orchestration "forest murmurs" and "water music" for special consideration. The reader can almost hear the rustling of trees in the rhythmic periods and tonal complexes of Brentano's language when he reports to Bettina in a letter of 1802: "Spring flies toward me from distant mountains across the flowering fields, gentle stream and ringing, singing, swinging forests and brings me floral fragrance, color and tone" (F 174). But whereas the singing of the forest, the song of flowers or other foliage[78] may occasionally have been music to Brentano's ears, it was primarily the flowing stream or bubbling spring that provided the most pleasing sounds in the bucolic milieu. The subdued, gently undulating lullaby of rivulets and brooks consoled many a disconsolate Brentano figure, whether in the interiorized world of dreams, in the garden Lindachara of the Spanish Alhambra, or in the mythical realm of the prehistorical Slavic nation:

> Träume freundlich ihn umschlingen, singen
> Ihm so süße Wiegen Lieder,
> Und die Töne die erklingen, springen
> Von Kristallnen Felsen nieder.[79]

> Der Springbrunn plätschert, und sein Lallen
> Singt mir ein buntes Schlummerlied;[80]
>
> (W I 577)

> Und der Moldau finsteres Rauschen
> Wieget mich ein wie ein Schlummerlied,
> Und meine Seele treibt hin unterm Lauschen,
> Wie der Kahn ohne Schiffer den Strom hinabzieht.[81]
>
> (W IV 589)

---

[78] See, for example, W I 661 and 578.

[79] "Dreams embrace him in a friendly fashion, sing / To him such sweet lullabies, / And the tones which resound, spring / Down from crystal crags." This poem is found in Hans Jaeger, *Clemens Brentanos Frühlyrik* (Frankfurt am Main: M. Diesterweg, 1926), p. 216.

[80] "The fountain splashes, and its babbling / Sings to me a gay lullaby."

[81] "And the somber murmuring of the Moldau / Rocks me as in a lullaby, / And my listening soul is swept onward / Down the stream, like a boat without a master."

Miller Radlauf, so closely affiliated with the aquatic element of "Vater Rhein," is also the son of the watersprite, Frau Lureley. His mother sings a lullaby, which fuses the most sublime sounds in the cosmos (the "music of the spheres") with the most sotto voce tones of nature:

> Singet leise, leise, leise,
> Singt ein flüsternd Wiegenlied,
> Von dem Monde lernt die Weise,
> Der so still am Himmel zieht.
>
> . . . .
>
> Singt ein Lied so süß gelinde,
> Wie die Quellen auf den Kieseln,
> Wie die Blumen um die Linde
> Summen, murmeln, flüstern, rieseln.[82]
>
> (W III 218–219)

The music of nature is also transmitted by the vast array of animal and insect singers that populate the pages of Brentano's works. Among these are two contrastive performers—the cat and the cricket. Although Brentano's musical menagerie includes guest cameo appearances by croaking frogs,[83] hymn-squeaking church mice,[84] clucking chicks, trumpeting fowl, or bleating goats, it is feline caterwauling and the chirping of crickets that occupy the limelight. Since these singers produce vastly different tones and timbres, they achieve diverse effects. As has already been noted in the case of Mores, the feline charivari arousd unpleasant and ominous sensations in the listener. Brentano expressed his aversion to their "nocturnal vocal academies,"[85] and in one of his didactic admonitions to Bettina he advised her not to be bothered by "caterwauling" (F 188). In contrast to the disruptive features of this "Katzenmusik" stands the beneficial effect exerted by the chirping cricket. For instance, in the lines spoken by the warrior-maiden Wlasta in *Die Gründung Prags*, the preponderance of "i-ie" vowels renders

---

[82] "Softly, softly, softly croon, / Croon a whispered lullaby, / Learn its cadence from the moon, / Slow in heaven drifting by. // Lisp a little lilting fable: / Bees about the honeysuckle, / Silver springs upon the gravel / Mumble, murmur, whisper, trickle." Translated by Herman Salinger in: *An Anthology of German Poetry from Hölderlin to Rilke in English Translation*, ed. Angel Flores (Gloucester, Mass.: Peter Smith, 1965), pp. 96–97.

[83] F 355.

[84] W IV 201.

[85] Reinhold Steig, *Clemens Brentano und die Brüder Grimm* (Stuttgart and Berlin: J. G. Cotta'sche Buchhandlung, 1914), p. 189.

the chirping sounds quite vividly while the verses themselves tell of the calming force of this unique lullaby:

Aufsinnend aus des Winters Stille, liegen Friede
Und Segen, von der Grille Wiegenliede
Erwecket, in der Wiesen grünen Wiegen,
Wie Kinder spielend in den Wiegen liegen
Und beim Geschrill der Siberklingeln lächeln.[86]

(W IV 682–683)

Finally, in the idyllic fairy tale world in which Brentano so willingly tarried, the question is posed in *Myrtenfräulein*: "Hörst du, wie die Brunnen rauschen? / Hörst du, wie die Grille zirpt?" (W III 320),[87] and is answered affirmatively by those whose ears are attuned to such assuaging sounds. In a rather significant scene in the *Rheinmärchen*, Frau Mondenschein's maidens dance as "the crickets chirped the rhythm" (W III 138), and Frau Nachtigall warbles an elaborate accompaniment.

The allusion to Frau Nachtigall in the above passage brings to mind the function of the third category of nature music in Brentano's writings, the song of the birds. The array of such singers is, as one might suspect, legion, and therefore the avian performers will be treated selectively rather than exhaustively (with regard to both quantity and quality). Aside from a preference for generic designations (for example, "Vogel," "Vögelein") Brentano favors several avian singers because of the distinctive features of their songs (including those commonly acknowledged for melodious tones—the nightingale, the finch, the lark, the swallow, and the robin—as well as other less euphonious warblers—the swan, the owl, the quail, the cock, the vulture). Since in each of these respective groups one member clearly stands out above the rest (the nightingale and the swan), the following discussion will concentrate primarily on these two performers (after presenting a capsule survey of the manner in which the music of their less distinguished confreres is treated).

As a poet-singer, Brentano felt a natural affinity for his avian

[86] "Awakening from winter's stillness, peace and prosperity, / Awakened by the cricket's lullaby, lie about / In the verdant cradle of the meadow; / They lie like children playing in their cradles / And smile at the tinkling of little silver bells."

[87] "Do you hear how the fountains murmur? / Do you hear how the cricket chirps?"

counterpart and therefore tended either to identify himself directly with the latter or to project his emotions (and those of his poetic "self") into the music of the birds. An excerpt from a letter of 1805 to the poetess Karoline von Günderode will illustrate the first condition: "And above my window sits a little bird and sings such childish songs, I love to listen to the way it sings, and would like to sing that way myself. When I grow up, I will sit on the rooftops and sing too"(S I 281). To a certain extent the unlimited freedom of flight and fancy enjoyed by the birds was an attribute which must have attracted Bretano in addition to their song. Godwi, for instance, having rejected the "song of bourgeois righteousness," seeks a more congenial idiom: "no stereotyped song, no, like the singing of the birds above us . . . free and without fetters, natural and unpretentious" (W II 37). The extent to which Brentano's poetic imagination could be sparked by the music of the birds is indicated by his reaction to their morning concert, which he heard while traveling from Berlin to Bohemia in 1811: the finches, titmice, siskins, thrushes, and others which warble at his window in the bright sunlight are nothing but the "orchestra for a great opera" that appeared in his dreams the previous night, complete with ballet and stage props; now he himself dances from his bed and performs in operatic fashion and in proper costume, an aria while gargling (S II 77–78).

A very common phenomenon to be observed with regard to Brentano's fondness for the song of the birds is, as was indicated earlier, the tendency to find his own emotions expressed by this music from an external source. Such examples of the "pathetic fallacy" are found in the following lines: "I step into the field, the lark carries my dawnsong upward; . . . isolated finches greet me with song from all the trees; I walk into the forest, the full orchestra of delight is already there; . . . and at night the cry of the bird of ill omen . . . the cock crows— trumpet of judgment . . . and the swallow sings again, it is morning once more, it is like yesterday, yet today I understand the song of the swallow" (W II 1073–1074). Even though this passage constitutes— strangely enough—the introduction to a theatrical review, it does reflect the poet's proclivity to discover his innermost feelings echoed in the mood of nature's music. In a similar fashion, the fisherman in the poem "Auf dem Rhein" awakens after having spent the night with his beloved and detects a note of exhilaration in the singing of the birds:

> Es rauscht der grüne Wald,
> Vor wildentbrannten Weisen,
> Der Vogelsang erschallt.[88]
>
> (W I 100)

For Libussa, the heroine of *Die Gründung Prags*, a similar effect is exerted by the swallow's dawnsong, which sounds "like nuptials" (see also SW IX:2 374) to her eager ears (W IV 739). The fervor which the listener finds in such music is more often the result of his spiritual disposition at the moment of apperception than an actual attribute of the song. Consequently, Aloys in a fit of emotional despondency, can declare: "But leave me alone now, . . . here in this dark and lonely realm of nature where wild vultures sing 'woe, woe' " (W IV 462). On the other hand, the total absence of any form of birdsong has even more ominous overtones, signaling—as did the silence on the part of the beloved—a world "out of joint." In the fairy tale *Fanferlieschen*, for instance, the phrase "and not one little bird is singing" recurs in leitmotivic fashion throughout the scene in which Ursula is immured in a tower to die. Later, however, when the course of her life takes a more propitious turn with the birth of her son, Ursulus, a joyous accompaniment rings out: "The next morning the birds sang so sweetly" (W III 414). When Brentano and Luise Hensel went their separate ways, the poet could lament: "Es wollt' kein Vogel singen / Als wäre dieser Stein verflucht" (W I 385),[89] even though his new-found faith appeared to revive this music on a more transcendental level: "Und der Himmel scheinet weiter / In der Vögel Lustgetön."[90] Later, in the poem "Alhambra," when it appeared that the garden of Lindachara would be forever lost, these sad tidings were accompanied by hollow silence: "Die Vögel schmachten stumm und krank, / Kalt seufzt das Echo aus den Steinen" (W I 585).[91]

Based on the evidence of avian song cited up to this point, two stimuli seem to give rise to this form of music: love or religious devotion. The first of these catalysts, it will be remembered, was a necessary

---

[88] "The verdant forest rustles, / From the passionately enkindled melodies, / The song of the birds resounds."

[89] "No bird sought to sing / As if this stone were accursed."

[90] "And heaven shines on / In the birds' song of delight." This poem is found in *Werke*, ed. Max Preitz, I, 113.

[91] "The birds languish, mute and sick, / The echo sighs coldly from the stones."

ingredient in the poetic plea to Auguste Bußmann, "Auf einen grünen Zweig," where the implications of the poem's title could only be realized after the sick bird in the enchanted forest was prodded to song. The song of the finch from 1817 begins with the same optimistic spirit with which Brentano approached his relationship to Luise Hensel:

> Vom Gesange lust'ger Finken
> Durch das Fenster aufgeweckt
> Lasse ich den Schleier sinken,
> Der mir meine Seele deckt.
>
> . . . .
>
> Wie die kleinen Sänger schweben
> Wie es sehnt und lockt und zirpt.
> O wie herrlich klingt das Leben
> Wenn's zu neuem Leben wirbt.[92]
>
> (W I 379)

The spirit of utter frustration and bitter disillusionment expressed by the closing lines of the same poem stem from the fact that the message of the finch proved to be renunciation rather than romance: "Also aus Kamelgedanken / Sang ich dir dies Finkenlied" (W I 383).[93] The patronizing melodies of the avian singer in another poem from the same era dispense advice with which the speaker is not in full accord:

> Es singt ein Himmelvögelein
> An meiner Kerkerwand,
> Er könnte wohl Bessers tun,
> Ich käm' um den Verstand.[94]
>
> (W I 426)

There is no discrepancy here when the erstwhile "desert angel" is transformed into a little bird from heaven, which sings ominous prophecies from the walls of his prison of life: "Es mahnet an dem Abgrund mich / Ein frommer Liedermund" (W I 427).[95] On the contrary, one finds an element of consistency here since both winged figures serve as intermediaries guiding the pilgrim and prisoner respectively on a

---

[92] "Awakened by the song of merry finches / Through my window, / I let the veil drop / That covers my soul. // How the little singers hover, / With their longing, tempting, chirping. / Oh, how gloriously life rings out / When new life is in the offing."

[93] "Thus out of idiotic thoughts / I sang to you this song of the finch."

[94] "A little bird from heaven sings / At my prison wall, / It could well do something better, / Then I would lose my mind."

[95] "A pious mouth, full of song, / Cautions me at the edge of the abyss."

journey from a barren (desert) or constrictive (the penitentiary) mode of existence to a life which holds the promise of ultimate deliverance.

That religion regained rather than love renounced might prove to be the panacea for his misdirected life is a subterranean theme with many variations in the song of the birds. In a poem from the critical Hensel year (1817) the resolute speaker declares categorically: "Hosianna ich auch singen mag" (W I 374),[96] to which he receives the antiphonal avian response: "Hosianna stimmten die Vöglein an" (W I 374).[97] Especially in the late revisions of the fairy tales, the religious aura surrounding the devotional music of the birds comes to the fore. The ultimate resolution of the conflict in *Fanferlieschen*, for example, is ushered in by pious avian liturgical music: "A blackbird, like a sable choir-master, brought in a small organ. Then a few nightingales flew in as songstresses and a number of finches and other warblers as chorus members. Then all kinds of little bells began to toll in the tower, and in the church the birds started to sing and resound as lovely as if the most solemn services were being held there" (W III 423). And in the *Gockel* narrative, the birds add their voices to the symphonic tribute paid by all of nature to its creator and sustainer:

> Zu dir, zu dir
> Ruft Mensch und Tier
> Der Vogel dir singt
> Das Fischlein dir springt
> Die Biene dir brummt
> Der Käfer dir summt
> Auch pfeifet dir das Mäuslein klein,
> Herr Gott, du sollst gelobet sein.[98]
> (W I 345)

The singer that embodies all gradations of the above thematic and motivic constellations in their most elaborate form is, coincidentally, the bird that symbolizes both the *grandeur* and the *malheur d'être poète*: the nightingale. Brentano's Orphean singers readily ally themselves and their fate with this most exalted of nature's performers. Radlauf, for instance, feels an elective affinity with this nocturnal warbler:

[96] "May I also sing 'Hosanna!' "
[97] "And the birds struck up their 'Hosanna!' "
[98] "To you, to thee, / Call man and beast / The bird sings to thee / The little fish leaps to thee / The bee buzzes to thee / The beetle hums to thee / Even the tiny mouse squeaks to thee / Lord God, thou art to be praised."

> Und ich hör dieselben Klagen,
> Und ich hör dieselbe Lust,
> Und ich fühl das Herz mir schlagen
> Hier wie dort in meiner Brust.[99]
>
> (W III 111)

The nightingale is moved to song by either erotic drives (the elation of longing fulfilled or the frustration of love's labors lost) or religious devotion. A poem from the hectic years with Auguste Buß-mann, "Wie in Gewölben von Smaragd!", opens with an ebullient concert to which the nightingale contributes its most fervent tones:

> Wie schallet und hallet der Hörnerklang,
> Wie rauschet der wilde Bronnen,
> Es wiederklinget der Felsenhang,
> Die Fliege tanzt in der Sonnen;
> Aber Frau Echo, Frau Echo, Frau Echo,
> Du wiederspiegelst die Wonnen!
>
> . . . .
>
> Da lispelt und wispelt die Nachtigall,
> Ihr Stimmlein wollt übersteigen,
> Es lacht und klagt der süße Schall
> Wie Orgel, Laute und Geigen.
> Aber du Amor, du Amor, du Amor,
> Vor dir muß Alles ja schweigen![100]
>
> (GS II 425–426)

What Brentano seems to be suggesting by these lines is his familiar complaint that unless the music of love stirs a responsive chord in the heart of his beloved, all external musical stimuli, echoing and reechoing throughout nature (this condition is undergirded in the poem by such echo devices as assonance, alliteration, and interior rhyme), serve no purpose. In the domain of the fairy tale, however, the nightingale remains the catalytic agent for love and marriage:

> Heb an, du liebe Nachtigall,
> Dein kunstreich Figurieren,

---

[99] "And I hear the same lamentations, / And I hear the same delights, / And I feel this heart of mine beating / In my breast, here as well as there."

[100] "How the horns sound and resound, / How the wild fountain rushes, / The craggy cliff repeats the sounds, / The fly dances in the sun; / But Dame Echo, Dame Echo, Dame Echo, / You mirror the delights! // Then the nightingale whispers and lisps, / Her dainty voice would excel, / The sweet sound laughs and laments / Like the organ, lute and fiddles. / But you Amor, you Amor, you Amor, / Before you everything must grow silent!"

Hilf uns mit deinem süßen Schall
Das Brautlied musizieren.[101]

(W III 925)

These lines come from the revised *Gockel* fairy tale, a work in which Brentano linked the music of this songstress par excellence etymologically—through its habitat, the linden tree—with the woman who dominated the last years of his life: Emilie Linder. Characteristically, Brentano fuses the erotic and the religious dimensions which this singing opens in the listener:[102]

Nachtigall, ich hör dich singen
Herz im Leib möcht mir zerspringen,

. . . .

Nachtigall, wohl ist gut wohnen
In der Linde grünen Kronen,
Bei dir, lieb Frau Nachtigall,
Küß dich Gott viel tausendmal![103]

(W III 697)

In the context of the *Rheinmärchen*, the religious implications of the nightingale's music were clearly delineated in terms similar to those cited above:

Wenn dir will das Herz zerspringen,
Lehret dich Frau Nachtigall,
Gott zu grüßen tausendmal;[104]

(W III 189)

Because of the aura of suffering and martyrdom that surrounded the mythological origins of this singer,[105] as well as the sublime nature of her song, the nightingale became a fitting symbol for that woman in Brentano's life who embodied these same qualities: Anna Katharina Emmerich. In his biographical sketch of this stigmatized nun, Brentano reports that when a dying nightingale was once brought to her, she

---

[101] "Commence, you dear nightingale / Your artful configurations, / Help us with your sweet sound / To compose the bridal song."
[102] For an analysis of the erotico-religious dimension in Brentano's work, see Wolfgang Frühwald's "Nachwort" to EL, pp. 310 ff.
[103] "Nightingale, I hear you singing, / My heart would burst in my breast, ... // Nightingale, it is good to dwell / In the verdant crown of the linden tree, / With you, dear Lady Nightingale, / May God kiss you many thousands of times!"
[104] "When your heart is about to burst, / Dame Nightingale will teach you / To greet the Lord a thousandfold."
[105] Hollander (n. 2 above), pp. 225–238.

cured the bird and restored its song simply by whispering to it (SW XIV:1 155). To the factual account of this event, Brentano appends the following exegesis:

> How touchingly the nightingale appears in this symbol as the Annunciation, as the voice of the loftier song of nature which lay unsealed on the lips of the blessed woman, while the nightingale, robbed of its song, died. She, however, had to restore it to the throat of the bird, where it is once again sealed as a secret in non-conceptual tones in order to awaken in man general compassion and a longing for the solution of all mysteries, and so forth. (SW XIV:1 155)

In the account of Anna Katharina's death in 1824, Brentano recalls the transfer of song and indicates that she is now about to receive her reward: hastening to her divine bridegroom, the soul of the long-suffering nun anticipates "not the song of prophecy which once, from her own lips revived the dying nightingale," but rather music of fulfillment, "the new song in the choir of virgins who follow the Lamb wherever it may go" (SW XIV:1 164).

A lyric poem which serves as a sort of companion piece to the above prose narration blurs the contours somewhat so that it is not clear whether the nightingale is meant to represent the suffering nun or the spiritually "sick" poet. In either case, the uplifting qualities of this form of song are stressed and play a significant role in the cycle of resurrection and redemption:

> Ich habe den Frühling gesehen,
> Es sind mir fünf Rosen erblüht,
> Ich hörte der Nachtigall Flehen,
> Sie lehrt mich mitleidig ihr Lied:
>
> . . . .
> Die Nachtigall sah ich erkranket,
> Da tränkt sie mit Leben mein Mund.
> "Nimm wieder dein Lied, sei bedanket,
> Du singst es noch einmal so rund."
>
> . . . .
> Nun singt sie die Lieder all wieder,
> Geht zu ihr, ihr Kinder, und horcht,
>
> . . . .
> Es half mir die Nachtigall flehen
> Ein lieblich mitleidiges Lied.

Ich habe den Frühling gesehen,
Es haben fünf Rosen geblüht.[106]

(GS I 104–105)

Whereas the nightingale performed in a dual capacity in Brentano's poetry (as an erotico-religious songstress), his other prominent avian singer, the swan, served only a single function: to capture the moment of death and transfiguration in song. After examining the many contexts in which the swan song is employed by Brentano, one should distinguish between what might be termed the standard *topos* and those cases in which the configuration is expanded and deepened to the extent that it becomes a unique expression of the poet's views on death as a fundamental human experience. As an example of the conventional or rhetorical usage of the swan song image, one might cite the Hensel poem "Einsam will ich untergehn" in which the growing sense of isolation is underscored by a series of similes such as the line "Wie ein Schwanenlied im Tode" (W I 390).[107]

Some of the unique additions which Brentano was to make to the traditional figure are already manifest when Biondette, "the most melodic of swans" (W I 883), performs her "swan song" in the theater:

Also tönt ein Schwan im Sterben,
Der im Spiegel klarer Wasser
Stumm sein Sternbild angesehen,
Grüßt es scheidend im Gesange.[108]

(W I 737)

The narcissistic element, the soul-searching self-analysis and the preoccupation with one's own image, result—at the moment of Biondette's theatrical "death" when she takes leave forever from the gaudy world

---

[106] "I have seen the spring, / Five roses bloomed for me, / I heard the nightingale's pleas, / She taught me compassionately her song: // I saw the nightingale grown ill, / Then my lips imbued her with life. / 'Take your song back, many thanks, / You will sing it once more so fully.' // ... Now it sings all the songs again, / Go to her, you children, and listen, ... // The nightingale helped me to implore / A lovely, compassionate song. / I have seen the spring, / Five roses have bloomed."

[107] "Like a swan song in death."

[108] "Thus sings a swan in death / While peering silently at its star image In the mirror of clear waters / Greeting it with song while passing on." The German term "Sternbild" in this and subsequent swan song passages has been translated "starry image"; by this is meant both the literal sense of "my reflection among the stars" as well as the figurative use of the term in German to signify the constellation Cygnus.

of operatic illusion—in a moment of clear insight, a glimpse into a transfigured mode of life ("his image . . . in the mirror of clear waters"), which is preceded, appropriately enough, by a form of music never heard before. In *Die Gründung Prags* the swan is lauded above all singers for this very quality: "Er weiß zu sterben, stärker als der Tod, / Singt er des Lebens Traum den Sternen vor!" (W IV 605).[109] In this same work the swan song concept is raised to a higher power, so to speak, or heightened to a cosmic dimension with surrealistic overtones: "Wo . . . ein Chor von Geisterschwänen / Sein Sternbild singt auf bittrem Meer der Tränen" (W IV 590).[110]

That the two components—death and transfiguration—are essential ingredients in this form of song can be seen in the stanzas from the *Rheinmärchen* in which Fräulein Schwanengesang explains to Frau Phönix Federschein (the embodiment of rebirth and rejuvenation) the difference between her music and that of Fräulein Nachtigall:

> Sängerin ist sie, ich bin Dichter,
> Dichte nur ein einzig Lied,
> Mich begeistern Himmelslichter,
> Wenn der Mond ins Wasser sieht.
>
> Und ich will dies Lied dir sagen,
> Das ich sterbend pfleg zu singen,
> Wenn die Flammen um dich schlagen,
> Dich im Feuer zu verjüngen.[111]
>
> (W III 189)

The distinction made here between the purely musical songstress (Sänger) and the poetic singer (Dichter) is significant. Whereas the singing of the former might, in times of duress, grow silent, the song of the latter never could. It is not a matter of mere accident, therefore, that in the verses of Hölderlin which Brentano took as his epitaph, the swans go to their death in song, while in the original an ominous air of silence prevails:

----

109 "It knows how to die, stronger than death / It sings life's dream to the stars."

110 "Where . . . a choir of swan spirits / Sings its starry image on a bitter sea of tears."

111 "She is a songstress, I a poet, / I compose a single song, / The lights of heaven inspire me / When the moon peers into the water. // And I want to recite this song to you / Which I am accustomed to sing while dying, / When the flames leap about you, / To rejuvenate you in fire."

Hölderlin, "Hälfte des Lebens":

>Ihr holden Schwäne,
>Und trunken von Küssen
>Tunkt ihr das Haupt
>Ins heilignüchterne Wasser.[112]

>Aber es tauchet der Schwan ins heilignüchterne Wasser
>Trunken das Haupt, und singt sterbend dem Sternbild den Gruß.[113]
>
>(S II 90)

Because of the close affiliations of the swan and its song with death, this avian singer could be regarded as nature's counterpart to Orpheus. But whereas the latter experienced tragedy in the wake of triumph, this sequence is, in the case of the former, reversed. The poem from the *Rheinmärchen* entitled "Schwanenlied" illustrates this situation most vividly. The opening lines express by means of a succession of anaphoric clauses of increasing length the sense of agitation welling up in the heart of the singer confronted with the prospect of imminent death:

>Wenn die Augen brechen,
>Wenn die Lippen nicht mehr sprechen.
>Wenn das pochende Herz sich stillet
>Und der warme Blutstrom nicht mehr quillet![114]
>
>(W III 202)

The release from this condition is brought about by music from a supramundane source—angels who know how to bring nature's blossoms to song and inspire fervent avian singing:

>O dann sinkt der Traum zum Spiegel nieder,
>Und ich hör der Engel Lieder wieder,
>Die das Leben mir vorübertrugen,
>Die so selig mit den Flügeln schlugen
>Ans Geläut der keuschen Maies-Glocken,

---

[112] "And swans divine, / With kisses drunk / You drop your heads / In the sublimely sobering water." Translated by Kate Flores in *An Anthology of German Poetry from Hölderlin to Rilke*, p. 26. The original German poem from Friedrich Hölderlin, *Sämtliche Werke*, ed. Friedrich Beißner, II:1 (Stuttgart: W. Kohlhammer, 1951), 117.

[113] "But the swan dips its head drunkenly into the sublimely sobering water / And, dying, sings a greeting to its starry image."

[114] "When the eyes turn sightless, / When the lips no longer speak, / When the pounding heart grows quiet / And the warm bloodstream no longer flows."

> Daß sie all die Vöglein in den Tempel locken,
> Die so süße wildentbrannte Psalmen sangen:[115]
>
> (W III 202)

Thus in 1812, before the advent of the "angel in the desert" (Luise Hensel) and Brentano's own reentry into the "temple" (1817), he envisaged such a moment of deliverance in the song of the swan. However, this sense of triumph is not spontaneous but rather the result of a titanic conflict waged in the soul of nature's Orpheus. It is only after the cycle of life has run its course, when all the "seasons of the spirit" have passed by, so to speak, that the swan gains insight into its existential condition:

> Stille wirds, es glänzt der Schnee am Hügel,
> Und ich kühl im Silberreif den schwülen Flügel,
> Möcht ihn hin nach neuem Frühling zücken,
> Da erstarret mich ein kalt Entzücken—
> Es erfriert mein Herz, ein See voll Wonne,
> Auf ihm gleitet still der Mond und auch die Sonne.
> Unter den sinnenden Denkern, den klugen Sternen,
> Schau ich mein Sternbild an in Himmelsfernen;[116]
>
> (W III 202–203)

This exercise in self-cognition through introspection at the moment of death opens to the singer new perspectives on the meaning of a life just concluded. Standing, Orpheus-like, at the crossroads between time and eternity, the swan views things from the dual vantage point of the finite and the infinite; peering inward and downward at the surface of the water in this "soulscape," the singer simultaneously glances upward and outward, seeing the firmament reflected in the interiorized mirror image. This mode of contrary movement (looking down to catch sight of what is above) and inverted perspective (finding the most distant at close range) is accompanied by other forms of sensual and spiritual interchange (heat and cold, joy and sorrow, pleasure and pain, all coalesce in a kind of *coincidentia oppositorum*):

[115] "Oh, then the dream descends to the mirror, / And I hear the songs of the angels again, / Who transported my life, / Who beat so blissfully with their wings / To make the chaste May-bells peal, / So that they enticed into the temple all the birds / Which sang such wildly fervent psalms."

[116] "It becomes quiet, the snow shines on the hill, / And I cool in the silver frost my sultry wing, / I would like to flap it toward new spring, / Then a cold delight benumbs me— / My heart freezes, a sea of ecstasy / Upon which quietly glide the moon and also the sun. / Among the pondering thinkers, the wise stars, / I behold my starry image in distant heavens."

Alle Leiden sind Freuden, alle Schmerzen scherzen,
Und das ganze Leben singt aus meinem Herzen:
Süßer Tod, süßer Tod
Zwischen dem Morgen- und Abendrot.[117]

(W III 203)

Orpheus from the realm of myth and the swan from the world of Brentano's "Märchen" have certain key features in common. Both singers straddle the threshold between life and death; Orpheus' lyre ultimately ascends to heaven to become a tonal constellation in the music of the spheres; the swan envisions itself transfigured as the constellation Cygnus in the firmament. But whereas Orpheus, by glancing back toward the domain of death, loses his beloved forever and spends the remainder of his days lamenting his loss, the swan, in its one and only song, looks forward to a new mode of life, a level of existence which reconciles mundane impotence with divine potential, thereby opening new vistas to both the depths of the human soul and the heights of its ultimate celestial haven.

The Cosmos and Chaos of the Dance

The "magically transfiguring power" of Orpheus' music enabled him either to control, order, tame, and organize the forces of nature or to inspire them to dynamic, dance-like movement.[118] To Brentano's mind the dance per se represents an art form that stands at the crossroads of discipline and disarray; it occupies a point of intersection where the coordinates of these diametrically opposed tendencies meet. The ambivalent aspect of the dance can be seen in the following excerpt from a letter of 1802 in which Brentano advises Bettina to pursue the study of foreign languages—an intellectual discipline which he compares with a dance:

> Languages are of great gain, they contain . . . a melodic genius, and this also produces a dancing genius in one's spirit. . . . Learning languages—following the most exciting dance music in one's spirit—is to delight in harmonious inflections and in ornamental, bold, labyrinthine dances, and this electrifies the spirit, even as dance music electrifies your senses. (F 96–97)

[117] "All sorrows are joys, all pains but jest, / And the sum of my life sings from my heart: / Sweet death, sweet death / Between the rising and the setting sun."
[118] Rehm, p. 62.

In this analogy between language learning and dancing, two aspects of the respective activities are distinguished (corresponding to the polarity of "intellect" and "senses" that runs through the entire letter): "harmonious inflections" (in both the grammatical and saltatorial sense of the term) and "ornamental, bold, labyrinthine dances." The response of the performer-spectator to these contrastive but coexistent (and, in the final analysis, complementary) elements in interplay is one of exhilaration ("electrifying," as Brentano puts it).

In a letter of 1816 to Luise Hensel, Brentano analyzes the polonaise, or Polish dance, with regard to its aesthetically pleasing fusion of apparently disparate melodic and rhythmic components:

> Often I am like a senile old man whose hands tremble so much that the children joyfully dance to the beat of it [his music], and nothing is more touching than when they—too tired to dance any more—approach me and thank me for having given them such a merry tempo with my hands, and tell me I should stop trembling, since they cannot dance any more. Perhaps this condition of mine helps explain why I have a particular liking for the polonaise, because the fast melody in it moves at a peaceful tempo, just as my vivacity moves in melancholy, or, to put it more honestly, in well-founded depression about my worthlessness or my heavy guilt. From this condition I deduce all my views or, more correctly stated, my feelings with regard to the arts in general. (S II 183)

Brentano's closing comment is particularly relevant, since he implies that the interaction of the two contrastive components in the polonaise reflects both his existential condition and his aesthetic credo. The ultimate reciprocity of what seem to be mutually exclusive forces results in a mood which Brentano here calls "melancholy" or "depression," but which could also be termed—as it has been throughout this discussion —the "crisis of conscience."[119] When Brentano wrote these lines he stood at the turning point of his artistic career as well as on the threshold of a new life (in which Luise would play a reluctant Eurydice to his ardent Orpheus). Therefore the ambivalence of the polonaise as a dance form provides a fitting counterpart to the Orphean framework on which this study is constructed.

Whereas stylized or stereotyped dance movements may reflect the

[119] For the most recent analysis of the problem of melancholy and its constituent elements, see Klaus Wille, *Die Signatur der Melancholie im Werk Clemens Brentanos*, Europäische Hochschulschriften, Reihe I, No. 36 (Bern: Herbert Lang, 1970).

spirit of tradition and ritual which, akin to modes of morality and manners, has withstood the test of time and therefore offers the individual reliable guides for his actions in the complex panoply of life, they also entail adherence to a prescribed order, acquiescence to established norms, and reliance on patterns from the past, which, if imposed dogmatically or followed blindly, could stifle initiative and ingenuity. On the other hand, the spontaneity engendered by the rhythms of the dance music might be interpreted as the attempt of the individual to throw off the restrictive shackles of society, to behave in a manner more amenable to his personal disposition. Yet the aftereffects of such an exercise in unbounded freedom can border on exhaustion and ennui, depression and disgust—especially when the liberation of the senses deteriorates into libertinism. Even though these two contrastive approaches to the dance are treated as independent phenomena in the following analysis, in the continuum of Brentano's life and art these seemingly centrifugal forces operated in perpetual play and interplay.

On the basis of both statistical and contextual evidence, the positive benefits stemming from the dance as an ordering and organizing medium are outweighed by the negative effects of such a predetermined "cosmos." Illustrative of the positive features of measured rhythmic patterns and movements in a particular dance form such as the waltz is the following passage from a letter of 1804 in which Brentano, while journeying from Eisenach to Jena in a darkened coach in the deep of winter, notes how some sprightly melodies restored some semblance of order to his distraught spirit:

> Then a half dozen xylophone tones, under the direct command of a bagpipe, braved the elements and strolled through the cold night in the manner of a waltz, double file, and peered into my ears right under my cap.
>
> It was fun to see these bold tones, plump and healthy, as they danced through the cold winter, for the whole world was frozen solid. . . . The honest tones led me with rustic hospitality up a type of human henroost; they gave me courage, for the rhythmic beat hopped about in front of me, and in its measured strides I forgot fear and boredom. (S I 227)

In Brentano's fairy tales, the dance frequently serves as a reminder that the universe depicted in this idealized milieu was, in spite of occasional disruptions and aberrations, still basically intact. For instance, the maidens of Frau Mondenschein encircle their mistress in

solemn rhythmical procession, while in the *Tagebuch der Ahnfrau*
the structure of the graduated medieval society is reflected in the
stylized "Reihentänze" or round dances (W III 855) performed by
the ancestress together with her entourage. Even when forces that
might upset the balanced symmetry of such dancing hover on the
periphery, Brentano can suggest by means of stylistic devices (such
as the regular, measured rhythms and rhymes of the verse) the tempering of any uninhibited license which the text otherwise implies.

> Es umgrenze und umglänze
> Duftberauscht und mondlichttrunken
> In dem Lenze unsre Tänze
> Glühend der Johannisfunken.[120]
>
> (W III 137)

However, the negative aspects of the dance as an "ordering" principle
far exceed its positive attributes. Especially when dancing infers
conformity, rigidity, or inflexibility in such areas as social intercourse,
political life, religious belief, and aesthetic creativity, then the drawbacks of this tightly structured art form become sharply silhouetted.
On the social level, for example, the dance may be dangerous when it
requires blind obedience on the part of the individual to norms arbitrarily established by the community in its educative function. "Alas,"
Godwi notes, "it is very sad how awkward our education makes us;
our soul is forced by bourgeois ways of life, as by a dancing instructor,
into a strange, stiff consistency and into a variety learned by heart"
(W II 151). Having seen his own upbringing regimented in this fashion
by Winterwerber's "Palatine Public Educational Institute for Pupils
of the Male Gender of All Three Factions of the Christian Religion,"[121]
and by his aunt in Coblenz (the infamous "Tante Möhn") Brentano
remembered the adverse effects of such traumatic experiences throughout his lifetime. Having learned from the Winterwerber school about
"Dancing as a Means of Training the Body," [122] Brentano recalls in
the "Dedication" section of his revised *Gockel* story almost half a
century later how he practiced "bodily exercise through dance for all

---

[120] "May the glow-worm / Intoxicated with fragrance and drunk with
moonlight / Surround and encircle with brilliance / Our dances in the spring."
[121] Wolfgang Pfeiffer-Belli, *Clemens Brentano* (Freiburg im Breisgau: Herder,
1947), p. 14.
[122] Pfeiffer-Belli, pp. 15 ff. For an account of the effects on Brentano of im-
proper educational training, see Carmen Kahn-Wallerstein, "Clemens Brentanos
Verhängnis," *Schweizer Rundschau*, 50 (1950–1951), 611–619 and W III 1105.

three Christian religious factions" (W III 622) in his youth. With regard to the pedagogical principles advocated by his Aunt Möhn, on the other hand, he gave indirect expression to his resentment of her authoritarian control in the figure of Mamsel Cephise Marquise de Pimpernell, the pedantic tutor of Schnürlieschen in the late fairy tale of the same name. The Marquise not only "crumples," "crushes," "mangles," and "dismembers" her charges (W III 609), but, as the following lines indicate, she also teaches superficial social graces while neglecting educational essentials:

> Vom lieben Gott hört ich nicht viel,
> Doch vom Tarock und L'hombrespiel,
> Von Tanzen und Manieren
> Und auch von Gratulieren.[123]
>
> (W III 609)

In his own life Brentano found a suitable contrast figure to this misguided pedagogue in the headmistress of a Catholic school for girls, a woman whose personality he had once lauded as "harmonious" and whose teaching methods revealed "no trace of the schoolmaster, of the dancing instructor" (GS IX 284).

The political rigidity and naïveté of the German middle class is attacked by Römer in terms of dancing terminology when he characterizes the bourgeois mode of life as a spiritual masquerade at which they dance jubilantly in order to conceal the frustrations they harbor in secret: "On the dance floors . . . vexation is suppressed by the clinking of glasses and the squeaking of fiddles" (W II 56). Godwi, for his part, rebels against the arbitrary restrictions imposed upon living and loving by society, in the following terms: "Joy whirls about us like the bantering of love, and the wedding dance, which tracks its jubilant rounds through our senses, drowns together with us in allegories of life, around which bourgeois mores have drawn mystic curtains" (W II 78). One illustration of the manner in which empty gesture stifles genuine emotion is the dance image used by Römer to describe the dandy who pursues Lady Hodefield with hollow words and stereotyped mannerisms: "The exclamation mark, which the fop boldly appended with his feet to his despairing exit [came] from the orthography of his dance master" (W II 65).

---

[123] "I did not hear much about God above, / But about the games of tarot and l'hombre, / About dancing and manners / And also about congratulations."

The drawbacks to conformism in artistic matters can likewise be paraphrased in terms of adherence to prescribed dance patterns. For instance, already in 1801 Brentano regrets having become a disciple of the apostate Friedrich Schlegel, "of David in Jena [Schlegel] who dances on ahead with his harp" (U 236), instead of remaining an apostle of the true Messiah, Goethe. By the same token, the prospect of engendering a host of shallow imitators of his own induces Brentano to comment to Arnim in 1802: "The poet lives as in a desert, the wild beasts attack him, since one cannot tame them all by singing, and the monkeys dance to his tune."[124] The impression that the field of art in general was being inundated by second-rate and derivative productions induced Brentano to comment to Bettina during the same period: "The whole windmill-works of the arts are constantly in motion, the hand of the musician and the foot of the dancer fit in with each other" (F 315). Toward the end of his career, Brentano looked to the writer Ferdinand Freiligrath as the rising star on the new literary horizon; comparing his own accomplishments with those of Freiligrath, Brentano makes use of the dance image both to express his conviction of the precarious nature of the aesthetic artifact per se and to indicate his feeling of inadequacy in competition with this outstanding representative of the younger generation:

> Tanzt' auch auf dem Seil ich grad,
> Wollt' ich balancierend bleiben,
> Schrieb auch keine Zeil' ich grad,
> Ließ doch meinen Kiel ich treiben,
> Kläng' es auch langweilig fad,
> Wollt' ich doch sechs Blätter schreiben,
> Für ein Blatt von Freiligrath.[125]
>
> (W I 623)

The transition from the dance as an embodiment of order in life and art (in both cases with positive and negative connotations) to the concept of dancing as the incarnation of disorder and dissolution is exemplified in the *Romanzen vom Rosenkranz* by the fate of the "pious dancer," Biondette. An indication of the fact that the dance can de-

---

[124] Reinhold Steig, *Achim von Arnim und die ihm nahe standen*. 3 vols. (Stuttgart: J. G. Cotta'sche Buchhandlung, 1894–1913), I, 106.

[125] "Even if I danced straight on the rope / I would want to stay in balance, / Even if I were not to write a single line straight / I would nevertheless let my pen flow freely, / Even if it were to sound boringly bland, / I would still want to write six pages / For a single page of Freiligrath."

teriorate into a force of moral and spiritual corruption is Moles' disclosure that Eve presented herself to Adam in dancing fashion (W I 788), whereby her sensuous allure contrasted with the divinely sanctioned "dance of the hours" (W I 789). Apo, who projected a kind of pan-eroticism into his astronomical interpretations, likewise envisions a form of Dionysian dance in the heavenly constellations:

> Nach des Bechers süßem Weine
> Greift der Wassermann und trinkt,
> Bär und Hund, der groß und kleine,
> Tanzen, der Triangel klingt.[126]
>
> (W I 870)

The magical spell cast by the old hag in order to make Biondette more amenable to Apo's advances also contains elements of orgiastic dancing: "Tanzend um den Bock den Reih'n" (W I 943);[127] "Und der Irrwisch hüpft betrunken, / Wo der Musikant versunken" (W I 944).[128] The apex of moral degeneration associated with some form of dance occurs in the words of Älia Lälia Crispis who, by means of the legendary ring of Herodias, hopes to wreak havoc and destruction:

> Bei der blut'gen Weihnachtsfeier,
> Bei der Kindlein lust'gem Mord,
> Daß er tanz' nach ihrer Leier,
> Schenkt' sie es dem Vater dort.[129]
>
> (W I 958)

The allusion to Herodias brings to mind the infamous dance of her daughter, Salome, who cavorted before Herod in order to acquire the head of John the Baptist. This entire scenic complex is recorded in vivid detail by Brentano in the *Leben Jesu*; the degree to which performer, audience, and reader are "carried away" by Salome's voluptuous gyrations is clearly evident:

> Salome appeared with some dancers, dressed very daringly and quite transparently. . . . She danced in the middle, the others around her. This dance is not as wild and brisk as our country dances; but it is a constant

---

[126] "Aquarius reaches for the sweet wine / Of the beaker and drinks, / Bear and Hound, Great and Lesser, / Dance, the triangle plays."

[127] "Dancing the roundelay around the ram."

[128] "And the will-o'-the wisp hops about intoxicatedly, / Where the musician has disappeared."

[129] "So that he might dance to her lyre, / At the bloody Christmas festival, / At the merry murder of the children, / She then presents it to her father."

bending, turning, and twisting of the body, as if they had no bones at all; and scarcely do they assume one position, than they already have a new one. It is a continuous turning and swaying and bending like a serpent; . . . this particular dance was based on pure lewdness and imitated the most disgraceful passions. Salome outdid all the others, and I saw the devil at her side, as if he were turning and twisting all parts of her body in order to bring forth this abomination. Herod was utterly captivated and confused by her confounded positions, and when she finally came to his throne, the other dancers danced on.[130]

The intimation that the Devil may have been the instigator of this voluptuous dance recalls the scene in the *Romanzen* in which Älia Lälia Crispis waltzes with Apo to the accompaniment of Moles' violin:

> Und in buhlerischem Eifer
> Tanzet, wie der trunkne Lot,
> Mit der Braut er einen Schleifer
> In fatalem Teufelstrott.[131]
>
> (W I 961)

Finally, it is significant that in Brentano's *Leben Jesu* Maria Magdalena's dancing is also described as "a perpetual display and enticement of her body," and that the mother of Christ's betrayer, Judas, is characterized as "a dancer and singer,"[132] the same combination of talents exhibited by Brentano's most prominent and problematic performer, Biondette.

The sensuous appeal and the feeling of uninhibited freedom evoked by the dance may, on the other hand, prove to be a blessing in disguise for someone like Jacopone; this bookworm, hearing Rosarosa's song, exclaims: "Sieh, es tanzet meine Seele / Auf dem frohen Strahl des Bronnens" (W I 806).[133] The dance of the heroine of *Fanferlieschen Schönefüßchen*, Ursula von Bärwalde, reflects by its spontaneity of movement the natural freedom of her spiritual disposition: "Oh! And Princess Ursula . . . is for everyone an angel in human—or better, up to the present, in bear form; she dances every polonaise spon-

---

[130] From Brentano's *Das Leben unseres Herrn und Heilandes Jesu Christi. Nach den Gesichten der gottseligen Anna Katharina Emmerich aufgeschrieben*, 3 vols. (Regensburg: Friedrich Pustet, 1858–1860), II (1859): 269–270, as quoted in Joseph Adam, *Clemens Brentanos Emmerick-Erlebnis* (Freiburg im Breisgau: Herder, 1956), p. 290.

[131] "And in amorous zeal, / Like the drunken Lot he dances / A waltz with his bride / In the devastating devil's trot."

[132] Adam, *Clemens Brentanos Emmerick-Erlebnis*, p. 251.

[133] "Behold, my soul dances / On the joyous water spray of the fountain."

taneously by sight-reading; she sings or growls like the most perfect dancing master!" (W III 969). This flexible attitude enables her to endure the harsh punishment inflicted arbitrarily by Jerum—the constriction of her personal freedom by a forced marriage (indicated by the leitmotiv-like phrase "Tomorrow you too have to begin the dance") and by incarceration. Yet the sense of inner freedom experienced by the dancer is not an unmixed blessing either. For example, in a passage from a letter of 1799 to his grandmother, Sophie von Laroche, Brentano compares his spiritual disposition to a deserted ballroom in which, following the gay festivities shortly before, an air of fatigue and ennui lingers:

> My heart is a boudoir that is connected to my head by the winding staircase of my moods. In my head things now look like a ballroom; the masks have disappeared, the last chord of the final dance rumbles against the walls, and a few candle stumps are still burning, illuminating the barren emptiness like the moon that shines upon graves. (S I 25)

The imagery here is suggestive of a kind of void; the last vestiges of the celebration have faded leaving behind that empty emotional vacuum which often follows in the wake of overindulgence. The importance of this concept for Brentano's work can be seen in the fact that he incorporates the deserted ballroom into *Godwi* at the point in the story at which the protagonist has just declared that only an artist superior to Lady Hodefield could elicit more than "frivolous, trippling tones" (W II 76) from him; his life of sensuality with Molly constitutes a dance now concluded:

> Alas! thus the winding staircase of my mood spirals upward from the intimate, lust-gloomy boudoir of my heart to the desolate, stagnant life in my head. . . . Transversely I saw myself as the blueprint of a building, in my head there was a grand ballroom, but everything was over; I saw the last note of the last dance yawning as it slipped out the door right past the orchestra platform of my ears with a dying, tattered cloak. A number of my youthful plans stood around there, disturbed and out of sorts; the dance was finished, they had masks in their hands and wept tears of relief from their somber, inflamed eyes. (W II 26)

Frequently, the disruptive or destructive force of the dance is allied with two elements that played a major role in Brentano's repertoire of symbols, fire and water. In *Gustav Wasa*, for instance, the "frantic dance of the flames" (W IV 35) poses the threat of literal as well as figurative disaster, while in the *Tagebuch der Ahnfrau* the "dance of the glaring torches" (W III 866) helps to undermine the mental equilibrium of Amey. The function of water and its dancing waves is to arouse a feeling of chaos or insecurity, owing to the treacherous undercurrent and lack of firm footing often associated with the aquatic element. In the "Mosel-Eisgangs-Lied" of 1830, for example, the melting snows of a spring thaw fill the network of rivers to the flood stage as even the tiniest tributaries "press toward the dance" (W I 514). Brentano conceives of this union of streams as a kind of marriage of nature's forces, for which celebration such man-made constructs as bridges serve merely as "bridal attire in the dance" (W I 517), and the inundated fields become a ballroom:

> Die Fastnacht hat vorm Jahr
> Rhein, Mosel hier vermählt,
> Heut hat das Riesenpaar
> Den Tanzplatz sich erwählt.[134]
> (W I 517–518)

In a much more phantasmagoric and imaginative fashion, Brentano attempts in his fairy tale of *Schneider Siebentot* to explain etymologically the derivation of the German word for the English channel ("Ärmelkanal" = "sleeve" channel) on the basis of incompatible mythic dancing partners, Continent (the mainland) and Marinus (the sea.) At the wedding of these mythic forces, the figures represented on the coat-of-arms of England (the "Einhorn," or unicorn) and France (the "Hahn," or cock) perform conflicting dances, and the ensuing melee terminates in the hostilities of the Hundred Years' War:

> But the happy couple told them to go home, and began to dance so vigorously that the isthmus started to pull apart. But when the cock on the one side crowed a minuet and the unicorn on the other side sang an English dance, they lost the beat and tugged around on each other so much that Marinus ripped off one of his bride's sleeves; at the same time the isthmus broke in two, the ocean poured through between England and France and separated forever the cock and the unicorn. (W III 280–281)

The bellicose feelings incited by the ill-matched dances in the above excerpts touches upon a motif that comes to the fore in Bren-

---

[134] "Last year the shrovetide married / The Rhine and the Moselle here, / Today the giant couple / Has chosen their dancing place."

tano's writings during the Napoleonic wars: the military encounter as
a kind of "weapons dance" (GS VII 374; GS II 48) in which the Little
Corporal from France fares badly: "Da kam er schlimm vom Tanze"
(GS II 22); "Der französche Contretanz / Wird nicht aufgeführt"
(GS VII 416).[135] It should be noted, however, that the dance image is
associated not only with the chaotic shambles of Napoleon's defeat
on the battlefield, but also with the spirit of cooperation and coordination exhibited by the allies in their struggle against the conqueror
of Europe: "Deutsch, Kosackisch, Ungrisch wird, / Englisch auch
getanzt" (GS VII 416).[136]

In the sphere of religious devotion the dance retained its Janus-
faced countenance, on the one hand suggestive of the ordered ritual so
essential to the liturgy and, on the other, indicative of unruly elements
that may disrupt the otherwise smooth operation of an organization
such as the Catholic Church. This dual aspect of the dance comes to the
fore in a remark of 1822 concerning a certain Frau Hirn and her behavior in matters not regulated by Church dogma:

> How many admirable qualities are to be marveled at and learned from
> this ingenious, devout, pious woman! She always puts me to shame,
> even though the taste of her broader pastime may bore me, for she
> indeed dances this minuet before the ark of the covenant, and how
> lovingly and with what infinite patience does she allow the ecossaises
> and waltzes of the new age to swirl and hop about her ranks, and she
> interrupts herself humbly for the glory of God. (GS IX 12–13)

In 1827 Brentano employs similar contrastive dance styles to indicate
to his brother Christian the sad state of disarray into which the journals
dedicated to the dissemination of Catholic doctrine have fallen:

> What now appears has no unity; even though in part excellent, even
> powerful, things scarcely proceed as in a minuet, while evil storms
> obliquely through things like a thousand lascivious partners dancing
> schottisches, gallopades, and tempêtes. (GS IX 168)

Finally, art itself as well as the aesthetic temper may be examined
in terms of the duality of the dance. Whereas the danger of conformism has already been discussed in conjunction with the dance as an

[135] "He left the dance in bad condition"; "The French contredanse / Is not
being performed."
[136] "People are dancing German / Cossack, Hungarian / and also English."

"ordering" force in art, the threat stemming from its other component—
dynamic energy breaking all restrictive shackles—has never disappeared from view. Lady Hodefield in *Godwi* articulated this latter condition when she stated: "Moreover, in my ideals it is transition, change,
and motion which are too impetuous to ever seek them in the silent,
plastic and graphic arts; not the sight, but the moment of seeing is
the object of my yearning; not the pose of the limbs but rather the
dance delights me" (W II 99). The exact phrase used by Lady Hodefield in her closing remark is "carries me away" (reißt mich fort), and
the act of being "swept off one's feet" by a form of art had inherent
dangers as well as innate delights. Whenever the distinction between
these two elements became blurred, Brentano became worried and
spoke in derogatory terms about "sprained and bone-set goddesses
of the dance" (S II 382) in the field of literature, or in the case of the
pictorial arts of Bavaria, of a graphic representation "which muddles
about and stumbles indecisively between Alpine yodeling and the high-
strung sublimity of grotesque dancing" (EL 111). Characteristically,
it was in the realm of the fairy tale that he was able to capture most
memorably the dual role of the dance as harbinger of cosmic order and
as the embodiment of chaotic disruptiveness. The ingenious "art
figure" (Kunstfigur) contrived by the three wicked engravers in order
to induce Gackeleia to part with the philosopher's stone (which would
have enabled Gockel to restore order in his out-of-joint world) makes
use of a mode of dancing to heighten its magic allure: "sie soll als
Tänzrin tanzen" (W III 715); "Tamburin and Kastagnetten / Schnurrt
und rasselt ihre Hand" (W III 715).[137] On reading this description, one
is reminded of the deleterious effects of the satyr's music of Violette,
or of Älia Lälia Crispis' parody of Biondette's performance. However,
in the fairy tale milieu Brentano skillfully resolves the inequities which
disturbed the equilibrium of the earlier works. The author holds the
trump card in his hand, since he makes the generating force behind
the seductive "art figure" none other than the tiny white mouse, Princess Sissi Mandelbiss, that creature which, in return for services rendered it by the elder Gockel, has dedicated its musical prowess and
magic powers to the restoration of order in the lives of the Gockel
family.

---

[137] "She is to dance as a dancer; Her hand clanks and clatters / Tambourine
and castanets."

Metamorphosis and Catharsis: "Singen-Lobsingen"

Whereas the ancient Greek poet-singer Orpheus founded a religion in a remote, mythical age, his Romantic counterpart, Clemens Brentano, "found" a religion in 1817. It would be an oversimplification, however, to claim that the edifying forces of liturgy and liturgical music were entirely without precedent in Brentano's thought prior to this date.[138] Note, for instance, the favorable comments he made in 1805 concerning the singing of the "divine singers of liturgical music, the Finkenstein girls," with whom he had recently become acquainted: "Since hearing the singing of these girls . . . I too can only regard all other music as a sad potpourri" (U 327). On a very superficial plane, the revived and revised attitude of the poet after 1817 is manifested by the increasing prominence of the term "lobsingen" (and its derivatives), which, although it by no means displaces the previous, more secularly oriented concept of "singen," nevertheless strongly rivals the latter in his writings.

The verb "lobsingen" (to sing hymns of praise or adoration) signified a form of art that no longer had its focal point in the mundane sphere, but rather found its correlatives in the transcendental or metaphysical. In a letter of 1818 to Luise Hensel, Brentano outlined the requisites of the aesthetic media in terms that reflect his new attitude: "All true art is a precursor of rebirth, for its striving toward the eternal strives, without knowing it, toward the Lord. . . . Pray that art might become good; it teaches singing and praising, and lies, as does life itself, between heaven and hell, and opens the gates to both" (GS VIII 330). The dilemma that confronted and confounded the author, however, is contained in the closing comment: even when art directed his glance upward and transported his soul to purer realms of the spirit, he remained aware of its terrestrial components. Hovering between "heaven and hell," art could not only deify but defile. This juxtaposition finds clear expression in a letter of 1824 in which "the beautiful Christian tone and the melody of character" (GS IX 68) in the heart of the true believer are contrasted with the aesthetic code and ethical credo of the apostate: "Intoxicated with their odd brew . . . they talk drivel like

---

[138] In spite of some of the irreverent digressions in works such as *Godwi* or the blasphemous comments of Moles in the *Romanzen*, Brentano seems to have wrestled with the religious issue throughout his early life.

cavaliers tumbling about in the labyrinth of love . . . and sing praises
with blatant articulation, with acoustically measurable tones" (GS IX
70). The adherents of such a misguided way of life practice idolatry
(Götzendienst") rather than Christianity ("Gottesdienst"). During the
decade 1820–1830 Brentano envisioned a return to pre-Reformation
Christianity, to the era when there was "one general circle of humble
and obedient children of the Lord singing praises in His temple" (EL
42). Aside from the fact that the "world was too much with" Brentano
to enable him to reconcile completely the disappointments of life with
the dictates of the Church, the age in which he lived was too secularized
for such an ideal to succeed. Instead of experiencing a period of re-
surgence, established religion had entered a time of eclipse, an epoch
of debunking and demythologization that would culminate in the official proclamation of the "death of God" a generation later. Brentano's
last-ditch attempt (through the power of religious verse) to rescue the
expiring faith from interment in a Hades-like materialism and cynical
skepticism represented another phase of his Orphean calling and crisis.

The following discussion of the above trends—under the polarity
of "singen"-"lobsingen"—will entail three areas of investigation: the
motivation behind the desire to sing a more exalted song of praise;
the forces or figures that became the objects of this pious devotion;
works illustrating either the successful transition from the secular to
the spiritual mode of singing or, more significantly, the uneasy coexistence of the two.

There are several factors that induced Brentano to think in terms
of "lobsingen" instead of "singen": the awareness that his earlier
approach to art had been restricted and restricting; the contrite heart
of a penitent who, after acknowledging the errors of his past, seeks to
atone for his mistakes in the hope of attaining the salvation of his
soul; and the fear of retribution for his failure to undergo a complete
change of heart. Brentano's desire to "cleanse" or "purify" his artistic
practices is expressed in a letter sent to his brother Christian in 1817
(ten months after his actual conversion), in which he includes among
the handwritten copies of poems by diverse authors the following lines
under the title "Heimweh":

> Mich zieht ein stetes Sehnen
> Nach jenen reinern Tönen.[139]
>
> (GS VIII 244)

[139] "A constant yearning draws me / To those purer tones."

Such "purer tones" would constitute a "literary baptism" comparable to the actual sacrament received by Luise Hensel in 1818 and commemorated by Brentano in a poem of the same year:

> Du lerntest Lieder singen,
> Die dich zur Welt gewandt,
> Manch bunten Kranz zu schlingen,
> Der an die Welt dich band.
>
> Doch alle diese Künste
> Sie wurden heut gekehrt
> Zu einem heil'gen Dienste,
> Der nur das Ew'ge ehrt.[140]
>
> (W I 428)

The teacher-pupil relationship between himself and Luise ("Lehre mich, wie du zu büßen, / Tränenquell der frommen Lieder" [W I 364])[141] is the reverse of that which once existed between Brentano and Bettina. The poet is now willing to become "as a little child": "Daß ich lobsingend dringe / Durch Nacht und Morgenroth" (GS VIII 256).[142] Having apparently been convinced by Luise's example that such an artistic metamorphosis was possible, Brentano subsequently chides those who, like himself, have tarried so long in taking this step:

> Daß das heil'ge hohe Lied
> Mir konnt Sinnentaumel scheinen,
> Muß, der durch den Spiegel sieht,
> Himmeltrunken ich beweinen.[143]
>
> (GS I 424)

This stanza reads almost like an analysis of the dilemmas encountered by Biondette in the *Romanzen*, except that Brentano now ventures to describe the cause and to prescribe a cure for this situation:

> Doch die Schätze dieser Welt
> Sind so arglistig bedinget,

---

[140] "You learned to sing songs / That turned you to the world, / To braid many a garland / Which bound you to the world. // Yet all these arts, / They were changed today / Into one sacred service, / Which honors only the Eternal One."

[141] "Teach me to do penance like you, / You source of tears for pious songs."

[142] "That I, singing praises, might penetrate / Through night and dawn."

[143] "Looking through the mirror, enchanted with heaven / I must bewail the fact / That the sacred, sublime song / Could appear to me as sensual frenzy."

> Daß, wer sich an ihnen hält,
> Sich stets mehr und mehr verschlinget.[144]
>
> (GS I 425)

The question remains, however, whether lines such as these represent a prognosis for one who, having seen the light at the end of the cave, can now move relentlessly toward that goal, or whether they simply constitute a reaffirmation of the tragic plight of art and the artist.

After this brief examination of some of the factors that motivated Brentano to attempt a more exalted song, the next goal is to identify those figures which he made the focal point of attention after apparently forsaking "Frau Welt" and her charms. There are basically four objects of such devotional song: God the Father, Christ the Son, Mary the Virgin Mother, and the Saints (or Christian martyrs). In the course of revising and modernizing the *Trutznachtigall* of the seventeenth-century Jesuit poet Friedrich von Spee in 1817, Brentano found ample opportunity to develop the biblical *topos* of singing songs (or psalms) in praise of the Lord, as can be seen from the following example:

> Fröhlich singen sie und klingen,
> Geben ihrem Gott die Ehr,
> Auf das immerwährend Singen
> Sie zu singen wünschen mehr,
>
> . . . .
>
> Süßlich viele Instrumenten
> Mit dem Singen stimmen ein,
> Dieses Musikspiels Regenten
> Gottes liebe Geister sein[145]
>
> (W I 372–373)

In another reworking of Spee's poetry (in which Brentano incorporates ideas and entire verses written by his "mentor," Luise Hensel), the singer contrasts the inferiority of his present mode of "faithful and simple" song with the sublime tones he will one day perform for all eternity:

> O hör' auf meine Weisen,
> O sieh auf mein Gebet.

[144] "Yet the treasures of this world / Are so deceitfully constituted, / That whoever clings to them / Entraps himself deeper, ever deeper."

[145] "Merrily they sing and ring, / Paying homage to their God, / To supplement this perpetual singing / They wish to sing even more, // Sweetly many instruments / Join in with the singing, / The rulers of this joyous music / Are God's beloved spirits."

> Bin ich im Himmel oben,
> Da lern' ich andern Sang,
> Da will ich hoch dich loben
> Mein ewig Leben lang.[146]
> (W I 400–401)

However, both this interim music—a poor substitute for the exalted melodies he intended to offer—and the as yet unsung song which he conceives in his mind's "ear" have already found favor in the realm of the Father and His Son:

> Das Lied, das ich verschwiegen,
> Das Lied, das leis ich sang,
> Sah ich die Engel wiegen
> In Davids Harfenklang.
> Und sah, den ich gerühret
> Mit meinem Lerchensang,
> Zum Herrn von mir geführet
> Auf einem Dornengang;
> Er sang mit mir zusammen
> Mit sel'gem Flug und Fall
> In Gottes Liebesflammen
> Trotz Lerch,' trotz Nachtigall![147]
> (W I 401)

Not only God the Father, but also Christ as the only "begotten Son" became an object of musical adoration. The poem "Wie man das Christkind beherbergen soll" (ca. 1822–1826) illustrates the standard format for such hymns of praise:

> Gott in der Höhe sei nun Lob und Preis
> Und auf der Erde allen Menschen Friede
> Die guten Willens sind, das singe leis
> Dem lieben Kinde du als Wiegenlied.[148]
> (W I 468)

[146] "Oh, listen to my tunes, / Oh, heed my prayer. / When I am in heaven above, / Then I shall learn another song, / Then shall I praise Thee to the heights, / All my life eternal."

[147] "I saw the angels cradling / In the tones of David's harp / The song I left unsung, / The song I quietly sang. / And I saw the one I had touched / With my lark-like song / Led by me to the Lord / On a path of thorns; / Together with me he sang / With blissful flight and fall / In God's flames of love / In spite of lark and nightingale."

[148] "To God on high now be praise and glory / And on earth peace to all men / Who are of good will; sing that softly / To the dear child as a cradle song."

Brentano also has difficulty in finding an appropriate mode of articulation with which to address the second person of the Trinity:

> "Ach hätt' ich Engelzungen,
> Ich hätt' dir längst gesungen
> Das süße liebe Lied,
> Das mir so still und selig
> Im jungen Herzen glüht.
>
> Ich weiß ja keine Weisen,
> Dich Heiland so zu preisen,
> Dich Jesu fromm und mild,
> Wie meine ganze Seele
> Dir jauchzt und singt und spielt."[149]
>
> (W I 398–399)

And indeed, the Savior, in his infinite wisdom, apprehends and appreciates this inward devotion even more than outward display and, consequently, promises a commensurate reward:

> "Und auch sei dir bescheret
> Die Weise, die mich ehret,
> Mit freud'gem Flug und Fall,
> Das Lied, das mir lobsinget
> Trotz Lerch,' trotz Nachtigall."[150]
>
> (W I 399)

One noteworthy aspect to all of the above verses directed to either God the Father or Christ the Son, is the fact that they are not exclusively those of Brentano himself, but rather adaptations from the poetry of Spee or Luise Hensel, individuals of demonstrated piety whose words he could, at best, paraphrase. The same holds true of his songs of praise directed to the Virgin Mary. Instead of addressing the latter directly, Brentano interposes a saint or martyr figure as the mediating interlocutor to the greatest of mediatrices. For example, in the poem "Das Waldvöglein" of 1831, a pious friar, dedicated to the Mother of God "in prayer and song," chants ceaselessly the refrain: "Gegrüßt

[149] " 'Alas, had I but tongues of angels, / I would long ago have sung to Thee / The sweet, dear song / Which has glowed so quietly and blissfully / In my young heart. // Indeed, I know no tunes / To praise Thee, dear Savior, / Jesus reverent and mild, / As much as my entire soul / Shouts, sings and plays to Thee.' "

[150] " 'And may you also be granted / The melody which honors me / With blissful flight and fall, / The song which sings my praises / In spite of lark and nightingale.' "

seist du Maria!"[151] Even more persistent in his dedication is Saint Solinus who, while spending most of his time perched in a tree—a madman or a fool in the eyes of the world which he so eagerly avoids— calmly responds to the taunts of the nonbelievers with his "eternally sacred song," inwardly convinced of its redemptive force:

> O Seligkeit der beiden Worte
> Ave Maria fort und fort,
> Erlösend tönst du im Akkorde
> Gott, Mensch, im fleischgewordnen Wort.[152]
>
> (W I 505)

Brentano's poetry from the period after 1830 contains a large number of lengthy saints' legends in which the author's song in commemoration of the principal subject is combined with the singing of this protagonist to celebrate one or more of the three exalted figures mentioned above. Saint Agnes, for instance, continues to intone hymns of praise to the Lord even in the seething flames of the funeral pyre (GS I 224). The most ambitious attempt on Brentano's part to fuse songs of praise to, with the singing of, saintly figures was his "Legende von der Heiligen Marina," a long poem of 1839 based on a painting by the Viennese artist Eduard von Steinle. In the "Dedication" to this work, Brentano explains why he decided to supplement the pictorial representation with a poetic text:

> Und als auch mir dein Werk das Herz bezwungen,
> Das stumm und hart nur selten Kunst gerührt,
> Hab'ich Marinas Lob für dich gesungen,
> Der Heil'gen selbst ein höhres Lied gebührt:
>
> Ein neues Lied, das unter Harfenchören
> Dem Lamme Gottes, das auf Sion steht,
> Die Jungfraun singen und allein nur hören,
> Die rein dem Lamm gefolgt, wohin es geht.[153]
>
> (W I 627)

---

[151] "Hail to thee, Mary!" (W I 523 ff)

[152] "Oh, the bliss of the two words / Ave Maria on and on, / Redeeming, you resound in the chord / God, Man, in the Word become flesh."

[153] "And when your work conquered even my heart, / Which, being mute and hard, has seldom been touched by art, / I sang Marina's praises for you, the Saint herself deserves a loftier song: // A new song which the maidens, / Amid choirs of harps, sing to the Lamb of God / And which only those hear / Who, pure in spirit, have followed the Lamb wherever it goes."

The ensuing tale of "constantia" in the face of adversity has all the elements of a baroque martyr tragedy; the "antiphonal" form of song (the legend itself celebrating Marina, and the latter's stoic hymns of praise) together with the dual perspective from which the account is presented (the visual as well as the verbal media) evoke memories of the grandiose seventeenth-century Jesuit churches in which similar techniques were employed to produce an awe-inspiring and divinely sanctioned but mundanely conceived "Gesamtkunstwerk."[154]

One has the impression after reading legends such as that of Marina that they could be ranked aesthetically with the works of the Nazarene school of painters, those pious artists who flourished during the early decades of the nineteenth century and who—also somewhat anachronistically—dedicated their life and works to the propagation of Catholic Christian concepts. Whereas the sense of religious fervor which inspired their paintings is admirable, their art evokes a feeling of reverent transcendence instead of existential relevance. Consequently, the products of the Nazarene school have little more than historical interest for the modern observer. The same may be said of Brentano's legends of martyrs and saints: impressive in execution, but not lasting in effect. It might be recalled at this point that Orpheus' greatest accomplishments in art were also not the result of imposing conquests, but came rather in the wake of life's most crushing defeats. Orpheus moved men more deeply by his lament for Eurydice forever lost than with his all-powerful song, which vanquished the guardians of the Underworld. In the case of Brentano himself, it is the aimless wanderer, the errant pilgrim, who remains closer to the reader's heart than the confident—at times complacent—singer who knows he has found the pathway to God. This situation comes to the fore in those works which either depict the struggle involved in the transition from the secular to the spiritual plane or, even more convincing for the modern audience, which bear subtle traces of the persistent coincidence and co-existence of dichotomous forces operating "between heaven and hell."

In depicting the conflict between mundane singing and sacred song, Brentano either resorts to a pattern of sequential progression from "singen" to "lobsingen" (as in Biondette's attempt to lead a cloistered life following her experiences in the world of the theater) or he super-

---

[154] For an extensive analysis and interpretation of both the Solinus and the Marina legends, see pp. 233–298 and pp. 347–427 in Bernhard Gajek, *Homo poeta: Zur Kontinuität der Problematik bei Clemens Brentano* (Frankfurt am Main: Athenäum, 1971).

imposes a religious overlay on a work originally conceived in a more
secular tone (the contrafact).[155] In order to illustrate the first technique,
two late poems (one confessional, the other occasional) will be cited.
The narrator in "Durch die weite öde Wüste" (1835) recounts the
odyssey of his soul (since the poem is set in a desert of the Middle
East, one should perhaps speak of a "hegira") from Babylon, the me-
tropolis of sin, to the heavenly city of Jerusalem. This migration of
the spirit from the seat of corruption to the heart of salvation is symbolized by a transformation of song. The forces of temptation, to be
sure, do not surrender without a struggle:

> Weh' aus meiner Harfe Saiten
> Von dem weiten Babylon
> Klang wie Leiden, Meiden, Scheiden,
> Mir durch's Herz ein Klageton.
>
> Wie der Turteltaube Sehnen
> In dem Traume seufzend tönt;
> Wie der Flügelschlag von Schwänen
> Im Gesange sterbend dröhnt.[156]
>
> (GS I 50)

The symbolically significant ascent from the valley to the summit of
Mount Tabor is accompanied by the quest for a higher form of singing;
the swan song to the mundane is followed by a foretaste of the musical
delights awaiting the pilgrim at the goal of his journey:

> Aufwärts durch die Wolkenwogen
> Drang zum Tabor ich hinan,
> Der von Segen rings umzogen
> Wiegte meines Liedes Schwan.
>
> O, der Blumen Augenfriede
> Blicket auf aus glühem Traum,
> Kniet und küßt dem Hohenliede
> Thaues Perlen von dem Saum.[157]
>
> (GS I 52)

---

[155] For a discussion on the literary contrafact in Brentano's work, see Wolfgang Frühwald, "Clemens Brentano," in *Deutsche Dichter der Romantik*, ed.
Benno von Wiese (Berlin: Erich Schmidt, 1971), pp. 295 ff.

[156] "Woe from my harp strings, / From far-off Babylon / There sounded
suffering, shunning, departing / A plaintive tone through my heart. // As the
yearning of the turtle-dove / Sounds in a dream, sighingly, / As the beating
wings of swans / Drone, dying in song."

[157] "Upward through the waves of clouds / I made my way to Tabor, /

That this poem contains the promise of deliverance being held in abeyance for the penitent during his probationary term in the desert wasteland of life can be seen by the appearance of the rainbow at the conclusion of the poem. Extending from the firmament to terra firma, the rainbow literally bridges the gap between heaven and earth, between man and his maker, between time and eternity.

The occasional poem "In das Stammbuch einer jungen Sängerin" (1837) presents, in more heavy-handed fashion, a fire and brimstone sermon admonishing a young actress on the brink of worldly success to bear in mind her eternal salvation:

> Fange jetzt schon an zu klettern
> Von der Ton- zur Himmelsleiter,
> Denn der Weg ist von den Brettern
> In die Bretter zwar ein breiter;[158]
>
> (GS I 540)

The plethora of wordplay in this opening stanza is just a prelude to the verbal acrobatics calculated to overwhelm the reader. The *sic transit gloria mundi* theme is underscored not only by the obvious meaning of the terms employed, but also by the medium of ambivalence and double entendre. For instance, Brentano unmasks the duplicity of worldly splendor by the very duality of the words he uses to report it: the boards of the stage ("die Bretter, die die Welt bedeuten," the boards which signify the world, become—*mutatis mutandi*—the planks that fashion our coffin. What the audience today applauds from the pit ("Parterre") of the *theatrum mundi* they may tomorrow trample under foot ("par terre"). In a dazzling cascade of topical allusions, the speaker next warns his protégée:

> Darum sängst du süß wie Todi,
> Rein wie Sontag, klar wie Mara,
> So vergesse doch den Tod nie,
> Nie den Sonntag, nie das *muora*.[159]
>
> (GS I 540)

Which, surrounded all about by blessings, / Cradled the swan of my song. // Oh, the delightful sight of flowers / Peers upward from the fervent dream, / Kneels and kisses the pearls of dew / From the fringe of the Song of Songs."

[158] "Begin now to climb / From the musical scale to Jacob's ladder, / For the path from the boards / To the planks is a broad one to be sure."

[159] "Therefore, even if you were to sing as sweetly as Todi, / As purely as Sontag, as clearly as Mara, / Still do not ever forget death, / Nor Sunday, nor *muora*."

The full impact of these lines is blurred somewhat for the modern reader by the numerous references to contemporary performers such as Luiza Todi, Henriette Sontag, and Gertrud Mara, whose surnames fit the *memento mori* tone of the passage. However, we can still appreciate fully the bilingual interplay here (Tod = *muora*) and elsewhere in the poem, as well as such rhetorically effective devices as chiasmus:

Tod nie

nie das *muora*

Brentano displays his full verbal virtuosity in a *tour de force* stanza describing the hypothetical reception granted the singer by her severest critic after her final curtain call on the stage of life:

> Möge dann dein Engel sagen:
> Aufmerksam, wenn ich soufflirte,
> Hat sie Kreuz und Dur getragen,
> Nicht zum Moll sie inclinirte.[160]
>
> (GS I 541)

Not only does the author transfer technical jargon from the theatrical medium (the verb "souffler" meaning "to prompt" in French) to a religious context (the root of "soufflieren" signifying literally "breathe" and figuratively "inspire" and "influence"), but he also exploits the dual potential of words having multiple connotations—depending upon the language in which they are understood (French or German) as well as on the level of interpretation in a single language (literal or figurative). For example, the German term "Kreuz" in its literal sense of "cross" naturally evokes religious concepts, while the figurative usage of "Kreuz" as a musical sharp (which, incidentally, is also cruciform in shape) relates directly to the aesthetic sphere. At the same time, these lines traverse the border areas of both language and culture by the musico-moral dichotomy which they establish: "Dur" (in German, the major mode; in French, "courageous," "austere") informs the singer how to "endure" the "cross" which she is to bear in her *imitatio Christi*, while "Moll" (in German, the minor mode; in French, "soft," "indolent"—the form "molle" being the feminine of "mou") cautions her about the pitfalls of sloth.

[160] "May your angel then say: / Attentively, whenever I prompted / She endured sharp and major mode, / She did not incline to the minor."

Whereas these poems from the 1830s treat the theme of conversion from terrestrial "singen" to transcendental "lobsingen" as a chronological sequence, a similar trend away from the secular to the spiritual can be observed in earlier works from the standpoint of altered context and structure. In such cases, the designation "restructure" would perhaps be more appropriate, since the procedure involves the transposition of an originally worldly text into a religious context. This revamping technique will be sketched for three works: the poem "Durch den Wald mit raschen Schritten" (1803 and 1817), the novelle *Aus der Chronika eines fahrenden Schülers* (the Urfassung" of approximately 1802 and the published version of 1818), and the fairy tale of *Gockel* (1816 and the "Spätfassung" of 1835).

The two versions of the poem "Durch den Wald mit raschen Schritten" reflect a change in allegiance on the part of the speaker (in the guise of a hunter restlessly in pursuit of—or pursued by—some unspecified prey) from the shepherd who stabilized the course of his early career (Arnim) to the pastoral guide who, he conjectures, will henceforth (subsequent to 1817) direct his path. In both the original text and its later adaptation one finds a compendium of those forces of distraction which conspired to deter the hunter from his predestined goal. For instance, the speaker, after labeling himself a lutist, declares, in a variation of the "singen-weinen" motif, "Freude singt, was Leid gelitten" (W I 165).[161] His entanglement with the joys and sorrows of love is expressed in terms of this stringed instrument: "Und es schlingen sich mit Klingen / In die Saiten Ros' und Dorn" [W I 165]).[162] In the original poem, the eagerness of the speaker to abandon himself to the dictates of fancy and fantasy seems to have its roots in his own unstable character ("Und ich spring' durch ihre [ghosts] Chöre / Wie ein irrend Zauberlicht" [W I 165]);[163] only in the later version is this recklessness ascribed to the allure of demonic powers:

> Seh' ich Wunderschätze glimmen
> Locket bald durch Sumpf und Moor
> Mich der Irrwisch hin und stimmen
> Muß mein Lautenschlag dem Chor.
>
> Zu der Gnomen Hochzeitfeier
> Zu der Elfen luft'gem Tanz

[161] "Joy sings what sorrow endured."
[162] "And with a ringing sound / Rose and thorn become entangled in the strings."
[163] And I leap through their choruses / Like a wandering magic light."

> Tönet meine ernste Leier
> Unerschreckt im Mondenglanz.[164]
>
> (W I 391)

Whereas in 1803 there is a hint that the speaker does not entirely fall prey to those forces of magic because of an innate sense of alienation ("Denn auch ich bin nicht von hier" [W I 165]),[165] the adaptation in 1817 clearly indicates that this restraint ("Und ich singe ohne Graus" [W I 391])[166] is the result of a conscious effort on his part, that he defiantly sings "in a new key," as it were:

> Zu der Mainacht Hexenreihen
> Spiel' ich nun ein geistlich Lied,
> Daß die Schar mit Maledeien
> Vor dem fremden Sänger flieht.
>
> In Frau Venus' Berg die Leier
> Hab' mit Keuschlamm ich geschmückt.[167]
>
> (W I 392)

Having steeled himself against the treacherous lure of the witches' sabbath or the enticements of Eros, the now pious singer sings a swan song to those forces which once caused him anguish:

> Wo der Schwan im Wellenspiegel
> In sein Sternbild niedertaucht
> Bricht der Schmerz auch mir das Siegel
> Daß mein Leid im Liede haucht.[168]
>
> (W I 392)

---

[164] "I see wonderful treasures gleaming, / The will-o'-the-wisp lures me / Away through moor and bog, I must / Tune my lute to the choir. // For the wedding ceremony of the gnomes / For the airy dance of the elves / My earnest lyre plays / Unafraid in the light of the moon."

[165] "For I, too, am not from here."

[166] "And I sing without horror."

[167] "For the witches' roundelay in May night / I now play a sacred song, / So that the throng with curses / Has to flee the unknown singer. // In Dame Venus' mountain / I adorned my lyre with *agnus castus.*" It should be noted that the name of the benevolent youth in the *Romanzen vom Rosenkranz* who intervened whenever the spiritual well-being of the protagonists was threatened was Agnus Castus (literally, chaste lamb, a term which immediately calls to mind the Lamb of God). However, Brentano also exploits the botanical potential of the name, since its Germanized form of "Keuschlamm" refers to the Vitex Agnus castus, "a plant which, according to Pliny, was strewn by the ancients in bed as an antidote to enchantment" (W IV 861).

[168] "Where the swan, in the mirrored surface of the waves / Plunges down into its starry image, / Pain also breaks the seal of my life / So that my sorrow respires in the song."

The interiorized tears shed by the speaker at this point ("Und ich singe viel Gesänge, / Doch im Herzen weine ich" [W I 393])[169] stem not from the reminiscences of personal transgressions committed in the past ("die Schuldner mahnen mich" [W I 393]),[170] but rather from his recognition of the tribulations endured by the Savior on the Cross for the collective guilt incurred by all mankind: "Einer schwebt am Kreuz erhaben" [W I 393]).[171] Consequently, the "shepherd" whom the huntsman encounters upon emerging from the Dantesque forest in which he had wandered aimlessly for so long, recalls the other pastoral guardian who came to tend the flock of His Father and to keep the errant lambs from straying too far. The bond established between this shepherd and the huntsman is expressed in terms of their respective instruments (the "Jäger" having forsaken the lute, which had led to his entanglement in the dangerous forest, and acquired a hunting horn):

> Hat der Jäger sich dem Hirten
> Flöte sich dem Horn gesellt.[172]
>
> (W I 393)

The tonal union established here is underscored syntactically by the rhetorical device of chiasmus, the linking of the two figures with their instruments in cruciform fashion:

Whereas the feeling of mutual dependence in the poem of 1803 is clearly a matter of personal ties on the human level (Brentano's friendship with Arnim), it assumes by 1817 the proportions of an errant prodigal finding a haven from the temptations and travail of life with a benign, deific companion. The interdependence of their lives and activities henceforth is expressed by linking them through assonance and a wealth of interior rhyme:

> Du kannst Kränze schlingen, singen
> Schnitzen, spitzen Pfeile süß

---

[169] "And I sing many songs, / Yet in my heart I weep."
[170] "My debtors admonish me."
[171] "One man hangs suspended on the cross, exalted."
[172] "The huntsman has joined with the shepherd, / The flute with the horn."

Ich kann ringen klingen schwingen
Schlank und blank den Jägerspieß.[173]
(W I 394)

The somewhat contrived nature of this stanza reflects, to a certain extent, the artificial resolution of the fundamental situation of the poem and the difficulty of transferring attributes previously ascribed to a friend to so exalted a figure as Christ.

The recasting of the *Chronika* from its original form of 1802 to the fragment of 1818 cannot be regarded as contrafact in the strict sense of the term; yet the work does undergo some significant revisions, owing to the author's altered view and values in life. The addition of religious motifs to the already pious tones and overtones of the "Ur-Chronika" could be considered a case of "gilding the lily," since the proximity of "prayer and song" is a motivic thread which permeates the fabric of the original text. For instance, when relating his experiences from the period of his wanderings, Johannes tells of a community in Franconia that exhibited an extraordinary degree of piety:

> Song arose in the church, resounding and delightful above all other voices, for they were all of pure heart and full of fervent, Christian spirit. When they worked together in the garden, then this became a living house of God, as it were, for they were there all united and devout as children of God and often sang in unison a joyous song of praise to the Lord. . . . I can indeed say that in them song and prayer had fused quite intimately. (W II 553)

Interspersed through the narrative are also numerous allusions to the solemn tolling of church bells which, according to Johannes' host, Ritter Veltlin, serve as heaven's summons for peace and order on earth (W II 558 ff.).

When reworking the text of the original *Chronika* in 1817, Brentano transformed many of the earlier instances of singing into examples of "lobsingen." For instance, the statement in the original concerning "the jovial singing of the birds" (W II 519) in the springtime is embellished to read "since the swallow, however, only sang out of joy at God's springtime" (W II 598). The sheer frequency with which the verb "lobsingen" occurs in the *Chronika* of 1818 (as opposed to 1802)

---

[173] "You can braid wreathes, sing, / Carve, sharpen arrows sweet; / I can grapple, clang, brandish / The huntsman's spear, shiny and slender."

is also noteworthy. Perhaps more important than the superimposition of elements of pious singing or the allusion to religious song is the elimination of two of the major musical figures who had performed extensively in the earlier story (the music of Pelagia, the orphan from Jerusalem, and the song of the "Perlengeist," or pearl spirit). Of course, the fragmentary form of the later *Chronika* may account for such omissions; on the other hand, the inability of the author to blot out the memory of those enticing sounds from his mind might have contributed, at least in part, to his failure to complete the revisions. However, since this act of omission could, in the case of such seductive music, actually represent an act of commission—or better, commitment—insofar as it removes a potential source of temptation from the scene, an examination of the exact nature of these two figures and their art would prove rewarding.

That Pelagia, the orphan from Jerusalem, is akin to Biondette insofar as her music hovers precariously between two worlds can be seen in the following description:

> When she becomes depressed, then she breaks out quickly into convulsive sobs, but just as quickly she grows jovial and sings. . . . Above all she is fond of music and she can play the organ beautifully; she also sings many religious and secular songs in a completely different, heart-rendering manner, even though they are the very same tunes. (W II 566)

The talent of Pelagia for contrafact is lauded by Johannes as "the blessed, beautiful bond between heaven and earth" (W II 569) and regarded by him as "the really highest of human callings" (W II 569). However, Ritter Veltlin is a bit more cautious in his assessment, seeing the possible threat to the soul of those who "wander on a dangerous path between heaven and earth" (W II 569). The ominous prediction which he makes at this point is reiterated later in the tale: "And they should hold fast to God with their arts and their deep thoughts, so that they do not become powerful servants of the world" (W II 569). Already in the *Chronika* of 1802 the author presents an analysis of the dual potential of music, which anticipates much of his attitude toward art in the post-1817 period.

Initially, Johannes cites examples of the salutary effect of music on man:

And when temporal man, surrounded by tools, works on the edifices of his age and, alarmed by their shortcomings and wearied by work, falls into earthly doubts, then art sings him a song so that the hewn wood again appears to grow green and the blow of the falling axe seems to be only the rhythm and sound of refreshing songs. . . . [Art] translates all spiritual wealth of all peoples into the generalized idiom of the senses and gives to inexpressible feelings the marvelous medium of music; it constitutes God's eternal, unceasing evolution, insofar as the latter is granted to man, His image. (W II 570)

Certainly no other contemporary poet wrote a more glowing panegyric to art (and music) than that expressed in these lines. Immediately after this remark, Pelagia, together with her sisters, performs a musical selection that illustrates such a form of edification:

Then we heard splendid organ music and several serene voices singing along with it. . . . Oh, that was glorious music, and they sang in the form of an alternating song, now querying, now answering, and then the voices again joined together in united ardor. . . . It was also wonderful to behold, for the sun set behind the cathedral. . . . And when the clouds fused together and their glow blended into a heightened purple, the pure voices of the singers and the full tonal configurations of the organ often coincided too, and it was as if the song and the colorful heavens understood one another and played together. (W II 571)

No sooner has Pelagia finished her "vesper music" (W II 572) than Johannes, in reading the parable "Concerning the Downfall of Temporal Love," illustrates that "dangerous path between heaven and earth" alluded to earlier by Ritter Veltin. Throughout this tale, two contrastive modes of musical expression wage a kind of contrapuntal war for the souls of the protagonists and, by indirection, of the writer and reader. The first of these is representative of the spiritual world and comes to the fore periodically in the tolling of church bells (W II 576), in the allusion to the music of the spheres (W II 590), and finally in the pious singing of nuns (W II 595). The second mode is the "strangely charming song" (W II 576) performed by the mysterious Pearl Spirit. This secular and highly seductive music runs like a *cantus firmus* throughout the narrative, sounding "more and more overpowering, lovelier and lovelier" (W II 576) with each repetition. The persistent use of intensifiers ("immer lieblicher") and the superlative ("die süßesten Lieder") stresses the growing attraction of these sounds (and could be compared with the use of similar techniques and terminology in conjunction with Biondette's "Song of Songs.").

The account of the corrosive musical magic of the Pearl Spirit illustrates that force which ensnares those who venture into the treacherous sea of life in a rudderless vessel and who, because of this lack of direction, are dragged down into the whirlpool of sensuality and temporality (W II 578; W II 584). The parable is told in a narrative form which might be compared with two concentric circles. In the outermost perimeter we learn the fate of three sisters, two of whom are enticed to their spiritual death by the allure of worldly splendor (pearls as precious jewels) and by sensuality (the "Perlengeist," being bisexual and thus reminiscent of the hermaphroditic Älia Lälia Crispis, assumes the form of a handsome youth and sings its "sweetest songs" and dances enticingly on a shimmering sea shell [W II 577; W II 579]). This display of worldliness alarms the third sister—who had spent her time praying in the chapel with an old fisherman—and she sets out in the company of the latter to rescue her wayward siblings. With a "pious song" (W II 578) on their lips, the girl and the aged boatsman approach the dangerous vortex and, with the aid of divine providence, hope to silence the seductive music: " 'When the evening star shines above the ocean and when *Ave maris stella* is sung, then the songs of the Pearl Spirit must grow silent' " (W II 579). Next, in what might be termed the innermost of the concentric circles, the fisher-boatsman recounts the story of the "Schöner Bettler" (the Handsome Beggar), a poet-singer who fell victim to the wiles of the "Perlengeist" after having resisted—and even successfully rivaled—its music for many years (W II 582). As a youth, the Handsome Beggar revealed considerable musical prowess of his own; he "cut out flutes for himself and blew them in the most charming manner. . . . He also composed beautiful songs and sang them with an enchanting voice" (W II 586). These descriptions suggest a natural affinity between this youthful artist and the mysterious Pearl Spirit, an affinity which is sustained by veiled allusions to the latter's relationship to the Beggar's mother. During the early stages of his life the lad heeded the admonitions of his father and avoided contact with the realm of danger and destruction: "Over there in the crags," his father cautioned, "dwells a siren, worldly pleasure and love, who can drag you down with her sweet song into the whirlpool of eternal sadness" (W II 587).

The "Perlengeist," assuming the shape of a siren in the case of a male victim, fails in its initial bid to overpower the Beggar; their confrontation in song is a variant of Orpheus' competition with and conquest of the sirens in Greek myth:

> Scarcely had he approached the old window—lyre in hand, to be sure—when, in front of him, an extremely beautiful woman emerged from the water and with all the amorous powers of song, of gesture, and of poetry sought to enchant him; he, however, refused to let himself be deterred and began, by means of his art, which was no less beautiful than hers, to mock in song her singing and her desires. (W 589)

> He . . . sat down on the shore with his lyre and with inexpressible artistry garbled the alluring songs of the siren, and one could say that whereas the foolishness of those who had been led astray consisted of the inability to choose correctly, he now was able to lead them to the good. Also he did not avoid direct confrontation with the water spirit; he was so proud that he summoned the latter and spoke to it, even tried to convert it by means of his songs. (W II 590)

The precarious nature of this triumph, however, is demonstrated by the subsequent fate of the Handsome Beggar (which is related in terms that recall the Christian concept of original sin). Prodded by a "zeal for knowledge," especially with regard to his origin, the Beggar ponders a mysterious book which he found in the proximity of the "Perlengeist" but which he is as yet unable to read (according to Brentano's conception, the quest for knowledge and the attempt to discover closely guarded secrets are acts akin to the eating of the fruit from the tree of the knowledge of good and evil). The second stage in the career of the Handsome Beggar is marked by his susceptibility to a form of music which he had heretofore scrupulously avoided: "he . . . listened to the songs of those who had been lost" (W II 590); so he no longer hears only the "music of the spheres." The final element in the course of the Handsome Beggar's development is presented in a framework which combines motifs from the myths of Orpheus, of Hero and Leander with an overlay of Christianity.

The pride of having vanquished the "Perlengeist" in head-to-head vocal competition eventually fills the Handsome Beggar with the desire to probe the depths of evil in order to understand its origins. This quest for knowledge is accompanied by his indoctrination into the sphere of love, for the girl who wins his favor ventures under the cover of dark-

ness to his island abode in order to teach him the art of reading. The
death of this maiden owing to the machinations of the Pearl Spirit (who
extinguishes the light that guided her across the waters to the shore
of the island) does not lead to any direct attempt to rescue her in Orphean fashion, but rather to the demise of the Handsome Beggar (after
recording a brief song about his downfall in the mysterious book which
he had learned to read in the interim, he took his own life and joined his
beloved in the whirlpool of the "Perlengeist").

Only after a cloister has been erected on one side of this treacherous site and a nunnery on the other—both edifices financed by the
"pearl tears" of mercy shed by the old fisherman and the pious girl
from the initial tale—is the deliverance of all those who fell victim to
the allure of earthly splendor and mundane love (and who now languish
in the stultifying realm of the "Perlengeist") possible. Significantly, it is
the Handsome Beggar who, with his music, paves the way for this release; "strumming impetuously on the strings of his instrument" (W
II 596) he not only celebrates their liberation from a death-like state
of suspended animation but he also destroys by the power of his music
the domain of the Pearl Spirit. As the entire assemblage boards a mysterious vessel and sets sail for an unspecified—but easily identified—
destination, the reader has the distinct impression that both the pas-
sengers and their guide are heading for "calm seas and a prosperous
voyage." This happy resolution of 1802 would certainly have appealed
to Brentano when he began revising the work in 1818, and yet the later
fragment breaks off long before such a denouement. This situation
may stem from the fact that in order to arrive at this point, Brentano
would have had to recapitulate the details surrounding the sensuous
allure of the music of the "Perlengeist." The temptations involved in
such an undertaking could have undermined the foundations which
the poet had just laid in 1817 and on which he hoped to construct the
framework for a different life.[174]

The third of those works which exist in two or more versions of
which the second could be regarded as a religiously oriented contrafact

[174] For a very informative account of the problems connected with the
various versions of the *Chronika*, see Elisabeth Stopp's "Nachwort" (Postscript)
to *Die Chronika des fahrenden Schülers: Urfassung* (Stuttgart: Philipp Reclam,
1971), pp. 112–136, and the article by the same author, "Brentano's *Chronika* and
its Revision," in *Sprache und Bekenntnis. Sonderband des Literaturwissenschaftlichen Jahrbuchs: Hermann Kunisch zum 70. Geburtstag*, ed. Wolfgang Frühwald and Günter Niggl (Berlin: Duncker and Humblot, 1971), pp. 161–184.

of the first is the *Gockel* story of 1816 and 1835 together with its sequel, *Blätter aus dem Tagebuch der Ahnfrau* (1835). Already at the
conclusion of the original *Gockel* tale an atmosphere of pious devotion
reigns as all the participants in the story gather in a church and sing:
"They played the organ and sang and preached" (W III 564). Two elements—organ tones and vocal singing—constitute the basic musical
motifs around which Brentano builds the *Gockel* plot. For instance,
the mouse princess, Sissi von Mandelbiss, who functions as a force
both of seduction and of salvation, enumerates the Orphean powers of
her singing by comparing her prowess with that of the famous operatic
soprano, Angelica Catalani:

> Und wie Frau Catalani singt,
> Mein Stimmlein bei den Mäusen klingt.
> Man hat mich drum als Gegensatz
> Oft Mausalani auch genannt;
>
> . . . .
> Verleugne nicht dein Zartgefühl,
> Laß rühren dich durch meinen Sang!
> Denn lockender als Flötenspiel,
> Als Harfen- und als Geigenklang
> Fleht er aus meiner Brust heraus:[175]
>
> (W III 497)

In return for the assistance which Gockel renders her, Sissi-Mausalani
vows to come to his service whenever he or his family needs aid. Although this promise leads to the ultimate resolution of the conflict,
Sissi's artistry, like that of Biondette, is also connected with the forces
of evil (represented in the fairy tale by the three seal-engravers) insofar as the mouse princess becomes the motivating force behind the
"schöne Kunstfigur" ("the lovely artifact") which induces Gackeleia to
part with Solomon's ring, thereby jeopardizing the well-being of her
entire family. During the period in which music is made subservient to
the forces of evil, the tones of Mausalani are supplanted by those of
another prima donna, Agatha Gaddi, whose fantastic fugues accom-

---

[175] "And as sings Madame Catalani, / So my little voice sounds among the
mice. / Therefore as a contrast, I / Have often been called also Mausalani; // ...
Do not deny your tender feelings, / Let yourself be touched by my song! / For
more enticing than flute music, / Than harp and violin tone / It pours entreat-
ingly from my breast."

pany the journey of Gockel and illustrate the need of art to curry the favor of generous patrons:

> In the distance an oratorio of six posthorns sounded, playing the composition of Cospetto di Bacco, and a fugue solo was performed by the renowned Agatha Gaddi. . . .
>
> Singing the fugal solo, Signora Agatha Gaddi went about with a plate among the assembled bakers and butchers and collected farthings and pennies; however, when she saw Gockel coming, she inserted a cackling rooster cry variation into her passage, and Gockel tossed into her apron a brilliant watch inlaid with snuff-boxes of lava, upon which the eagle of song—carrying off the Ganymede of emotion to heaven—was cut in stone. He simultaneously cried out "Bravissimo! da capissimo! cito citissimo!" . . . and the postilions cracked a finale with their whips, and they [the entourage] just arrived at the Eierburg as the Signora ended her trills of thanks, which ascended to the church tower. (W III 733)

The prominence of Agatha Gaddi's music in the revised *Gockel* of 1835 seems to suggest a function above and beyond that of a mere verbal frill or incidental addendum. The full significance of her fugal singing (the "Fuge Solo" cited above is a musical impossibility, since a fugue must be polyphonic, not monophonic) becomes apparent at the conclusion of the work after Gackeleia had been led to sophistic transgressions (she substituted the "schöne Kunstfigur" for the doll which Gockel and Hinkel had forbidden her) and then, with the aid of Sissi Mandelbiss, had atoned for her errors. The restoration of order is signaled by the music of the organ, that instrument which so often symbolized a divinely ordained harmony and which plays in the chapel as Gackeleia and Prince Kronovus are united in matrimony:

> But the organist sang a lovely artistically figured aria [kunstfigurierte Arie], to which men and fowl chimed in and the bells tolled—for behold, a curious event had strengthened the bond, both parts of the pretzel and the lad's thigh [a kind of baked goods] had become whole and united again, as if they had never been separated. (W III 793).

The concept of a reunification of entities which originally had formed an integral whole but which had become fragmented is expressed on diverse levels: symbolically, and in keeping with the *Gockel* context, by the piecing together of the "pretzel" and the "boy's thigh"—a kind of baked goods; on the aesthetic plane, by the musical quartet consisting of the organist's melody, the choral support provided by the ensemble of human voices together with the singing of the fowl and the tolling of the church bells. In view of such musical accord between man and beast, between the forces of the sacred and the profane, one can assume that the spirit of "re-ligio" is also expressed by the harmonious texture. Brentano even demonstrates that evil also has an essential part in the homophony; the description of the dominant melody as a "kunstfigurierte Aria" reveals that the "schöne Kunstfigur" which had threatened to throw the fairy tale universe into turmoil (German "aus den Fugen") has not been eliminated from the "grand finale," but rather incorporated and integrated. By the same token, it is no mere coincidence that the author complements the homophonic setting with a polyphonic obligato. The songstress, who had previously striven for the impossible (the "Fuge Solo") and had shown herself so dependent upon the patronage of a worldly audience, reenters the lists, no longer in quest of monetary reward for her services, but rather demonstrating by the *contrapuntal* texture of her vocal line a counterdirection to such subservience—a perpetual flight (Latin "fuga") from this world:

> Then the prima donna of Gelnhausen entered the chapel, just as the organist began the fugue: . . . in the future she refused to sing the fugues as a solo any longer, but together with him; however, because they always fled from each other and chased one another in song without ever uniting, their singing together was a *Fuga perpetua*, a perpetual flight. (W III 794)

The musical accompaniment in the pendant to *Gockel*, the *Blätter aus dem Tagebuch der Ahnfrau,* is likewise the result of a fusion of seemingly heterogeneous elements. In the life of Amey, the ancestress of the Gockel family and the founder of a charitable order of sisters, pure and pious song ("a soft, uncommonly pure and lovely song" [W III 797]) sets the initial tone. Amey's novitiates are thoroughly trained in devotional singing: "Sunday Cantata.—For one reads: Sing a new song unto the Lord" (W III 850). However, even though Amey is continually exposed to this form of sacred music, she still senses a terrible void in her life: "With pain and joy there should be an echo, a vibrant answer—but you are alone!" (W III 863). The singing of Klareta— her mentally unsound companion—together with the nocturnal proces-

sion of noisy torchbearers, does not prove to be a source of consolation,
but is rather a reaffirmation of her fundamental loneliness:

> Die Fackeln und Schalmeien,
> Sie brennen, reißen, schreien
> Mir tief durch Mark und Bein.
>
> . . . .
>
> Wenn Tön und Farben starben,
> Kömmt Nacht und bittres Darben,
> Arm, bloß, allein; allein![176]
>
> (W III 868)

Running throughout the *Tagebuch*, however, are two central and
contrastive refrains: "Feuerrote Blümelein" (fire-red flowerlet) and "O
Stern und Blume" (O star and blossom). The first of these with its stress
on the flame image and the crimson hue of flowers underscores the
sensuous side of life to which even Amey is susceptible: "Whenever I
saw the flame, I had to sing softly: 'Little fire-red flowers . . .'" (W III
865). On the other hand, the second—and more significant of the two—
speaks of flowers in conjunction with a transcendent source of light:
the stars. This latter refrain occupies a central position not only in the
Tagebuch but also in the author's entire lyric output in the post-1835
period. The fact that this key couplet is introduced at first rather un-
obtrusively at the close of the revised *Gockel* tale and then, gradually
but unmistakably, assumes an ever more important role in his writing,
gives the reader an indication that these two lines must have expressed
something essential which the poet sought to communicate in unique
fashion, quantitatively as well as qualitatively. Hence, a close examination of the "O Stern und Blume" refrain might prove to be a final
and connecting link in the thematic chain derived from Brentano's
adaptations of the Orphean myth.

The first occasion on which the "O Stern und Blume" refrain appears is that point when the participants in the story of Gockel (together with the readers) are encouraged to become again "as little
children":[177] "Laß, das hohe Lied zu singen, / Uns aufs Kinderstühl-

---

[176] "The torches and the shawms / Are burning, ripping, shrieking / Deeply
through my very marrow and bone. // When tones and colors died, / Night
and bitter want then come, / Poor, naked, alone; alone!"

[177] Several doctoral dissertations have dealt with this central problem of
the role of the child and the childlike (not to mention the "childish") in Brentano's
life style and his works. The earlier of these, however, Walter Dellers' *Clemens
Brentano. Der Versuch eines kindlichen Lebens*, Diss. Basel, 1955 (Basel: Cratander, 1960), and Reingard Ewald's "Das Bild des Kindes bei Clemens Brentano,"

chen schwingen" (W III 821).[178] Even the mysterious "restless youth," who for so long stood—book in hand—apart from the throng, now appears in transfigured light and participates in this song:

Und nun ist es hell zum Lesen
Wie in einem Chor gewesen,
Wo man wechselnd singt die Psalmen.
Als das Kind hat intonieret,
Haben auf des Mohnes Halmen
Gleich die Sterne respondieret:
"Stern und Blume, Geist und Kleid,
Lieb, Leid, Zeit und Ewigkeit."
Und den ganzen Widerhall
Sang das Lied der Nachtigall,

. . . .

Und ich sah das Kind im Singen
Sich zum höhern Chor erschwingen.[179]
(W III 829)

The only person not sharing in the miraculous return to childhood innocence is the unidentified "ich" who interjects himself at the close of the work. However, although doubts concerning the direction of his own life plague him, this unnamed speaker also harbors the hope that on the day of final reckoning, when truth shatters delusion, when all masks fall and we are judged on the basis of essence rather than appearance, the poetic justice that held sway in the fairy tale will also be meted out to him:

Und bis so das Märchen aus,
Sing ich in die Nacht hinaus:
"O Stern und Blume, Geist und Kleid,
Lieb, Leid und Zeit und Ewigkeit!"[180]
(W III 831)

Diss. Graz, 1966, have been superseded by Gerhard Schaub's comprehensive analysis *Le Génie Enfant: Die Kategorie des Kindlichen bei Clemens Brentano* (Berlin: Walter de Gruyter, 1973).

[178] "In order to sing the sublime song, / Let us sit upon a child's chair."

[179] "And now it was bright enough to read, / As in a choir / Where one alternately sings psalms. / As the child intoned / The stars on the stalks of the poppy / Responded immediately: 'O star and blossom, spirit and garb, / Love, sorrow, time and eternity.' / And the nightingale's song / Echoed this completely, / ... And I saw the child raise himself up / To the higher choir while singing."

[180] "And thus until the fairy tale is over, / I sing out into the night: / 'O star and blossom, spirit and garb, / Love, sorrow, and time and eternity!'"

Therefore, alienated from the rest ("sing *ich*") and still hovering under the shroud of darkness ("Nacht"), this stranger clings doggedly to the fragile surrogate he has for the serenity others have found—the magical refrain.

The cryptic message of the couplet (which becomes a virtual *idée fixe* in the *Tagebuch*) can perhaps be best appreciated if one considers it with reference to the other modes of music represented in the diary. Aside from the pious, devotional songs of Amey's order, there were the variations on the "Feuerrote Röselein" which emphasized the sensuous element in life and, finally, Klareta's music (principally the song of the weaver Jürgo of Vadutz) that told of escapist dreams ultimately destroyed by the malicious and nightmarish intrusion of reality. Throughout all these other modes of music runs—like a *basso ostinato* or *basso continuo*—the two-line refrain which, because of its deceptive simplicity, has proven the bane of Brentano critics. With no attempt at a resumé of the various schools of interpretation for these leitmotivic lines in such a specialized study as this, it is apparent that they acknowledge the basic "threshold" status of the Orphean myth by stressing the intermediary and indeterminate position of the speaker between heaven and earth ("Stern und Blume"), between the ethereal and the material ("Geist und Kleid"), between joy and sorrow ("Lieb, Leid"), as well as time and eternity ("Zeit und Ewigkeit"). Instead of adhering doggedly to one facet of human potential, or of striking out with uncompromising determination in either of the alternate directions, these verses affirm the uncomfortable "Schwebezustand" (condition of suspense and indecision) as a fact of life, they advocate the interdependence of both forces over the independence of either. The latter, single dimensional approach had led either to modes of behavior that were ethically untenable (Godwi), or to works of art that were aesthetically uninteresting (the endless saints legends) or that remained fragmentary (the *Romanzen vom Rosenkranz*). The latter cycle, incidentally, contained implicitly the theme of coincidence and coexistence which occurs explicitly in the "Stern und Blume" refrain. Therefore, a brief account of the failure of Biondette, Brentano's most Orphean singer, to resolve this dilemma, might serve to recapitulate the circumstances which gave rise to the "crisis of conscience" in the first place.

Biondette, it will be recalled, began her career as the acknowledged master of secular song (opera), who determined to forsake this sphere completely for a higher calling: "Und die arme ird'sche Harfe," she told her sister, "Klinge bald am Himmelstore" (W I 678).[181] Biondette sought to convince herself and others that such a metamorphosis was possible:

> "Hörst du, hörst du, wie vom Klange
> Mir des Herzens Saiten pochen,
> Wie von göttlichem Gesange
> Sich ein Netz um uns gezogen?"[182]
>
> (W I 681)

The sublimity and sanctity of Biondette's "new song" is underscored by the fact that her "golden tones" are brought into metaphoric relationship with what was to be the central concern of the work: the redemption of Kosme's accursed family (and, by implication, the entire family of mankind) through the institution of the Catholic Rosary. Biondette's sister tells her:

> "Durch die Rosen meines Kranzes
> Und durch meines Blutes Rosen,
> Die in Lieb' und Andacht wachsen,
> Flocht ich deine Töne golden!"[183]
>
> (W I 681)

Biondette is so intent upon fulfilling her mission that she eagerly teaches the children under her charge to sing pious songs, and they prove apt pupils: "Und sie singen dort im Chore / Die du sie gelehrt die Psalmen" (W I 839).[184] As Rosarosa lies dying, she envisions the cathedral that will one day tower above the ruins of the demolished theater and urges Biondette: "Lasse ... / Himmlische Musik erschallen" (W I 858).[185] The latter readily complies with this request and tells of the premonition of such exalted sounds which she had while unconscious in the flames. Biondette, having heard "der Engel Legionen" intone their majestic song (W I 860),[186] added her voice to the grandiose concert:

---

[181] "And the poor, terrestrial harp, / May it soon sound at heaven's gate."
[182] " 'Do you hear, hear how from the sound / My heart-strings vibrate, / How from the song divine / A net has been cast about us?' "
[183] " 'Through the roses of my wreath / And through the roses of my blood, / Which grow in love and reverence, / I wove your golden tones.' "
[184] "And they sing there in chorus, / Those whom you taught the psalms."
[185] "Let ... / There be heavenly music."
[186] "Legions of angels."

"Singend stand ich auf der Orgel,
Vor mir stand die goldne Harfe;

. . . .

In der Kirche hohem Dome
Schmetterten die Nachtigallen,
Ganz durchzucket von dem Tone
Fühlt mein Herz ich wieder schlagen.

Und ich bin empor geflogen,
Eine Stimme, singend Ave,
Bin des Engels Gruß geworden,
Ave, Salve, Dei Mater!"[187]

(W I 860–861)

The deterrent to such glorious prospects was, as we noted before,
Apo and his diabolic henchmen, whose earthy music methodically undermined such sublime sounds:

Doch du machst aus Weltenkreisen,
Wo der Engel Palmen schwingt,
Und, den Ewigen zu preisen,
Gloria die Sphäre singt,

Einen Tummelplatz der Heiden.[188]

(W I 873)

Not only are the heavenly harmonies and the music of the spheres
subjected to degradation, but the most formidable of earthly performers, Biondette, is humiliated after the ill-fated "Song of Songs" by her
association with the harlot, Älia Lälia Crispis. In the *Romanzen vom
Rosenkranz*, therefore, music stands in the service of either God or
Satan; however, this exclusivity is not sustained for any length of
time. This was a situation which Brentano acknowledged but found
perplexing. It was only after formulating the "theodicity" of 1813
—delineated in the letter to Rahel Varnhagen—in which he con-
ceded the "Devil" his part in the divine "score" composed by God for
man, that Brentano's resolution of the Orphean dilemma begins to

---

[187] " 'I stood, singing, on the organ / Before me stood the golden harp;
// ... In the high cupola of the cathedral / The nightingales warbled, / And I,
completely enthralled by the tone / Felt my heart beat again. // And I flew upwards, / A voice, singing Ave, / I became the greeting of the angel, / Ave, Salve,
Dei Mater.' "
[188] "Yet you are making out of the celestial orbits, / Where angels wave
palm branches, / And, to praise the Eternal One, / The spheres sing, // A gather-
ing place of heathens."

emerge more distinctly. As suggested previously, the *Romanzen* actually skirt the periphery of any obvious "catharsis." Toward the close of the work, however, Biondette catches a glimpse of her former pupils, "Singend vor des Himmels Tor" (W I 947).[189] Their number has been augmented by Samael, an erstwhile cohort of Moles'. The song performed by Samuel is highly indicative:

> Dann in wunderbaren Weisen
> Sang er stammelnd Gottes Lob,
> Der zu höhern Lichtes Kreisen
> Sein erbarmend ihn erhob.[190]
>
> (W I 949)

That such songs of praise to a deity he previously scorned and defied are not easy for one so steeped in sin to bring over his lips, can be inferred by the adverb "stammelnd." The fact that provision is made for him even to attempt such atonement, however, is reminiscent of the situation in *Gockel* when the "kunstfigurierte Arie" was performed by a harmonious consort. In the case of Samael, the report of his new mode of singing is presented by Aurora, the dawn, the mythological and mystical embodiment of that transitional period when night is no more and day has not yet come—a temporal threshold hovering between the broken promises of the past and a future of uncertain prospect.

Like the biblical deliverer Moses, Biondette catches a glimpse of the "promised land," but she herself is not permitted to set foot in it; and like the mythical Orpheus, she comes to the brink of success, only to lose what she cherishes most for all eternity. Whereas in the early stage of his development, Brentano delineated the fate of those who risk everything on an "either-or" commitment, he later came to acknowledge—if only grudgingly and resignedly—the dual citizenship conferred by the *condition humaine*. The "Schwanengesang" of 1812–1813 foreshadowed this insight, and the "Stern und Blume" refrain affirmed it. The extent to which the author ultimately came to grips with the oxymoron of life can be judged from the stanza of a poem of 1835 entitled, significantly, "Nach großem Leid," in which the speaker recapitulates his newly gained insights confidently and yet cautiously:

---

[189] "Singing before the gate of heaven."

[190] "Then in wonderful melodies / He sang stammeringly the praise of the Lord, / Who, taking mercy on him, / Elevated him to the higher orbits of light."

Ich darf wohl von den Sternen singen,
Mich hat die Blume angeblickt,
Und wird mein armes Lied gelingen,
Dann wird vom Stern mir zugenickt.
   O Stern und Blume, Geist und Kleid,
   Lieb, Leid, und Zeit und Ewigkeit.[191]
                              (W I 601)

---

[191] "I may well sing of the stars, / The blossom has looked upon me, / And should my poor song succeed, / Then the star shall nod to me. / O star and blossom, spirit and garb, / Love, sorrow, and time and eternity."

4. Musicalization of Literature

⒔T is apparent from the Orpheus legend that the tendency to regard the crafts of poetic and musical song as complementary
facets of a single creative process has its roots deeply implanted
in the cultural soil of Western Europe. Whereas the interrelationship
of the two media had been taken as a matter of course in the myths of
ancient Greece (for which activity the term *mousiké* was used),[1] subsequent epochs witnessed a gradual isolation of the kindred disciplines,
a symptom of the trend toward disintegration that beset mankind after
the breakdown of the hypothetical "golden age" of unity and homo-
geneity. In spite of occasional attempts at rapprochement during the
centuries following the decline of *mousiké*, (for example, in the fusion
of "wort unde wîse"—words and melody—by the minnesinger, in the
Reformation hymns of Luther, and in the operatic pageant or "Gesamtkunstwerk" of the baroque), the two media continued to grow
apart and develop independently. Their estrangement may be said
to have culminated in the aesthetic theories and "poetics" of the
eighteenth century in which the clearest possible distinctions between
the literary genres—and, as a corollary to this, the strictest lines of
demarcation between the various art forms—became a desideratum.

The dialectic of historical evolution came into play at this point,
as it so often does in intellectual thought. Several of the leading critics
of the later eighteenth century began to question the isolationist program of their predecessors and to advocate not a separation but rather
an amalgamation of the arts. Perhaps this demand resulted from what
these theoreticians felt had been the intellectual limitations of their
immediate forerunners. Or they may have shared the deep-seated conviction that the impact of a work which synthesized the "best of all
possible (aesthetic) worlds" and restored the "preestablished harmony"
of the arts would be greater than the sum total of these components
if they were considered individually.

---

[1] John Hollander states: "Like the folk balladeer's identification of the
notions of 'song' and 'story,' the Greek word *mousiké* designated neither a linguistic nor a tonal art but the craft of composing *song*, considered as a unified
entity." *The Untuning of the Sky: Ideas of Music in English Poetry 1500–1700*
(Princeton: Princeton University Press, 1961), p. 13.

The revival of interest in the figure of the poet-singer Orpheus by the Romanticists might be regarded as an expression of their tacit hope of regaining a perspective on life which sees isolated phenomena and the diversified activities of man as part of an integrated totality. The modern poet could expedite this process by arousing—through his verbal medium—our awareness of the inherent music in the world around us, sounds to which our ears, through centuries of apathy, had grown indifferent. This goal was postulated by Friedrich Schlegel at the outset of the epoch (1801):

> Durch alle Töne tönet
> Im bunten Erdentraume
> Ein leiser Ton gezogen,
> Für den, der heimlich lauschet.[2]

And it was still the ideal of Joseph von Eichendorff in the waning years of the period (1835):

> Schläft ein Lied in allen Dingen,
> Die da träumen fort und fort,
> Und die Welt hebt an zu singen,
> Triffst du nur das Zauberwort.[3]

Ever since the Romantic attempt to regenerate literature by restoring its lost ties with music, critics have examined and evaluated the theoretical programs and practical accomplishments of these pioneers, rating the success or failure of their project from various standpoints. In general, these appraisals can be divided into three categories.

There are proponents of the theory that a literary work not only can aspire toward the condition of music, as Schopenhauer claimed ("To become as music is the goal of every art"),[4] but can attain virtual identity. The poet Sidney Lanier, who had some provocative comments about music and love, postulated that music and poetry were simply

---

[2] "Throughout all tones / In the colorful dream of earth, / There sounds a gentle tone / For him who listens in secret." These lines are from the longer poem, "Die Gebüsche," contained in Friedrich Schlegel, *Kritische Friedrich-Schlegel-Ausgabe*, ed. Ernst Behler, V (Munich: Ferdinand Schöningh, 1962), 191.
[3] "Slumb'ring deep in every thing / Dreams a song as yet unheard, / And the world begins to sing / If you find the magic word." Translated by Alison Turner in: *Anthology of German Poetry*, ed. Alexander Gode and Frederick Ungar (New York: Frederick Ungar, 1964), p. 213. The original is found in Joseph von Eichendorff, *Werke und Schriften*, ed. Gerhart Baumann and Siegfried Grosse, I (Stuttgart: J. G. Cotta'sche Buchhandlung, n.d.), 112.
[4] Arthur Schopenhauer, *Schriften über Musik im Rahmen seiner Ästhetik*, ed. Karl Stabenow (Regensburg: Bosse, 1922), p. 159.

"two species of the genus art of sound," and he stated aphoristically: "Music is not a species of Language, but Language is a species of Music."[5]

And there are advocates of the view that any claim of identity between poetic and musical "song" is, at best, a misnomer and, at worst, a mistake. René Wellek and Austin Warren follow this line of argument in their *Theory of Literature*: "The Romantic and Symbolistic attempt to identify poetry with song and music is little more than a metaphor, since poetry cannot compete with music in the variety, clarity, and patterning of pure sounds. Meanings, context, and 'tone' are needed to turn linguistic sounds into artistic facts" (p. 160).

A third faction takes a position somewhat less extreme than either of the above, conceding a fundamental similarity (but not *identity*) between some aspects of the two media, and at the same time tempering or qualifying the extent to which common terminology can be applied to any acoustical or rhythmical features that form the sum and substance of the respective arts. Oskar Walzel, one of the first adherents of a "reciprocal illumination of the arts," offered this word of caution:

> Music and poetry have in common an appeal to the ear. In both, the ear perceives accents, beats, rhythm, melody. Even the contrasts of major and minor, of staccato and legato can be figured in here. Yet precisely these contrasts are often used in their figurative sense, not merely as differences in audible values, but rather as differentiations of a spiritual nature, as representations of contrastive emotional reactions, whenever the verbal art is involved. Ample variation of tones is observed when actually only a polymorphic reflection of feeling is manifest.[6]

In the *Reallexikon* under the heading "Literatur und Musik," one finds the following qualification: "In short, the 'musical elements' of poetry, in spite of the same designation and originally related properties in essence, have, to a certain extent, assumed traits and functions which are quite different, owing to their varied development."[7]

It is not possible within the confines of a study devoted to Bren-

---

[5] *The Science of English Verse* (New York: Scribner, 1880), p. 340.

[6] Oscar Walzel, *Gehalt und Gestalt im Kunstwerk des Dichters* (1929; reprinted, Darmstadt: Wissenschaftliche Buchgesellschaft, 1957), p. 266.

[7] *Reallexikon der deutschen Literaturgeschichte*, founded by Paul Merker and Wolfgang Stammler, ed. Werner Kohlschmidt and Wolfgang Mohr, 2nd ed., II (Berlin: Walter de Gruyter, 1965), 155.

tano to present a detailed account, or even a synoptic survey, of the
arguments offered by the respective camps in support of their position.[8]
However, after an analysis of the vast bulk of critical literature on the
subject of musico-poetic affiliations, several areas of investigation common to both the proponents and the opponents of the "marriage of
the media" can be distinguished. These encompass four basic considerations: problems of form, sound patterns, rhythm configurations,
and the nature of the imagery evoked in the listener by music and
poetry respectively in response to the audible stimuli presented. One
valid generalization that can be made with regard to the musicality of
literature is that, of all the genres available to the writer, the lyric is,
by general consensus of opinion, the mode of verbal expression most
akin to music, both in its treatment of the element of sound and in the
associations which its unique syntactical structures evoke.[9]

The close relationship of music and prosody is of considerable importance in a study of Brentano, since he was basically a lyric poet
(who, nevertheless, also dabbled in almost every other form). However,
even though the investigation of his methods of musicalization will
concentrate primarily on the lyric genre, contingent factors dictate that
attention be paid to his prose and stage works as well. For example,
one finds in his novels and plays evidence of a "sym-syndrome," that
is, the desire to fuse distinct modes of perception or different means of
artistic expression into a single act of receptivity or creativity. Since
both these synthesizing activities—which will be referred to as "synaesthesia"[10] and the "syn-aesthetic"[11] respectively—could be considered
preliminary stages on the pathway to lyric musicality, they will be discussed first, before turning to a detailed analysis of the specific forms
of musicalization in Brentano's poetry.

[8] For a succinct account of the various schools of thought on this subject,
see Steven Paul Scher, *Verbal Music in German Literature* New Haven: Yale University Press, 1968), the chapter entitled: "The Problem of Music and Literature:
Trends in Criticism," pp. 155–166.

[9] J. P. Dabney, *The Musical Basis of Verse* (1901; reprinted, New York:
Greenwood, 1968). Until the appearance of Scher's book on "verbal music" in
German prose, this phenomenon was generally restricted to the lyric, as seen
in Calvin S. Brown's study *Tones into Words* (Athens, Georgia: University of
Georgia Press, 1953).

[10] Scher, p. 166, states: "Literary synaesthesia may be defined as the metaphorical verbalization of real or imaginary experiences perceived by one sense
and employing expressions and concepts semantically related to another."

[11] The term "syn-aesthetic" has been introduced in order to provide an
English concept for the German "Gesamtkunstwerk," or "total work of art."

Synthesizing the Senses: Synaesthesia

The practice of transferring sense impressions or of recording sense data normally associated with one channel of perception in terms of another is a phenomenon frequently encountered among the writers at the turn of the eighteenth century. Undoubtedly the belief that one might actually see sounds or hear colors reflected the conviction that the spectrum of sensual experience could be broadened. Brentano touches upon the need for a wider range of sensitivity when he comments to Bettina in 1801: "The normal, healthy person hears, sees, feels, speaks; for the educated person, however, hearing becomes music, seeing becomes painting, feeling becomes form, and language becomes a lovely, cultured mode of speech" (F 18). Since these lines do not call for a radical commingling in the reception and assimilation of sense data, they cannot, strictly speaking, be classified as synaesthesia. There are, however, numerous examples of synaesthetic interchange in Brentano's early works. It is often very difficult to distinguish statements that reflect a genuine experience on the part of the speaker (or the poet) from those representing concession to popular fads and literary fashions. What leads one to suspect that synaesthesia was more metaphorical than actual in Brentano's work is the fact that the incidence, although high in the early works (up to approximately 1810), tapers off markedly in his later writings.

The appearance of the figure "Wolltemehr" in the satiric farce *Gustav Wasa* represents more than a mere parody of Friedrich Jacobi's hero from the novel *Woldemar*. This individual who "wanted more" becomes the spokesman for those seeking a heightened dimension of sensitivity. Recalling in elegiac tones "all the gay melodies of life" (W IV 35) which he perceived when "the harmony of love" (W IV 35) prevailed, "Wolltemehr" describes this lost Arcadian existence in synaesthetic terms:

> Wir lebten, zwischen Blumenschlaf der Sterne
> Geheiligt, hohes Leben ruhig wieder,
> Und sangen durch der Farben Stummheit Lieder,
> Aus Mondeshell und Sphärenklang gewebet.
>
> (W IV 34–35)

Und ferne sprach das Licht in leisen Tönen,
Wie wenn der West der Laute Küsse raubet.[12]

(W IV 36)

The contrast to this "golden age" is the prosaic present dominated by
men like Kotzebue, whose small minds bureaucratically divide what
superior intellects boldly fuse:

Es bricht das Ganze in *Fragmente*,
Und diese werden Elemente,
Aus denen, rein und unversehrt,
Ein schöneres Ganze wiederkehrt.[13]

(W IV 33)

The unifying force of love in Wolltemehr's past was a major
factor in determining his synaesthetic approach to life. The same can
be said of Godwi, whose language parallels that of Wolltemehr in
many important respects. For instance, after finding what he considers
an idyllic relationship with Otilie, Godwi claims to understand "the
silent, solemn weaving of love through nature, with which it entwines
us close together in the variegated color-melodies of life" (W II 114).
Wolltemehr's "gay melodies of life" and Godwi's "variegated color-
melodies of life" can be correlated with each other, as can the "colorful" songs which the former composed and those which the latter heard:
"The morning is here again," writes Godwi, "and all colors, all tones
and forms sing a song to the morning which was never sung before"
(W II 131). The melodies "woven out of moonlight" and fashioned
from the "harmonies of the spheres" reecho in Otilie's rendition of the
poem "Sprich aus der Ferne" depicting the nocturnal *unio mystica* of
entities which, in the harsh light of day, appear isolated:

Glänzender Lieder
Klingender Lauf
Ringelt sich nieder,
Wallet hinauf.[14]

(W II 156)

---

[12] "We lived, sanctified between the flowery sleep of the stars / A sublime
life once more, / And sang through the muteness of the colors songs / Woven
out of moonlight and the harmony of the spheres."

"And far off, the light spoke in subdued tones, / As when the west wind
steals kisses from the lute."

[13] "The whole breaks into *Fragments*, / And these become elements / From
which, pure and undamaged, / A lovelier whole returns."

[14] "The resonant course / Of radiant songs / Undulates upward, / Wends
its way downward."

The "gentle tones" which Wolltemehr perceived in the distant "murmuring" of the light become for Godwi nature's antiphonal response to Otilie's music: "The entire temple of night celebrated above her, and her tones, which resounded in the dark bushes, appeared to envelop her with golden, singing blossoms" (W II 156).

The unique fusion of light and sound in these colorful blossoms calls to mind what is perhaps Brentano's favorite and most frequent synaesthetic concept, "golden tones." The lyric poem "Der Abend," for instance, which appears later in the novel, expands this familiar motif; the "hue" of these sounds stems from the rays of the setting sun as Helios completes his orbital journey and the nightingale plaits them into "golden knots" (W II 355). Biondette, too, sang "Mit der Saiten goldnem Tone" (W I 680),[15] but the *non plus ultra* formulation of the synaesthetic experience in Brentano's writings is furnished by the poem "Abendständchen":

> Hör, es klagt die Flöte wieder,
> Und die kühlen Brunnen rauschen.
> Golden wehn die Töne nieder,
> Stille, stille, laß uns lauschen!
>
> Holdes Bitten, mild Verlangen,
> Wie es süß zum Herzen spricht!
> Durch die Nacht, die mich umfangen,
> Blickt zu mir der Töne Licht.[16]
>
> (W IV 286)

The concepts "Golden strains are wafted downward" and "Light of music shines on me" certainly seem to constitute further proof of the blending of audible and visual sensations. However, when one remembers that the above lines were not originally published as a separate lyric poem, but rather formed part of a dialogue in *Die lustigen Musikanten* between the love-struck girl, Fabiola, and the blind old man, Piast (to whom, incidentally, the last two verses in each stanza are ascribed), then the claims of full-fledged synaesthesia must be modified.[17] The golden tones of the flute brighten the life of the sightless

---

[15] "With the golden tone of the strings."
[16] "Hark, once more the flute's complaining, / And the rustling fountains glisten; / Golden strains are wafted downward—/ Quiet, quiet! let us listen! // Gracious pleading, gentle longing, / To my heart they make their plea, / Through the dense night that surrounds me, / Light of music shines on me." Translated by Anne Jennings in *Anthology of German Poetry*, p. 193.
[17] For a very cogently argued analysis of this point, see Friedrich W. Wollen-

Piast and illuminate the otherwise dark and drab horizon of his existence in a fashion totally different from that experienced by the individual in possession of the visual faculty.

Whereas Brentano later widened his synaesthetic color palette to
include darker shades (such as the "coal-black raven melody" sung as
a funeral dirge for King Laudamus in the early *Fanferlieschen*, or its
later adaptation as "black songs of mourning" [W III 388; W III 957]),
the proclivity toward *audition colorée* in his works decreases markedly
with the passage of time. The same generalization may be made for
audition tactile (whereby musical sound waves are perceived in terms
of the undulating movement of water). Rosablanka, for example, had
responded to Biondette's tones in this manner:

> Ihr zum Herzen hingedrungen
> Sind die Fluten des Gesanges,
> Ihr im Busen ist entsprungen
> Eine Quelle des Verlangens.[18]
>
> (W I 673)

As an alternative to pure synaesthetic experience, Brentano either re-
verts to standard forms of comparison such as the simile: "Suddenly
right next to the bower some lute chords sounded; from the golden
tones a song hovered through the night like a faintly glimmering ray"
(W II 487), or he resorts to unreal modes of description: "Her song
was so lovely and flowed through my ears like a sweet brooklet, and my
heart became as cool as if I were bathing in clear waves in the hot
summer . . . and it seemed to me as if I were sinking down deeper and
deeper" (W III 457). Whereas the act of combining the senses to
achieve "synaesthesia" may only have been a passing fancy in Brentano's career, the art of combining the aesthetic media—the syn-
aesthetic—proved to be a much more stimulating challenge and of
greater duration.

Synthesizing the Arts: The Syn-Aesthetic

One searches in vain through Brentano's correspondence or his
critical writings for a definitive statement regarding the feasibility or

---

berg, *Brentanos Jugendlyrik: Studien zur Struktur seiner dichterischen Persönlichkeit,* Diss. Hamburg, 1961 (Hamburg: Private Printing, 1964), pp. 77 ff.
  [18] "To her heart have rushed / The floods of song, / In her bosom has sprung
up / A fountain of desire."

the desirability of combining the arts. The closest he comes to delineating his position on the subject are the remarks contained in a letter of 1810 to the painter Philipp O. Runge concerning the marginal illustrations which the latter was to provide for the *Romanzen vom Rosenkranz*:

> The spirits, which will appear on the margin by means of your pen, shall redeem mine, and the whims of the artist shall surround my strange song, as if it were a pile of ashes. (It is one of our legends that when crickets sing under the oven, they are the souls of birds that once sang in the trees . . .). (S II 9)
>
> The entire work might be compared with a sequence of arabesques for interrelated paintings, where the form is inexpressible and where the symbol intervenes, where the form blossoms or resounds . . . indeed, it would delight me if your pictures resembled the dreams of an artist, dreams, which I tried to accompany with my songs. (S II 10)[19]

It appears that the benefits to be accrued from the syn-aesthetic would be comparable to the heightened sensitivity deriving from "synaesthesia." Such a composite medium might, Brentano conjectures, articulate ideas and emotions that were inexpressible in any single art form. The death of Runge in the same year in which this proposal was made dashed all hopes the poet may have had of collaborating on such a joint venture.

The view that music would play a decisive role in synthesizing the arts was advanced by Brentano both directly and indirectly. When writing to Bettina early in 1801, for instance, he speaks of his association with the music director of a theatrical group in Düsseldorf: "I will remain here a while longer," Bretano notes, "for to see, to hear, indeed to experience how all thinking and inventing suddenly flows in musical laws, laws which set poetry's head aright, all that really enthralls me" (F 229). The similarity between this statement and the assertion by Kleist that in the laws of music he hoped to find principles applicable to poetic creation,[20] is striking. A more indirect acknowl-

[19] The concept of the "arabesque" with reference to Brentano is discussed by Wolfgang Frühwald in "Das verlorene Paradies. Zur Deutung von Clemens Brentanos *Herzliche Zueignung* des Märchens *Gockel, Hinkel und Gackeleia* (1838)," *Literaturwissenschaftliches Jahrbuch*, N.S. 3 (1962): 129–141, and by Elisabeth Stopp in "Brentano's 'O Stern und Blume': Its Poetic and Emblematic Context," *Modern Language Review*, 67 (1972): 95–117.

[20] The reference is to the often quoted statement by Kleist that music is the "root" or "algebraic formula" of all other arts, and that he hoped to find in the "thorough-bass the most important disclosures about poetry." For the full

edgment of the hegemony of music in any process of unification is found in the poem to Karl F. Schinkel, the architect responsible for so many neoclassical structures in nineteenth-century Berlin. In resuscitating the austere style of ancient Greece, Schinkel was guided, Brentano feels, by musical principles: "Saitenklang Dir brach das Schulgerüst," "Grundtöne führen Dir den Plan," "Harmonieen wiegen Dir ihn [den Plan] aus," "Melodieen treiben bis zum Strauß / Des Gipfels Dir die Linien hinan" (W I 342).[21] This daring feat of rescuing architecture—which some claim to be "frozen music" ("erstarrte Musika" [W I 342])[22]—from the stagnation of the gaudy rococo is comparable to that of the Thracian singer:

> Bist Du mit *Orpheus* glaubend eingeschifft,
> Und wie in Klangfiguren Schöpferruf,
> Wie im Kristall der Ton Gestalt sich schuf,
> So Saitenklang in Deine Seele trifft.[23]
>
> (W I 341)

Rather than present any theories on the advantages of a "synaesthetic" in ex cathedra pronouncements, Brentano preferred to demonstrate them firsthand in practice. Consequently, the investigation of this phenomenon must be inductive rather than deductive, deriving its conclusions from a posteriori evidence rather than a priori premises. Brentano's attempts at a rapprochement of the diverse art forms under the aegis of music will be traced initially with reference to his prose writings (represented by the novel *Godwi*) and his stage works (treating in chronological overview such different theatrical genres as the farcical parody *Gustav Wasa*, the melancholy comedy *Ponce de Leon*, the tragedy *Aloys und Imelde*, the historical-mythical spectacle *Die Gründung Prags*, and the allegoric pageant *Viktoria und ihre Geschwister*). Then, following a brief glance at Brentano's theatrical reviews and his comments on the opera (a genre which seemed to offer unlimited potential for reviving *mousiké* or creating the "Gesamtkunstwerk")

---

text see Heinrich von Kleist, *Werke*, ed. Erich Schmidt (Leipzig: Bibliographisches Institut, n.d.), V, 429.

[21] "The sound of strings broke the pedantic framework. . . . Fundamental tones brought you the ground plan. . . . Harmonies measured it [the ground plan] out for you. . . . Melodies drive the lines upward / To the crest of the peak."

[22] The concept of architecture as "frozen music" has been attributed to various writers including Goethe, A. W. Schlegel, Schelling, and Schopenhauer.

[23] "Believing in good faith, you set sail with *Orpheus*, / And as creative renown manifested itself in sounding figures, / As tonal form became evident in crystal, / So the sounds of strings will penetrate into your soul."

the discussion will conclude with an investigation of his lyric poetry, since this mode of expression remained, in the final analysis, the most congenial to the author and the one in which he achieved his unique brand of musicality.

GODWI

Godwi oder Das steinerne Bild der Mutter (Ein verwilderter Roman von Maria) has long been recognized as a work that fulfills many of the canons for a "progressive Universalpoesie" established by Friedrich Schlegel in his famous *Athenäum* aphorism of 1797.[24] In addition, it has been claimed that this novel incorporates, within the limits of prose narrative, a wide variety of subsidiary literary forms and that it seeks to make a maximum appeal to the senses by transposing into the verbal medium the essential features of the pictorial, plastic, and tonal arts.[25] The contention that a synthetic or synthesizing approach to life and art constitutes both the thematic and structural core of the book (in spite of its frequent proclamations of uninhibited individualism or its ostensibly diffuse format—"verwildert") becomes clear if one focuses attention on the central section and then interprets the peripheral areas surrounding it in the light of these findings.

The complete text of *Godwi* consists of approximately 450 pages (in the Hanser edition), of which the middle segment (pages 200–275) is devoted, in both theory and practice, to a program for unification. The theoretical aspects come to the fore initially not in expository prose, but in a poem with the significant title "Als hohe in sich selbst verwandte Mächte," appearing almost at the numerical midpoint of the novel (pages 215–217). According to this lyric introduction, the ultimate binding force in the universe remains, as it had been for Lady Hodefield in Part I, love; Eros joins together that which the exigencies of time and destiny have severed. The mysterious-mystical realm in which such an all-embracing reunion can be achieved is circumscribed by various terms: "homeland," "poetry," and "fatherland." The access route to this primordial unity passes through a halfway-house located at the crossroads of synaesthesia and the syn-aesthetic:

---

[24] See, for instance, Franz Norbert Mennemeier's article "Rückblick auf Brentanos *Godwi*. Ein Roman 'ohne Tendenz,' *Wirkendes Wort*, 16 (1966): 33.

[25] Eugene Reed, "The Union of the Arts in Brentano's *Godwi*," *Germanic Review*, 29 (1954): 102–118.

Die Töne ziehn dich hin, in sanften Wellen
Rauscht leis ihr Strom in Ufern von Kristall,

. . . .

Die Wimpeln wehn in bunten Melodieen,

. . . .

Der Marmor wird in süßem Schmerz erklingen,

. . . .

Die Töne singen Liebe dir und fliehen;

. . . .

Gesang der Farbe, Formen-Harmonie,
Gestalt des Tons, du hell lebendig Weben
In Nacht und Tod, in Stummheit Melodie,
In meines Busens Saiten tonlos Beben,
Ersteh in meiner Seele Poesie[26]

(W II 216–217)

Throughout this poem, which, toward the close, reads like a magical incantation, Brentano makes it clear that the realm of "Poesie" is not a region unknown or alien to man, but, on the contrary, one which has become alienated from him (the "Fremde") because of his self-inflicted exile. This banishment might be considered a kind of spiritual "death," a "mortification" of the soul in the desert of daily life from which the poet, Orpheus-like, would one day rescue him. It will be recalled that the novel concludes with a summons to Clemens Brentano to assume the role of an Orpheus incarnate and release love and art from the state of suspended animation in which both are languishing.

The scene in *Godwi* which represents the apex of the synthesizing approach to the arts is found in Part II of the novel when Maria and the Tasso-translator, Haber, visit the secluded forest retreat of the protagonist. The reader actually learns what transpires here from three intersecting perspectives: that of Godwi, who produces and directs the performance, that of Maria, who reports and interprets it, and that of Haber, who distorts and misunderstands it. The full appreciation of the complex exposition (incorporating background music, dancing, an allegorical operatic tableau, startling light and color effects, poetic interludes, and expository prose passages) requires the active

---

[26] "The tones take you there; in gentle waves / Their stream laps quietly on shores of crystal, // . . . The pennants wave in many-colored melodies // . . . The marble will ring out in sweet pain // . . . The tones sing love to you and flee // . . . Song of color, harmony of forms, / Configuration of tone, you brightly vital weaving / In night and death, in muteness melody, / In the strings of my heart a toneless quivering, / May poetry arise in my soul."

cooperation of the reader, since he must act as the synthesizing agent in whom the various artistic media merge and converge. With Maria as a guide, the reader is encouraged to draw together the diverse strands and stimuli which, owing to the nature of the narrative prose, must be presented sequentially and in what appears (to Haber) a helter-skelter fashion.

The performance opens, appropriately enough, on a musical note:

> Several hunting horns sounded in a very cheery manner. It was a beckoning melody, and I [Maria] soon distinguished three horns that were answering each other from various points in an exchange of song. The echo doubled the tones and brought a pleasant confusion of shimmering tones to the harried melody. Soon even the echo appeared to double, and from all the depths of the forest it pursued the melody, as if a mysterious musical life were moving through the tree tops. (W II 246)

Whereas Maria is delighted by this antiphonal introduction, Haber's reaction is decidedly negative: "The secret music," he complains, "has led us astray" (W II 247). Nevertheless, this pedestrian translator, a true son of the enlightened eighteenth century with its credo of clear and distinct boundaries between the arts, has unwittingly supplied the theme for a lyric interlude as Maria develops the above complaint in verse form:

> Irrende, flüchtige,
> Tönende Geister,
> Die ihr mit schäkernden
> Lispelnden Worten
> Irr mich geführt.[27]
>
> (W 248)

Whereas Haber has literally been "led astray" by the sudden appearance of the musicians, Maria encourages the tonal spirits to lead him to that promised land of "Poesie" announced at the outset of Part II: "Lead me to my homeland!" (W II 249).

By the same token, the "homeward" journey could also signify the pilgrimage to Godwi's sequestered retreat. The events here hold more perplexity in store for Haber because the interior of the walls is lined with mirrors arranged in such a manner that reality and illusion

---

[27] "Straying, fleeting, / Sounding spirits, / You who with jesting / Lisping words / Led me astray."

combine to produce a complex network of reflection and refraction. The entire milieu is a deceptively composite creation. For example, a towering oak tree proves to be the concealed entrance to the park, the exterior walls of the forest lodge are painted to resemble shrubbery, even the water faucet is camouflaged as a butterfly. In order to enhance the impression of the coincidence of diverse spheres, Godwi supplies an appropriate bit of background music:

> At this point Godwi took a small silver hunting horn from the wall and gave a few sharp blasts, which ran up along the domed ceiling through the green walls like flames.
>
> "The tones are a wonderful, vibrant breath of darkness," I [Maria] said; "how everything rustles and comes to life and speaks with us in the secret hall through which the tones quivered like glowing pulse-beats."
>
> Godwi said: "The tones are the life and the form of night, the sign of everything invisible, and the children of longing." (W II 252)

These tones, in conjunction with the architectural design and the elaborate decor, supply an invisible but indispensable dimension to what is gradually emerging as a total work of art.

To the above components the dancer Flametta next adds the element of ballet as she performs to the accompaniment of the hunting horns. Her dancing is not observed directly by the audience, however, but rather as it is reflected in the mirrors that adorn the walls—so that not only Flametta's movements, but also the orchestral instrumentalists and the decor are projected into a single nexus of reflection fusing several angles of perspective (W II 253). The ability of such a synthesizing experience to raise the imaginative faculties of an individual to a "higher power," as it were, can be seen in Flametta herself. She believes that the figure of the hunter carrying a "golden lyre" (W II 255), which she next sees, is the incarnation of her beloved stag with the golden antlers (the animal had been slain). Godwi, who is said to have "his own peculiar instrument in his heart" (W II 258), uses this variation of the Orpheus-Eurydice situation as the springboard from which to launch into an analysis of Romanticism. The central issue, according to his interpretation of this phenomenon, involves the problem of mediation and translation: to what extent, namely, does the mediating agent—because of its unique mode of apperception—"color" the portrayal of an objective fact or the description of a particular object? Since Haber is unable to grasp this type of abstraction, Godwi and

Maria shift the topic to a province with which he should be familiar: the translation of Tasso from Italian into German. In a passage delineating the role of rhyme in the respective languages, Maria compares poetic translation and musical transcription:

> The Italian rhyme is the tone from which the whole is played. Will your [Haber's] rhyme have the same tone? I do not believe that you are the type of musician who can transpose from all keys and clefs to another instrument, without having the song come to a standstill here and there. . . .
>
> Every language . . . resembles a unique instrument, only those can be transposed which are most similar to each other; but a piece of music is its own music and not a composition stemming from the performer's soul or from his type of instrument. It comes into being when the instrument, the composer, and the music per se come together with equal excellence. Many translations, especially those from the Italian, will always be tones of the harmonica or of brass instruments which have been transposed to tinkling or percussion instruments. (W II 261–262)

At this point in the discussion, the rays of the setting sun pass through an emerald-green basin and bathe the entire room in an ethereal light. The transfigured interior of the secluded retreat provides Maria with a perfect example of this theory concerning the importance of the mediating agent in the Romantic process: "Tone, color and form have come here into a wonderful confusion. One does not know in the slightest what one should feel. Things . . . stand in all points at the transition stage" (W II 263). The use of a singular verb in this passage when referring to a grammatically plural subject (the original German reads: "Hier *ist* Ton, Farbe und Form . . .") acts as a subtle reinforcement of the aesthetic synthesis that is taking place. The fact that Maria experiences "wonderful confusion" corresponds to the "pleasant confusion of shimmering tones" which he had noted earlier, and gives a sense of unity and cohesion to the entire chain of events.

Maria's apparently parenthetical remark about not knowing what to feel at this moment contains a significant germinal idea. It stresses the unbridgeable gulf between "knowing" and "feeling," between the intellectual and emotional "grasping" of a situation. Haber, for whom such fusion has meant nothing but confusion, is not satisfied with this explanation and demands that the "idea" behind this unusual adventure in the cottage be clarified. Godwi, who had just expounded at length upon the inability of any form of rational discourse to articulate adequately such a complex experience, retorts categorically: "And I veiled this idea in my words for the very reason that I did not want to speak it out" (W II 264). Sensing, perhaps, that the auxiliary "want" in this comment might be misinterpreted, Maria reiterates his statement, substituting the more apropos verb "to be able," thereby underscoring the fundamental incommunicability of such a moment: "Everything lost its form and sank into a unity. There was only a single heaven and a single earth. . . . Oh! to whom could I have explained how I felt? who would have understood me and deciphered the wretched fragment of my language? and who would have deserved doing so?" (W II 270). Certainly the "wretched fragment of language" could never convey in its isolation what the "syn-aesthetic" experience achieves in its totality. In any case, Haber does not even "deserve" the attempt. For those who willingly suspend disbelief, no explanation is necessary; for those unwilling to believe, no explanation is possible.

The importance of this section of the novel for an understanding of the role of syn-aestheticism is twofold. On the one hand, it attempts to impart some appreciation for the expanded horizons opened to the human spirit by such an integrating approach; on the other, it reveals the frustrations of those who preach a new gospel to deaf ears. Whereas Haber serves as the foil for the latter point, the initial premise deserves one further illustration. Among the paintings hanging in the portrait gallery on Godwi's country estate is one of Annonciata-Kordelia, a mysterious acquaintance of Lady Hodefield's and sister of the protagonist's mother. Annonciata sought in vain to find a unifying factor in the manifold of existence. For her, the solution lay not so much in the acquisition of, but rather in the transition toward, a synthesis: "Reverent is he," she declares, "who perceives in the process of thinking not a dissecting finality but rather a gentle transition into eternal love" (W II 347). According to Annonciata, the pangs of isolation and the pain of individuation cease when one attains that condition "which opens our closed form from all sides and shows us our kinship with much that we have neither ever seen nor known. Thus are the semitones of music and the gentle colors of transition in painting . . . for they all stand at the divine portal of transition" (W II 347). Annonciata's existential plight confirms her aesthetic preferences, for she wavers between the possibility of living and the potentiality of dying. Her portrait reflects this semitone condition in its finely nuanced color scheme

("The colors are mobile, they all flee toward the distant glow of heaven and appear to flutter already in the echo" [W II 350]) as well as in the "syn-aesthetic" techniques employed by the artist: " 'before his pictures the eye becomes a sharp sense of hearing which hears the fluctuations of individual tones in the full chord, and I [Maria] would like to call his painting rhythmic and declamatory; it is as if the waves of gentle iambics were undulating through his painting' " (W II 351).

The stress placed on the "divine portal of transition" by Annonciata and by Maria after his experience at Godwi's retreat ("Things . . . stand at all points at the transition stage") resembles the "threshold" condition that characterized Orpheus' life and art. At the same time, one remains aware of the precarious nature of such an ambivalent situation. The Habers in this world constitute an "eternal recurrence" and inevitably carry the day, while the Annonciatas and Marias are dispatched ignominiously from the scene, and with them vanishes all hope of actually attaining or retaining the ideals for which they stood. Maria's death without the slightest hint of Orphean grandeur marks the demise of the "syn-aesthetic"; the wretched outcome of his enterprise, however, is intended not to demean the basic conception, but rather to make us acutely aware of the potential value of what has been lost.

STAGE WORKS

The unsympathetic attitude of the pedant was not all that curtailed the synthesis of the arts in the novel *Godwi*; the natural restrictions imposed on the genre by the prose medium precluded any unqualified success, in spite of the author's innovative experiments in breaking down boundaries. There was, however, another mode of literary expression in which the marriage of the media could be consummated: the theater. As Wagner demonstrated later in the century, the stage was to become the means of appealing en masse to every avenue of human apperception. Although Brentano's early phantasmagoric parody *Gustav Wasa* was ostensibly written for stage production, its wild medley of scenes and unwieldy array of dramatis personae (including such figures as "Arabesque" and "the Tuning of the Orchestra") made a performance in the theater of 1800 impossible. Interspersed between parodistic snippets from Kotzebue's melodrama, *Gustav Wasa*, one finds a potpourri of fragmentary vignettes, most of which are only obliquely connected with the slender thread of satire on which Brentano's piece is strung. One such segment depicts a library in which classical authorities are reincarnated in order to comment upon the abuses of contemporary playwrights. Ovid is particularly disturbed whenever he hears "a general rebellion of tones coming from strange, wooden coffins, which they call violins" (W IV 25), but his objection is soon overridden by Brentano, who hopes to reveal how the poet can enhance his art by drawing upon musical effects.

The first stage in the integration of music into this work is, as indicated earlier, the appearance of the Wolltemehr and his panegyrics to the age of uninhibited synaesthesia. After the introduction of music into the dialogue in this metaphoric context, the next step is the incorporation of actual musical tones, as, for instance, when "Subscription" and its entourage depart from the scene "singing a canon" (W IV 46), or when "in the orchestra the tones touch each other, individual sounds break forth one by one, seek each other with wonderment, find each other with love; the bass violin grumbles monosyllabically" (IV 55). At this point, the organizing talents of the "Theatergeist" (the spirit of the theater) are called into play in order to establish some semblance of order:

Töne entspringen,	Laute und wilde
Irrlichterfunken	Geisterblicke
Beben und ringen	Hin und zurücke,
Taumelnd und trunken,	Die in gelinden
Ehe der Meister	Wechseln sich finden,
Löset mit Kühnheit	Daß sich verhüllte
Tönender Geister	Ähnlichkeit bilde,
Heilige Stummheit.	Daß sich die Einheit
Vor dem Erstehen	Im Wechsel verkünde
Aller Gebilde	Und in der Einheit
Zucken und wehen	Der Wechsel verschwinde.[28]

(W IV 59)

This summons for unity amidst diversity, the quest for "hidden correspondences" in the face of apparent differences, becomes the domi-

---

[28] "Tones leap forth, / Straying will-o'-the-wisp sparks / Quiver and wrestle / Tumbling and intoxicated, / Before the maestro / Unbinds with boldness / The sacred muteness / Of sounding spirits. / Before the arising / Of all creatures, / Spirit glances, / Loud and wild / Quiver and flutter / To and fro, / Finding each other / In gentle fluctuations, / So that hidden correspondence / Might be formed, / So that unity be proclaimed / In change, / And that in unity / Change may disappear."

nant theme of the piece, a persistent melody which, however, only the objections of a Kotzebue and his clique can dispel.

Certainly the Habers in the audience are shocked to discover that each of the three "acts" in Brentano's mangled version of Kotzebue's play is introduced not by a prologue, but rather by a prelude (or overture, which is called, in accordance with the musical practices of the age, "Symphonie").[29] The thematic content of this verbal music had already been anticipated by the "Theatergeist"—the triumph of the artist over his recalcitrant material. The composer-conductor first performs the Orphean feat of summoning tones from the realm of "silent death":

> Ruhe!—die Gräber erbeben;
> Ruhe!—und heftig hervor
> Stürzt aus der Ruhe das Leben,
> Strömt aus sich selbsten empor
> Die Menge, vereinzelt im Chor.[30]
> (W IV 60)

The maestro, however, although allowing these scintillating and "sparkling" sounds free play, nevertheless does not permit them to run rampant: the "dance" they perform harnesses both elements characteristic of this genre—chaotic force *and* cosmic form:

> Schaffend eröffnet der Meister
> Gräber—Geborener Tanz
> Schweben die tönenden Geister,
> Schimmert im eigenen Glanz
> Der Töne bunt wechselnder Kranz.[31]
> (W IV 60)

The genuine "Gesamtkunstwerk" not only demands the mutual interplay of all the senses and the incorporation of the various art media, it also integrates measured calculation with spontaneous exuberance:

> Alle in einem verschlungen,
> Jeder im eigenen Klang,

---

[29] *Musiklexikon*, ed. Hans J. Moser (Berlin-Schöneberg: Max Hesse, 1935), pp. 837–838.

[30] "Silence!—the graves are quaking; / Silence!—and violently / Life storms forth from silence, / The throng, individuals in the choir, / Streams upward and out of itself."

[31] "Creating, the maestro opens / Graves—the sounding spirits / Hover as dance come to life / The colorfully changing wreath of tones / Shimmers in its own brilliance."

Mächtig durchs Ganze geschwungen,
Eilet der Geister Gesang
Gestaltet die Bühne entlang.

Heilige brausende Wogen,
Ernst und wollüstige Glut,
Strömet in schimmernden Bogen,
Sprühet in klingender Wut
Der Geistertanz silberne Flut.[32]

(W IV 60)

Such apparently contradictory terms as "Gräber-Geborener" and "Gestaltet-Strömet" (and "Sprühet") do not imply contrast or contraries as much as they do a *coincidentia oppositorum*. With the maestro as the synthesizing factor, even individual differences become a means to illustrate underlying coincidence:

Alle in einem erstanden,
Sind sie sich selbst nicht bewußt,
Daß sie sich einzeln verbanden;
Fühlt in der eigenen Brust
Ein jeder vom Ganzen die Lust.

Aber im inneren Leben
Fesselt der Meister das Sein;
Läßt sie dann ringen und streben;
Handelnd durcheilet die Reihn
Das Ganze im einzelnen Schein.[33]

(W IV 60)

Having affirmed the principle of orchestral coherence and cohesion in this verbal overture, Brentano adds a coda section in which the piano—the instrumental counterpart to the orchestra with regard to its panoramic tone-producing capacity—restates the theme. The fact that the piano, in acknowledging the authority of the maestro, disguises itself "as a fountain in which the whole is reflected" (W IV

[32] "All entwined in one, / Each in its own sound, / Powerfully whirling through the whole, / The song of the spirits, having acquired form, / Rushes along the stage. // Sacred, surging waves, / Serious and sensuous ardor, / The silver flood of the dancing spirits / Streams in glittering arches, / Sprays in resounding fury."

[33] "All arisen simultaneously, / They themselves are not aware / That they banded together as individuals; / Each one in its own breast / Feels pleasure from the whole. // But in the inner life / The maestro fetters their being; / He allows them toil and striving then; / Actively, the whole rushes through the ranks / In each individual brilliance."

61) is reminiscent of the many forms of dual identity and the mirror images in the scene at Godwi's cottage.

As if to illustrate an intrinsic correlation between the instruments of the orchestra and the individual forces in the vast panoply of nature, Brentano subsequently portrays a musical tempest, underscoring, in the process, the dual capacity of each performer ("glowing trombones" are also lightning bolts, the clarinets become gypsies, the flutes serve as shepherds, and so forth). Once this tempest of sound has subsided, an atmosphere of calm serenity sets in, evoking a feeling of reverence and awe for the conductor-composer of this grandiose symphony. The sotto voce sounds of the "still small voice" of the receding storm are reminiscent of the mood which Klopstock evokes at the close of his "Frühlingsfeier":[34]

> Der Geister einzeln tönend Spiel verschlang
> Sich leise atmend durch das süße Schweigen.
>
> (W IV 72)
>
> Wie Mondeslied tönt himmlisch ihr Gesang,
>
> . . . .
>
> Der sanften Töne leise ernste Lieder
> Erwachen in des Beters zartem Ohr,
> Und klingen heilig ihm im Innern wieder.[35]
>
> (W IV 73)

This morendo passage is followed by the solo prayer of a hermit (the horn), which links the role of this cosmic maestro with his musical counterpart in the verbal overture to the entire work: "Die in Ordnung er gereihet / Und geweihet" (W IV 73).[36]

However, the type of atmospheric-aesthetic theodicy envisioned here is violated when "mortal hands" intervene. Because he lacks the divine insight to fathom the "great chain of being" which the Creator has fashioned, man no longer synthesizes, he merely sins. We get some indication of this development in the version of the "Symphonie" which precedes the second installment of the truncated *Gustav Wasa*. An army officer from the campaign in France, upon hearing the orches-

---

[34] Friedrich Gottlieb Klopstock, *Ausgewählte Werke*, ed. Karl A. Schleiden (Munich: Hanser, n.d.), p. 92.

[35] "The music of the spirits, sounding individually, breathing softly, / Intertwined with the sweet silence. // Their singing sounds divine, like the moonsong, // ... The subdued, earnest songs of gentle tones / Awaken in the tender ear of him who prays, / And re-echo solemnly in his heart."

[36] "Which he arranged and consecrated / In a certain order."

tra tuning in the pit, blurts out convulsively a garbled paraphrase of
the earlier overture. The spectral tones summoned from beyond the
grave by the maestro now become the sounds of an apocalyptic "Ça
ira" emanating from the lips of French troops about to ambush a German contingent (W IV 93). The ensuing conflict resembles the upheavals of the storm-tossed sea in the original "Symphonie" and the
orchestral tempest that followed; however, the "Ça ira" does not prove
to be an Orphean invocation to life, but is rather an invitation to the
dance of death. The confusion among the German forces is finally dispelled by the cavalry officer's call to battle, and order returns, enabling
them to defeat the French (the thousand sabres of the German troops—
"tausend Klingen"—produce in unity a brilliant sound—"helles Klingen" [W IV 94]), and establishing peace once again: "Die Ruhe kehrt,
und alle Chöre sammeln /Sich wieder" (W IV 94).[37]

At this point the target of Brentano's satiric attack, the playwright
Kotzebue, appears on stage and objects, in Haber-like fashion, to the
adverse "effect of the overture [Symphonie]" (W IV 95). Consequently, the decision is reached to reduce the orchestral accompaniment to
the bass viol alone—an appropriate touch in view of what has already been established concerning Brentano's attitude toward this
instrument. However, in an ensuing melee the double bass is damaged,
whereupon it is decided that the final section of Kotzebue's *Gustav
Wasa* will have no musical introduction at all: "Humanity requires
that no symphony be played, particularly out of respect for the faithful
services rendered by the bass viol; this time, when storms rage, the
symphony will be silent. . . . Humanity demands that instead of the
symphony with its convulsive effect, the noses and not the ears [of the
audience] be engaged" (W IV 108). Brentano could not have dealt a
more telling blow to the contemporary stage than by substituting for
the ethereal delights of a symphonic overture the aromas of an "ol-
factory orgy" (W IV 108). The progression from an ambitious verbal
introduction in musical form to a "battle symphony" and, finally, to
a rejection of the musical idiom serves as a sad commentary on the type
of "humanity" in whose name such aesthetic atrocities are committed.

Whereas the early farce *Gustav Wasa* made bold—even though
fruitless—strides in the direction of the synaesthetic mode of art, the
later stage works of Brentano are, for the most part, more reserved
and conservative in their attempts at artistic fusion. In *Ponce de Leon,*

[37] "Peace returns, and all choirs / Assemble once more."

for example, the dance is a major ingredient: at the opening of the comedy, Ponce dances somewhat absentmindedly at a court ball, holding an unlit torch in his hand while all the other participants carry burning tapers. At the close of the work, however, Ponce participates in a round dance with Isidora, and his behavior conforms with that of the other happy lovers (in contrast to the opening scene in which he had been the exception, the individual for whom the "light of love" had not, as yet, been kindled). The principal musical element in *Aloys und Imelde* is, aside from the leitmotivic love song of the heroine, the musical battle waged by the rival suitors for Imelde's hand: Benevides and Aloys. The contrastive serenades presented by the lovers anticipate the confrontation of Sixtus Beckmesser and Walther von Stolzing in Wagner's *Die Meistersinger*. Brentano's most serious effort to integrate orchestral background music into the dramatic context can be seen in *Die Gründung Prags*, a work that was inspired to some extent by the triumphant processional music he once heard in the Czech capital[38] and which, according to Arnim's comments, was originally intended to be an opera.[39] The programmatic element in the music prescribed by Brentano comes to the fore in the second act when Libussa, listening to the strains of a "melancholy horn melody" (W IV 615) with her warrior maidens, is suddenly jolted out of her reverie by the onslaught of the Avars—the attack being accompanied by a fortissimo passage: "The full orchestra interrupts the hunting-horn melody at the first arrow shot and accompanies the tumult of battle diminuendo into the distance; ... gradually, at the greatest distance, the music grows silent" (W IV 616). On another occasion, the music attempts to express the sense of concord between Libussa and her sister: "Meanwhile Kascha comes forward as the flute players advance. Maidens follow her, the horns of Libussa greet them and play in concert with the flutes, the

[38] In his preface "Die Entstehung und der Schluß des romantischen Schauspiels *Die Gründung Prags*," Brentano tells that after seeing the city of Prague one morning at sunrise, he was inspired to put his visionary drama down on paper. "The noise of the populace, the pealing of the bells, the singing of the processions, and the harmonious din of military music, all this awakened in me once more the vivid desire—indeed, the calling, to celebrate in a romantic drama the founding of this city, shimmering before me in the joyous glow of spring" (W IV 532–533).

[39] Rudolf Kayser in *Arnims und Brentanos Stellung zur Bühne*, Diss. Würzburg (Berlin: W. Kuhlisch, 1914), p. 128, cites (without giving the source) the following comment of Arnim: "These are lovely, individual scenic groups, strange events, so that I am sorry that he did not go through with his first plan of treating it as an opera."

sisters embrace" (W IV 644). Finally, all throughout Brentano's "resounding play" *Viktoria und ihre Geschwister*, battle music, marching songs, drum rolls, and trumpet fanfares blare. The closing tableau depicting the reunion of Viktoria with her kin following the cessation of hostilities incorporates a number of musical elements that echo, so to speak, the restoration of the harmonious "body politic" in both the German states and Europe. The panoramic allegorical pageant concludes with a ballet performed by a chorus of dancers consisting of both allied and enemy troops while the rest of the entourage joins in song. Paradoxically, Brentano's *Viktoria*, although approaching the concept of a "syn-aesthetic" on a most ambitious scale, remains, from the artistic standpoint, one of his weakest creations. A parallel phenomenon might be mentioned in the case of "Wellingtons Sieg oder Die Schlacht bei Vittoria" by Beethoven, a work that commemorates the same victory as Brentano's play. Although inspired by the spirit of the times to present a vivid portrayal in music of the sights and sounds of battle, Beethoven's composition is, notwithstanding the lofty idealism which engendered it, an artistic disaster.[40]

Brentano's theatrical reviews of the stage productions of Schiller's plays incorporate elements of the synaesthetic approach by underscoring certain features—as, for instance, his comment that in the *Braut von Messina* the various choral groups on stage become "echoing columns" and "resounding statues, pillars of Memnon from the ancient world which ring out because the wonderous Aurora of modern Romantic art touches their brow with its rays" (W II 1080). In contrast to the stone-like symmetry of the choruses stands the musicality of individual performers: Beatrice, for example, has "something musical" in her (W II 1080), a "melody" of character (W II 1081), which the actress may best express through the "purely ringing tones of her voice" (W II 1085), avoiding in the process, any tonal "gluttony" (W

---

[40] Note, for instance, the characterization of Beethoven's work given by Wallace Brockway and Herbert Weinstock, *Men of Music* (New York: Simon and Schuster, 1939), p. 194: "Vienna responded [to 'Wellington's Victory'], not enthusiastically, but deliriously, ... It seems unlikely that calling the piece the *Battle of Leipzig* would have added a single leaf to his [Beethoven's] laurels. Besides, the fact that between artillery charges and cannon shots the only music to be heard was *Britannia Rules the Waves*, *Malbrouck s'en va-t-en guerre*, and *God Save the King* provided three insuperable obstacles to a patriotic change of title. Some faint conception of this atrocious potboiler—unquestionably ... the worst trash ever signed by a supreme genius—may be achieved by imagining a mixture of the '1812' Overture (with real cannon) and Ernest Schelling's *A Victory Ball* (with rattling bones, offstage bugle, and bagpipes full orchestra *fff*)."

II 1084) or, as he later termed it, "tinsel-" or "hangover tones" (W II 1103). Brentano proved particularly sensitive to the musicality of stage declamation and cautioned against the "painting manner" of speech, which "even in music borders on the ridiculous" (W II 1083). In a review of *Kabale und Liebe*, Brentano delineates what to him constitute the ideal conditions of performance—and he does so using musical analogy: "Every play is like a piece of music written down in notes; but music becomes wretched if each one plays in a different key and some are loud and the others are soft. The best proof of how much further advanced music is than acting comes from the fact that musicians have a conductor while actors perform *ad libitum*" (W II 1112).

It was unfortunate that in his encounters with the one genre that offered the greatest potential for a satisfactory "syn-aesthetic" experience—the opera—Brentano discovered a plethora of those very abuses against which he cautioned in the drama. There are several phases through which Brentano passed in his attitude toward operatic composition. Early in his career he sketched a libretto for an opera based on the poem "Die lustigen Musikanten" from *Godwi*. In the preface to this text Brentano, after minimizing the significance of his efforts, curries the favor of a prospective collaborator: "Moreover, I do not ascribe any value to the whole thing, but it would please me immensely if some musician would credit me with having a degree of talent for musical poetry and would like to collaborate with me on a larger opera, the character of which I will gladly allow to be prescribed to me" (W IV 275–276).

In sharp contrast to this almost embarrassing self-deprecation are the remarks in operatic reviews which Brentano wrote for the *Spenersche Zeitung* of Berlin in 1815.[41] The general tenor of his often polemic pieces is that the opera should not become a vehicle for the vocal acrobatics of some pampered prima donna, nor should the libretto merely serve as a poor excuse for a text of high literary quality, enabling the composer to exhibit his technical mastery. At best the music is "language raised to a higher power" (W II 1138), a medium of expression to undergird the emotions of the protagonists (W II 1137) but not to override the dramatic structure as a tonal tour de force. By the same token, other subsidiary facets such as stage decor or costume

---

41 John F. Fetzer, "Clemens Brentano on Music and Musicians," *Studies in Romanticism*, 7 (1968): 218–230, presents a comprehensive analysis of Brentano's operatic reviews.

should not be allowed to get out of hand either. Should this, however, come to pass, Brentano conjectures, there is a remedy which he—with tongue in cheek—proposes to counter the dangers of distortion: allow the music to take over completely, as in the most stilted opera. "With such a complete departure from all historical truth," he goes on to add, "a departure which in many forms of music represents a deeper understanding of the matter than modern theatrical wisdom . . . one would excuse everything with the magic of Orphean music, to which the rivers paid heed, standing still within their shores, and which accomplished still other miracles; everything marvelous would then not be distracting . . ." (W II 1139). It was perhaps in this spirit of dramatic musicalization that Brentano prescribed the accompaniment of his projected opera, *Phaon und Sappho*, a work which exists only in fragmentary form but which, in this skeletal state, anticipates much of what Wagner incorporated into *Tristan und Isolde* a generation later:

> The overture begins with a distinctly feminine tenderness; dance and declamation evolve in it; it sinks down, an offer of love is made, it resists, cries for help, hunting horn music approaches and becomes festive, enticements appear and a dance of the flutes follows, and closes on a serious note. Amorous celebration makes itself manifest and rises to the highest festivity. Now and then solemn tenderness intervenes . . . the entire overture becomes lamentations of love's despair and concludes with serious, tender solemnity. (FDH)

Lyric Musicality

Although Brentano's sporadic remarks concerning the musicality of poetry—"Is a poet conceivable who is not a musician?" (W II 1230); "the musical element in him [Tieck] is what I like best" (S I 192); "if some musician would credit me with having a degree of talent for musical poetry" (W IV 275–276)—are more numerous than his statements on either "synaesthesia" or the "syn-aesthetic" approach to art, they tend to be no more edifying on the subject than the vague pronouncements of his contemporaries and predecessors. Somewhat more helpful, however, are the observations Brentano made to his "brother in song" Arnim in 1802 concerning the folk songs which the two were collecting. With reference to the problem of form, for example, Brentano maintains that this consists of finding a "proper costume," a concept which he then amplifies in the following manner: "However, the artist who is simultaneously a genius, rediscovers for the costume a higher unity of nature, and thus without anachronisms he achieves the highest costume—free form in itself, music, rhythm through thought. All his rhythms will be the original melodies of his poems . . ." (S I 126).

To these musical constituents of poetry—form and rhythm—one could add the sounds of language itself. On this point, Brentano is also not very explicit, but he skirts the periphery of how the tones of music might be correlated with the sound structures and imagery of poetry in the following passages:

> Now I like to speak very much with that distant world; it seems to me then as if I were making music, which is no doubt only a form of communication with a higher world. (L 42)

> . . . as music speaks, which utters no words that are first borrowed from language, no, that takes, I should like to say, from the innermost heart of nature, from the secret workshop of God, the simple, eternal tones, understandable to all, and expresses their will. (S I 121)

> Music also does not speak, and yet I understand it. Only devout, good people have learned from God . . . what the tones wish to say; these secrets, this sustenance of eternal innocence, youth and love must not come into the hands of the vulgar, who even treat the divine as if it were a local product and who would sell eternity as a piece of material —by the yard—if they could. (S I 122–123)

The views expressed here resemble those articulated earlier by Herder, Schiller, Wackenroder, and Novalis, and expanded later by E. T. A. Hoffmann. Two salient points for Brentano's own poetry, however, can be found in the stress placed on music as an idiom that conveys ultimate truths even while circumventing rational discourse, and the fact that such nonsemantic communication is the prerogative of an elite group of kindred spirits. It would follow, then, that the greater the extent to which the sound complexes constituting the verbal mode of expression could be made to conform with these standards, the more closely such literary utterances would approach music. Whereas the superior poet grasps this situation intuitively, the second-rate writer will never comprehend the mystery. Thus, Brentano warns his friend August Winkelmann: "One cannot speak to the peoples other than through music, . . . and because you have no music, you speak to the peoples and your pain is merely lack of belief in mankind" (U 237). Because the musical word is a matter of faith rather than fact, any attempt to analyze its "musicality" fully in terms of cognitive speech—just like the "sale of the eternal by the yard," to use one of Brentano's own images—is doomed to failure. The futility of such an undertaking has already been demonstrated in the case of Haber and the "synaesthetic."

Brentano's appreciation of the intimate relationship between musical and poetic expression was undoubtedly also enhanced by certain "extrinsic" factors: the close ties between text and tune in the folk songs gathered for the *Wunderhorn* anthology; the practice of writing a poem to an already extant melody; the inspiration for poetic creativity stemming from a musical performance or a particular piece of music. However, an analysis of the works produced under these conditions would not necessarily yield information germane to the central concern of this phase of the study: the intrinsic qualities of lyric poetry, which, in Brentano's work, create in the reader a sense of musicality. Therefore, primarily those factors suggested by the author himself will be considered. On the basis of the aforementioned discussion of his scattered thoughts on the subject, there are four areas of concentration: form, rhythm, sound, and imagery. The significance of imagery stems from Brentano's allusion to the "magic of Orphean music" (cited in conjunction with the opera critiques), since the purely tonal art led to "a complete departure from historical truth," a condition whereby nothing concrete was said and yet the most profound statement resulted.

MUSICAL FORM PATTERNS AND THE FORMS OF BRENTANO'S POETRY

Critical opinion is divided into two camps with regard to the extent to which the transposition of musical form patterns (defined as "the arrangement of material within a composition")[42] to poetry could contribute to musicality. There are those who maintain that literature in general becomes musical to the extent that it disdains any clearly discernible elements of form.[43] The adherents of this view ascribe to poetry such features as "loose musical properties,"[44] "music, no struc-

[42] Donald Jay Grout, *A History of Western Music* (New York: W. W. Norton, 1960), p. 662.

[43] This faction undoubtedly bases its position on remarks such as the following by Novalis: "A fairy tale is really like a dream vision—without continuity—an ensemble of strange things and events—for example, a musical fantasy—the harmonious sequence of an Aeolian harp" (*Werke*, I, 390).

[44] Leonard A. Willoughby, *The Romantic Movement in Germany* (London: Oxford, 1930), p. 108.

ture,"[45] "music, fluidity,"[46] and "the really rambling or freely fantasizing element."[47] Brentano himself, it will be recalled, spoke rather vaguely in terms of "free form in itself, music" in his letter to Arnim. The musical genre, therefore, which would best correspond to this kind of approach would perhaps be the "Phantasie." According to an authoritative source, the fantasia is "a composition of rather free form which should arouse the impression of impromptu invention."[48] Significantly, one of Brentano's earliest lyrics bears the title "Phantasie" (1799) and betrays its musical affiliations by "scoring" the individual stanzas for diverse instruments (flute, clarinet, bassoon, hunting horn) and instrumental combinations in the manner inaugurated by Tieck a few years before.[49] Yet if the musical or poetic fantasia were completely devoid of recognizable patterns, there would be little point in examining such whimsical and arbitrary conglomerations in either discipline. However, in both instances, the artist *is* concerned with matters of form, only these are the product of his own invention rather than the imposition of prescribed norms. One need only recall Mozart's "Fantasia in C minor" (K. 475), Schubert's "*Wanderer* Fantasia in C major," Chopin's "Polonaise-Fantasia," and—perhaps the best example of all, since it underscores the close alliance between the pictorial, literary, and musical media favored by the Romantics—E. T. A. Hoffmann's *Phantasiestücke in Callots Manier* and their adaptation by Schumann for piano as *Phantasiestücke*. In all of these examples, there are clear manifestations of conscious craftsmanship and artistic design, the only distinction being that, unlike the established literary genres (novella, sonnet, drama, and the like) or standard musical forms (sonata, song, rondo, and so forth), they follow no extant paradigm, but rather create one of their own, which is unique and not intended for duplication.

From the standpoint of form and structure, Brentano's poem "Phantasie" (W I 28–30) combines artistic freedom and aesthetic free play with a thematic and formalistic pattern that, to all appearances, is original with the author. Of the ten stanzas that constitute this poem,

---

[45] Karl Glöckner, *Brentano als Märchenerzähler*, Deutsche Arbeiten der Universität Köln, 3 (Jena: E. Diederich, 1937), p. 6.

[46] Emil Staiger, *Grundbegriffe der Poetik* (Zurich: Atlantis, 1959), p. 70.

[47] Willi Reich, in "Musik in der Literatur," *Stimmen*, 1 (1947): 379, states: "Only the really rambling or freely fantasizing element of many romantic literary works is comparable to certain musical forms."

[48] *Musiklexikon*, pp. 623–624.

[49] For the most recent and comprehensive discussion of Tieck's poetic composition, see the chapter "Tieck's 'Topsy-Turvy' Symphony" in Scher, *Verbal Music*, pp. 36–55.

numbers one through four and six through nine are assigned to the
solo instruments; at the midpoint and at the finale of the fantasia
(stanzas five and ten), there are "tutti" passages for the entire ensemble. The order in which the instruments perform in each of the two
segments or "movements" is not fixed. Even more important, however,
is the fact that neither the metric pattern nor the rhyme scheme is
identical in any of the eight solo passages—not even in the two performed by the same instrument. This means that Brentano employs
eight different stanzaic forms together with eight distinct rhyme
schemes. In addition, the number of verses in each of these solo stanzas
varies greatly. Whereas in the first section there is a certain uniformity
(7–7–8–8), in the second this is abandoned completely (6–4–8–15).
The length of the individual lines, too, is variable, ranging in scope
from a single word to as many as eight. Enjambement is the dominant
principle in every one of these solos, so that the impression of freedom
from restriction and of unimpeded flow is evoked by the syntactical
structure as well as by the imagery (which, incidentally, enhances the
impression of fluidity through the use of water concepts and flowing
liquid consonants—*l*'s and *r*'s). The spirit of uninhibited freedom
found in the solo passages is counterbalanced by that of interplay and
interdependence in the "tutti" sections (which are identical in their
verse form, their rhyme scheme—although not in the actual rhymes
used—and their avoidance of enjambement). Finally, a comparison of
themes also reveals the juxtaposition of freedom and restriction. The
solo stanzas deal with the problems of isolation and alienation, the
"tutti" parts stress the inevitable integration of the individual and
society, of inner and outer worlds, of essence and appearance, and so
forth. Because of its ostensible improvisation and yet overriding
concern with the problem of freedom versus formalism, Brentano's
"Phantasie" could be considered, from both the thematic and the
structural standpoints, a poetic counterpart for that musical genre
which exhibited similar qualities: the fantasia.

    If one were to proceed on the basis of the title alone, then an
analysis of Brentano's poem "Symphonie" (discussed previously in
conjunction with *Gustav Wasa*) would most likely be devoted to un-
covering elements of sonata form in the work. Disregarding for the
moment the fact that the designation "Symphonie" is used in the
older sense of overture, it would also be possible to trace in the poem
a thematic development characteristic of the sonata form—the standard

paradigm for the first movement of the classical symphony in the era of Mozart and Haydn. The poem opens on a solemn, funereal note (tombstones quake, spirits come forth out of the silent realm of death), which is reminiscent of the *grave* introduction that characterizes many a Haydn symphony. Following this somber introduction, the principal themes (A and B) are announced. In contrast to the dynamic effervescence of theme A ("storm forth / Mightily," "stream up," "colorfully changing") stands the element of controlled craftsmanship of the maestro (theme B), the "Meister" who is responsible for summoning these sounds to life and the one who actually gives direction to their apparently spontaneous movements. There follows, then, a "development" section, which explores and expands the thematic and motivic possibilities of the principal subjects, juxtaposing to the impression of unbounded playfulness the idea of underlying control. The development constitutes the major portion of the poem—stanzas two through five. The concluding quatrain brings a "recapitulation," which includes the final restatement of theme B ("But in the inner life / The maestro fetters their being"), theme A ("toil and striving"), and a brief "coda" passage. The latter gives a sense of continuity and circularity to the poem by paraphrasing a key motif from the introduction: "The throng, individuals in the choir" becomes "the whole rushes through the ranks / In each individual brilliance" (W IV 60).

To a certain extent, a musico-poetic analysis such as this represents a tour de force of critical intrepretation rather than an unbiased account of authorial intention. Numerous objections could be raised which either question or invalidate its premises. For example, would such an approach even have been conceivable, if the title of the work had not suggested a musical genre? Could Brentano, whose declarations of musical ignorance are well documented, have successfully accomplished such a transfer? And finally—what is perhaps the most telling criticism—can one in this instance treat symphonic form in the modern sense of the term? Or should one perhaps analyze the poem as an overture (a theory that is supported by the function of the "Symphonie" to introduce the three segments of Kotzebue's parodied play)? Pursuing this line of attack, it would be possible to discover in Brentano's work, as Oskar Walzel did with reference to Tieck's "Symphonie" in *Die verkehrte Welt*,[50] a thematic progression characteristic of the overture (such as the popular "French" type introduced by Lully with

---

[50] *Gehalt und Gestalt*, pp. 355–356.

the format "Slow-Fast [-Slow]") especially in view of the solemn opening and the vivacious second section.

There was, however, a form of music that coincided more closely with the poetic practices of Brentano and that was congenial to his style without overtaxing either his ability to devise or the reader's patience to discover complex parallels of technique: the theme and variations. Literal repetition and variation of themes or motifs are all-pervasive in music and very prevalent in poetry.[51] Just as the composer creates a feeling of artistic economy and aesthetic continuity by re-working previously introduced material (ranging in scope from small motivic threads to extensive themes), so too does the poet in his literary context employ similar devices to achieve comparable aims. That the Romantic writers regarded both repetition and variation as a valid literary adaptation of musical techniques is apparent from their many pronouncements on the subject.[52] In contrast to the enthusiastic claims of his contemporaries and later critics, however, Brentano's views on the possibilities of variation are modest. In his famous letter to Runge, for example, he voices the hope that the painter will find the *Romanzen* "an inducement . . . for the most lively and ideal variations" (S II 10). Whether this taciturnity with regard to specific details of technique for variation is the result of musical ignorance or of restraint, it nevertheless compels one to study Brentano's poetry inductively and cautiously. From the outset, a few qualifications must be made in order to dispel the impression that a blanket comparison can be drawn between repetition and variation in music and in lyric poetry. In the first place, extent as well as intent must be considered. As one modern critic notes:

> Not when poetry here and there presents a repetition or variation . . .
> does musical structure come to the fore. That is found almost always
> and everywhere in the broad confines of literature, not only in the

[51] Percy Goetschius in *Lessons in Musical Form* (Boston: n.p., 1904), p. 7, writes: "Nowwhere is the principle of return more significant and imperative than in music, which, because of its intangibility has need of every means that may serve to define and illustrate its design."

[52] Novalis, for instance, states in one of his aphorisms, in *Werke*, II, 186: "The sermon of the Protestant preacher should be musical, and indeed, a variation." Friedrich Schlegel declares, concerning *Wilhelm Meisters Lehrjahre*: "The second book begins by repeating musically the results of the first book." *Friedrich Schlegel: Kritische Schriften*, ed. Wolfdietrich Rasch (Munich: Hanser, 1964), p. 455.

lyric. . . . The deciding factor, on the other hand, is to what extent these principles of form are used. Only when all these form-media become an end in themselves above and beyond the content, when pure joy in these principles reigns supreme, only then does a musical structure come about in the literary work.[53]

In addition to the above stipulations, the reader should also bear in mind the limitations imposed upon poetry by the verbal medium. Whereas the composer has at his disposal a wide range of techniques and technical devices to vary the presentation of his themes (changes in harmony, rhythm, and instrumentation; modulation, augmentation, diminution, inversion, ornamentation, legato versus staccato style, and so forth), the possibilities open to the poet are much more restricted. Even though he may employ synonyms or paraphrase, modify the metric or rhythmic scheme of his verses, alter the stanzaic pattern, or reverse his attitude toward the subject matter (change the tone from serious to satiric), the inescapable semantic ties of words, and the limited acoustical range of verbal utterances, set greater limits on the degree to which the poet can repeat and vary his themes without running the risk of tedium. A close examination of Brentano's lyric style reveals that he made extensive use of these techniques throughout his entire career and, in so doing, did not always avoid the concomitant pitfalls.

Even a cursory review of Brentano's lyrics reveals that he tended to repeat and vary not only the smallest syntactical and semantic units in his verses, but also entire lines, stanzas, and even stanzaic complexes. Although literal repetition seems, at least on the surface, to entail less ingenuity than variation, it could be argued that the reiteration of individual words, phrases, and larger segments of text shifts the emphasis from the transmission of meaning to the concern for sound. Words and word groups no longer appeal to the cognitive faculties of the reader as much as to his mind's "ear"—in the form of recurrent acoustical patterns. For instance, the lilting lines of Frau Lureley in the *Rheinmärchen*: "Singet leise, leise, leise, / Singt ein flüsternd Wiegenlied" (W III 218),[54] together with her famous exhortation:

---

[53] Hans Klein, "Musikalische Komposition in deutscher Dichtkunst," *Deutsche Vierteljahrsschrift für Literatur und Geistesgeschichte,* 8 (1930): 694.
[54] "Softly, softly, softly croon, / Croon a whispered lullaby."

Singt ein Lied so süß gelinde,
Wie die Quellen auf den Kieseln,
Wie die Bienen um die Linde
Summen, murmeln, flüstern, rieseln,[55]
(W III 219)

employ verbatim repetition ("leise, leise, leise"), repetition with slight
alterations ("Singet . . . / Singt"), and variations of larger syntactical
units ("Singt ein flüsternd Wiegenlied"; "Sing ein Lied süß gelinde")
in order to instill the feeling of reassurance and repose. The aim of
any lullaby, of course, is to comfort and console; and to achieve this,
one tends to repeat key concepts. The verb "summen" in the last line
above, is then picked up as "Summ, summ, summ" in the choral refrains which follow the lullaby and which themselves constitute variations on the Harper's theme "Wer nie sein Brot in Tränen aß" (W III
219ff.) from *Wilhelm Meisters Lehrjahre*.

In contrast to the soothing and assuaging effect of repetition and
refrain in this fairy tale of 1811 stands the jarring *idée fixe* "Treulieb,
Treulieb ist verloren,"[56] which resounds in forty-four of the forty-five
stanzas of the ballad of 1812. This ominously ironic refrain never lets
us forget the anguish of the narrator and the persistent disillusionment
to which he is exposed as he pursues the checkered career of the heroine
in the hope of saving her from self-destruction. In both the literal and
the figurative senses, however, "Treulieb" is and remains lost; the refrain acts as a painful reminder of the futility of these quixotic dreams.
Judging from the contrastive refrains in the fairy tales and in the
"Treulieb" ballad, it would seem, then, that Brentano—whom Wolfgang Kayser has labeled the master of this device[57]—saw in such an
artistic technique two basic functions: either to imprint indelibly on
the reader's heart and mind the hope that things will be better, or to
impress him with the fact that they could not be worse. The best refrains, however, take the form of a "mixed blessing," insofar as they
open vistas in both directions simultaneously.

Into this latter category fall three of Brentano's most famous refrains, each of which comes from a different epoch in his life: From
"Die lustigen Musikanten" (*Godwi*, 1801):

[55] "Lisp a little lilting fable: / Bees about the honeysuckle, / Silver springs
upon the gravel / Mumble, murmur, whisper, trickle."
[56] "True-Love, True-Love is lost."
[57] *Das sprachliche Kunstwerk*, 6th ed. (Bern: A. Francke, 1960), p. 168.

Es brauset und sauset
Das Tambourin,
Es prasseln und rasseln
Die Schellen drin;
Die Becken hell flimmern
Von tönenden Schimmern,
Um Kling und um Klang,
Um Sing und um Sang
Schweifen die Pfeifen, und greifen
Ans Herz,
Mit Freud und mit Schmerz.[58]

(W II 396ff.)

From the untitled poem dated "25. August 1817," written initially for Luise Hensel and then reworked for Emilie Linder under the title: "Kettenlied eines Sklaven an die Fesselnde zur letzten Stunde des Jahres 1834 geschlossen" (W I 596):

Einsam will ich untergehn,

. . . .
Will ich einsam untergehn.[59]

(W I 389 ff.)

From the poem "20. Jenner nach großem Leid" (1835) the lines:

O Stern und Blume, Geist und Kleid,
Lieb, Leid, und Zeit und Ewigkeit.[60]

(W I 601 ff.)

As was indicated earlier, the latter verses appear throughout the *Gockelmärchen* and the *Tagebuch der Ahnfrau*, and are also incorporated into such poems as "Es ist ein Schnitter, der heißt Tod" and "Was reif in diesen Zeilen steht."

The first of these refrains, consisting of eleven lines, is repeated virtually unchanged (the only variations are the inversions 'sauset und brauset" and "rasseln und prasseln" in certain instances) after all eleven of the stanzas in which the merry minstrels tell of their sorry

[58] "The tambourine / Is hustling and bustling; / The bells join in / With jingling and jangling; / The cymbals glimmer brightly / From the shimmering sounds, / With tinkling and tone, / With singing and song / The pipes ramble and seize / The heart / With joy and with pain."

[59] "Alone I want to perish ... / I wish to perish alone."

[60] "O Star and blossom, spirit and garb, / Love, sorrow and time and eternity."

lot in life. On the one hand, the boisterous music in the refrain offers these tragic figures an outlet for their pent-up frustrations—they pound the percussion with reckless abandon. For a few fleeting moments the minstrels became oblivious to the sad plight in which they find themselves. Their performance exerts a similar effect on the audience—a momentary escape from the tragedy of existence: "Wir wissen alle hinzureißen / In unsrer Töne Zauberzug" (W II 397).[61] However, a marked shift in meter signals a change of mood: in contrast to all the previous lines of the refrain, which contain two principal stresses, the verse "Schweifen die Pfeifen und greifen" has three, thereby placing greater emphasis on the concept "Herz" in the following line. The isolation of the heart suggests that it is the prime target for the lilting fife melodies, those ambivalent tones which, as the closing comment indicates, are both pleasant and plaintive.

The original Hensel poem of 1817, with the haunting refrain "Einsam will ich untergehn," as well as the much expanded version of 1835, complements the statement of this principal theme with a variation in the form of partial inversion: "Will ich einsam untergehn." The function of this device is a reaffirmation of the speaker's stoic resolve to face the crisis standing alone, on his own two feet. Although for Brentano such self-reliance may, at times, be more a literary pose than an act of actual bravery, the dogged determination with which the lyric of 1817 reiterates the theme and its counter-subject makes it a commitment worthy of a modern existentialist thinker. The later version of the poem, however, loses some of this relentless consistency. Aside from being tripled in length—and, consequently, sacrificing some of the terse poignancy of the original—it seeks a resolution of the existential dilemma in a transcendental-metaphysical realm: the falling star of the old year ("untergehen") may signal the rise of his fortunes in the new ("auferstehen"). The leitmotivic refrain "O Stern und Blume," on the other hand, retains throughout a bittersweet quality to the extent that the oxymoron of life is acknowledged and articulated in the most succinct terms. Whereas the refrain of the merry minstrels has served as a mask for spiritual and physical shipwreck, and that of "Einsam will ich untergehn" became a stoic concession to and acceptance of the harsh facts of life, the "O Stern und Blume" couplet stands

[61] "We know how to transport everyone / In the enchanting procession of our tones."

alone as a positive affirmation of the threshold which Orphean man straddles.

Brentano's development of the theme-and-variations technique on a more complex level than that of repetition and refrain comes prominently to the fore in two poems separated by almost forty years: "Guitarre und Lied" (1799–1800) and "O Traum der Wüste, Liebe, endlos Sehnen" (1838). The first of these applies the technique of literary variation from the smallest verbal unit (individual words, phrases) to entire stanzaic complexes. Small-scale modifications are found in synonymic exchange and rhythmic alterations:

> Guitarre: Wo die Liebe nicht wacht,
> Ist alles leer,
> Kein Freuen mehr.
> Lied: Alles leer, und nimmer freuen....[62]
> (W I 32)

The principal theme of the poem—the stifling of the song of love through the cold silence of feminine indifference—is first expressed tersely by "Lied":

> Stille Liebe, süße Blicke,
> All die Töne, all die Lieder
> In der kühlen Nacht verwehen;[63]
> (W I 32)

In response to the optimistic rejoinder of "Guitarre" that such an appeal will not go unheeded, "Lied" continues and expands its initial complaint:

> Alle Lichter bald versinken;
> Alle Töne stumm ersterben;
>
> . . . .
>
> Aller Himmel bald verschwindet,
> Alle Sterne bald vergehen,
> Alle Töne niederfallen;[64]
> (W I 33)

[62] Guitar: "Where love does not watch, / All is empty, / No more joy." Lied: "All empty, and no more rejoicing...."

[63] "Silent love, glances sweet, / All the tones, all the songs / Are scattered in the cool of night."

[64] "All lights soon sink down; / All tones die away; // ... All of heaven soon is gone, / All stars soon perish, / All tones descend."

Whereas in the initial formulation of the problem the stars descend
and all tones die away in the night of unrequited love, in the next
variation this process is reversed, with the result that tones now "fall"
and stars "perish."

On a more comprehensive scale, it can be shown with reference
to thematic distribution and development that "Guitarre und Lied"
illustrates what Oskar Walzel labeled the "pro-musical" ternary song
structure: A-B-A,[65] with the modification that A-B-A becomes A-B-A¹.
Part A consists of a long "solo" passage in which "Guitarre" outlines
the benefits of serenading the lady to the somewhat skeptical "Lied";
the second section, Part B, is composed of a duet or dialogue between
the two principals in which they combine their talents in an attempt to
break the barrier of silence; finally, in Part A¹ "Guitarre" returns once
more in its solo capacity and systematically recalls and retracts each
of the suggestions in Part A. In order to illustrate this more graphically,
the two passages will be shown side by side:

PART A	PART A¹
Guitarre	*Guitarre*
Wache auf, Du süßes Lied,	Schlummre sanft Du süßes Lied;
Öffne Deine goldnen Augen;	Schließe Deine goldnen Augen,
Mondschein still herniedersieht.	Mondschein ist schon abgeblüht.
Leise, kühle Lüfte hauchen	Leise Lüfte Dich verhauchen,
Durch die tiefe dunkle Nacht.	Kühler Morgen schon erwacht.
Lasse Deinen hellen Blick,	Lasse Deinen trüben Blick
Leuchtend, durch die Schatten schweben;	Stille zu den Schatten schweben,
Antwort kehret bald zurück,	Sehne nimmer Dich zurück;
Wenn des Echos Wechselleben	Denn der Liebe Wechselleben
Hallend an dem Fels erwacht.	Ist verhallt in tiefer Nacht.
Sag', wo willst Du hin?	Ach, wo bist Du hin?
Soll ich Dich begleiten,	Konnt' Dich nicht begleiten,
Durch die Dunkelheiten	Durch die Dunkelheiten
Deine Schritte leiten?	Deinen Schritt nicht leiten;
Soll ich stiller Liebe	Konnt' nicht stiller Liebe
Deinen düstern Sinn	Deinen düstern Sinn
Freundlich deuten?	Freundlich deuten?
Willst Du Deine Triebe	Konntest nicht Deine Triebe
Durch den Abend singen;	Durch den Abend singen;
Oder höher,	Auch nicht höher,
Immer höher	Immer höher

<hr>

[65] *Gehalt und Gestalt,* pp. 351 ff.

Zu den Sternen klingen?   Zu den Sternen klingen;
Laß Dich traulich umschlingen;   Mußte Dich traurig umschlingen—
Sprich Deine Worte   Schlummert freundlich
In meine Akkorde.   Ihr letzten Worte,
                    (W I 30–31)   Im letzten Akkorde.[66]
                                                            (W I 35–36)

Several types of variation can be distinguished in Parts A and A¹ of
the poem:

Direct contrast:
    Wache auf   Schlummre sanft
    öffne . . .   schließe . . .
    tiefe, dunkle Nacht   kühler Morgen
    hellen Blick   trüben Blick
    bald   nimmer
    Sprich Deine Worte   Schlummert freundlich/Ihr
                                      letzten Worte

Subtle shadings and nuances of meaning because of prefix or suffix variations:
    hauchen   verhauchen
    hallend   verhallt
    traulich   traurig

[66] Wake up, you sweet song,   Slumber gently, you sweet song;
   Open your golden eyes;   Close your golden eyes,
   Moonlight silently peers down.   Moonlight has already faded.
   Gentle, cool breezes breathe   Gentle breezes carry you off,
   Through the deep, dark night.   Cool morning awakens already.
   Let your bright gaze, radiating,   Let your somber gaze
   Float through the shadows.   Quietly float into the shadows,
   The answer will soon return,   Never long to return;
   When the antiphonal life of the echo For the antiphonal life of love
   Awakens resonantly by the crag.   Has died away in deep night.
      Tell me, where do you wish to go? Alas, where have you gone?
   Shall I accompany you,   I could not accompany you
   Through the darkness,   Through the darkness
   Direct your steps?   Nor direct your steps.
   Shall I interpret   Could I not interpret
   Cordially, the somber meaning   As friendly the somber meaning
   Of your silent love?   Of your silent love?
   Do you wish to sing your impulses You could not sing your impulses
   Through the evening;   Through the evening;
   Or higher,   Nor higher,
   Ever higher,   Ever higher,
   Ring them out to the stars?   Ring them out to the stars.
   Let me embrace you as a friend,   I had to sadly embrace you—
   Speak your words   You last words
   Into my chords.   Now slumber pleasantly
                                    In the last chord.

Verbatim repetition of phrases with a radical shift in meaning owing to negation of constituent elements:

Durch die Dunkelheiten	Durch die Dunkelheiten
(begleiten)	(nicht begleiten)
Deinen düstern Sinn /	Deinen düstern Sinn /
Freundlich deuten?	Freundlich deuten?
(soll ich)	(Konnt' nicht)
Durch den Abend singen;	Durch den Abend singen;
(Willst)	(Konntest nicht)
Immer höher /	Immer höher /
Zu den Sternen klingen?	Zu den Sternen klingen;
	(nicht)

Finally, the above poem could also be regarded as Brentano's earliest set of variations on the Orphean theme insofar as "song" (that is, the singer) is given the task of passing through the "shades" (Schatten) in order to free his beloved ("Mädchen, lieb Mädchen" [W I 31]) from the realm of darkness. The guitar (a modern adaptation of the lyre) volunteers its services in a cooperative venture of *mousiké*. The rhetorical question posed in Part A, whether "song" prefers to continue singing in the darkness or to transcend to the stars should the mission fail, also has a familiar ring, for these queries parallel the course of Orpheus' career. Part A¹, however, in its concluding lines presents a heightening of the Orpheus tragedy, which Brentano and his progeny were to experience: unable to sing in the night of life and, contrary to Orpheus, no longer convinced that art is a means to overcome misfortune, the poet-singer is confronted with the grim prospect of abject silence.

The poem of 1838 "O Traum der Wüste" bears witness to the fact that the technique of theme and variations was not discarded by Brentano, but rather refined and intensified even toward the close of his career, especially when poetry became the vehicle in which to express his dismay at unresolved personal tensions. In this poem, as in the 1817 version of "Einsam will ich untergehn," there is no progression toward a goal which holds the promise of relief from the "desert dream" of love; the latter, because it is constantly unrequited and fraught with disappointment, becomes a nightmarish mirage. Whereas in "Einsam will ich untergehn" the form of the lamentation could have been compared to a musical rondo in the form A-B-A-C-A-D-A-E-A-F, and so forth (whereby A denotes the major motif and the letters B, C, D, etc., the various images invoked by the poet in order to exemplify different types of loneliness), "O Traum der Wüste" represents a further development of the rondo form which, in the first fourteen stanzas, follows the pattern A-B-A^1-C-A^2-D-A^3-E-A^4-F-A^5-G-A^6, and so forth, and only in the final stanzas hints at a stopping point by repeating the refrain unchanged in two successive stanzas: A^{15}-P-A^{15}-Q. At times the consistency with which Brentano pursues this technique borders on a pathological obsession and a morbid phobia of love's "eternal recurrence." Nevertheless, verses A-A^{14} furnish a veritable compendium of all possible linguistic and stylistic devices with which to characterize the deceptive dream:

(1) O Traum der Wüste, Liebe, endlos Sehnen . . .

(2) O Wüstentraum, wo Lieb' auf Herzschlag lauschet . . .

(3) O Wüstentraum, wo Liebe träumt . . .

(4) O Liebe, Wüstentraum der Sehnsuchtspalme . . .

(5) O Wüste, Traum der Liebe, die verachtet . . .

(6) O Wüstentraum der Liebe, die sich sehnet . . .

(7) O Wüste, wo das Wort der ew'gen Liebe . . .

(8) Lieb', Wüstentraum . . .

(9) O Durst der Liebe, Wüstentraum . . .

(10) Durst, Liebe, Wüstentraum . . .

(11) O Liebe, Wüstentraum des Heimatkranken . . .

(12) O Liebe, Wüstentraumquell, beim Erwachen . . .

(13) O Wüstentraum, wo Sehnsucht Feuer trinket . . .

(14) O Wüstentraum der Lieb'! in der Oase . . .

(15) O Liebe, Wüstentraum . . .

(16) O Liebe, Wüstentraum . . .[67]

(W I 624–626)

[67] (1) O dream of the desert, love, endless longing . . .
(2) O desert dream, where love listens for a heartbeat . . .
(3) O desert dream, where love dreams . . .
(4) O love, desert dream of the palm of longing . . .
(5) O desert, dream of love, which scorns . . .
(6) O desert dream of love, which yearns . . .
(7) O desert, where the word of eternal love . . .
(8) Love, desert dream . . .
(9) O thirst of love, desert dream . . .
(10) Thirst, love, desert dream . . .
(11) O love, desert dream of the home sick one . . .
(12) O love, spring of the desert dream, upon awakening . . .
(13) O desert dream, where longing drinks fire . . .
(14) O desert dream of love! in the oasis . . .
(15) O love, desert dream . . .
(16) O love, desert dream . . .

Many of the poetic techniques employed here anticipate the inno-
vations in language of such twentieth-century writers as Gertrude
Stein. As Hans Magnus Enzensberger has shown,[68] Brentano not only
employs neologisms and striking word compounds to uncover hidden
layers of meaning and arouse a wealth of associations ("Wüstentraumquell"), but he also makes use of a host of other techniques—ambiguity
between subjective and objective genitive ("Traum der Wüste"), com-
pression or extension ("Traum der Wüste-Wüstentraum"), combinations and re-combinations of unique verbal constructs and standard
rhetorical devices (polyptoton: "Wüstentraum, wo Liebe träumt";
alliteration: "O Wüste, wo das Wort der ew'gen Liebe . . .")—in
order to give a litany-like expression to what was obviously a static,
perpetually unresolved, and on the basis of his Orphean experience,
ostensibly insoluble dilemma.

RHYTHM

Brentano's contention that the outstanding lyric artist attained
"a higher unity of nature" in his work by approaching "free form in
itself, music, rhythm through thought" was followed by the explanation: "All his rhythms will be the original melodies of his poems"
(S I 126). In spite of the ambiguity surrounding the exact constitution
of "free form," "music," and "rhythm" (or rhythms as the basic melodies), it should be clear from these remarks that rhythmic factors were
of paramount importance for Brentano's conception of lyricism. There
exists today a considerable bulk of scholarship concerning the nature of
"rhythm" in both music and literature. What Brentano labels, somewhat cryptically, "rhythm through thought" might coincide with the
definition given by the modern critic Gilbert Highet in his book *A
Clerk at Oxenford*: "Rhythm is the pulse which, through its regularity,
enhances our interest and sustains our excitement, and through its
variations, emphasizes the meaning."[69] What emerges from this con-
cise formulation is the fact that rhythm consists of two elements:
regularity and variety. In order to avoid some of the complications that
arise in this connection, it would perhaps be best to use the term
"meter" to refer to the aspect of regularity (or "the pattern of stressed
and unstressed syllables") and reserve the designation "rhythm" per

[68] *Brentanos Poetik* (Munich: Hanser, 1961), pp. 56–70.
[69] *A Clerk at Oxenford* (New York: Oxford, 1954), p. 134.

se for those alterations of the metric pattern which "intensify the expression of what is said."[70]

After having made this basic distinction between meter and rhythm, it is still necessary to add a qualifying word concerning these attributes in music and literature respectively. Even though both poetry and music are "temporal arts" (that is, they are acoustical modes of expression that reveal their form and content sequentially in time), music can control the "time" factor to a much greater degree than poetry. The tempo at which a piece of music is to be performed, for instance, can be indicated precisely by a number on the metronome scale. The rate of speed at which a poem is read, however, remains a highly subjective matter and, under normal conditions, cannot be regulated by the author. Consequently, whereas attention will be given to the problem of meter and rhythm with reference to both media, any conclusions reached are provisional, leaving more questions open than answered.

When dealing with meter as "the pattern of stressed and unstressed syllables," one could, by substituting the concept "tones" or "notes" for the word "syllables," correlate certain phenomena in music and poetry somewhat more closely. For instance, the pronounced triple time so characteristic of the minuet and the waltz (or the "scherzo" movement in a symphony) has been compared with the distinctive stress pattern of the dactylic foot: / − − / − − / − − . In a similar vein, the duple time of the trochee (/ − / − / − .) might be likened to the strong beat of the march. However, if one were to apply these hypotheses to selected poems of Brentano's, their validity would be open to question. Even though the meter found in the refrain of the "lustigen Musikanten" is predominantly dactylic, one would not be tempted to consider these verses ("Es brauset und sauset / Das Tamburin . . .") as a literary waltz—not even a "Valse triste"—let alone a drawing-room minuet or a lighthearted scherzo. By the same token, the following lines—although in trochaic meter—would hardly qualify as a poetic "march":

> Lieb' und Leid im leichten Leben
> Sich erheben, abwärts schweben

[70] Karl Beckson and Arthur Ganz, *A Reader's Guide to Literary Terms* (New York: Noonday Press, 1960), pp. 121 and 178.

> Aus dem Spiegel schauen Bilder,
> Blicken milder, blicken wilder.[71]
>
> (W I 129)

If the attempt to establish precise metrical correspondences between music and poetry leads to a blind alley from the beginning, the investigation of rhythmic factors—although potentially more rewarding—likewise ends in a cul-de-sac. Rhythm as the element of metrical variety which, by breaking the regular pattern, "emphasizes the meaning" can be seen in the merry minstrels' refrain by the verses "Schweifen die Pfeifen, und greifen / Ans Herz." The single trimeter line just before what seems to constitute the climax of a crescendo passage underscores through the dimension of rhythmical variety the manner in which the musical tones break through and break down any barriers of restraint in the lives of both the performers and their audience. The significance of rhythmic variety amidst metric regularity can also be illustrated in the basically trochaic quatrain cited above. The manner in which joy and sorrow fluctuate periodically in life—especially in a devil-may-care type of existence ("leichten Leben")—is captured, in part, by the lilting, lighthearted flow of these lines. The element of flux is enhanced by syntactical parallelisms and internal rhyme ("erheben . . . schweben"; "Blicken milder, blicken wilder"). Such devices also contribute to the sprightly vigor of these verses, to the extent that parallel phraseology prepares the reader subconsciously for what is coming as his mind's eye glances across the page. The impression of uninhibited movement is also fostered by the preponderance of alliterative *l*'s in the opening line, as well as concealed alliteration (together with augmentation) in the third: "*Spiegel schauen Bilder*." In order to prevent the reader from falling into an uninterrupted sing-song routine, however, Brentano incorporates certain rhythmic modifications. For example, the enjambement from line one to line two causes one to read "Lieb' und Leid im leichten Leben / Sich erheben" as a single unit followed by a pause. The next phrase ("abwärts schweben") is elliptical, insofar as "Lieb' und Leid im leichten Leben" is implied but not repeated. The pause after "schweben" gives the reader sufficient time to reflect on this situation. However, the counterpart to verse one ("Aus dem Spiegel schauen Bilder") is a complete syntactical unit in itself and does not involve enjambement. In this case, both of the following

[71] "Love and sorrow in carefree life / Soar up, sink down / From the mirror pictures gaze / Glancing milder, glancing wilder."

phrases "blicken milder, blicken wilder" are dependent upon the preceding verse for their raison d'être. Whereas they form a visual counterpart to the "Sich erheben, abwärts schweben" of line two, they actually stand in a different relationship of dependence to the preceding line than the above. This quatrain illustrates one manifestation of rhythmical variation in a context in which the metrical pattern remains relatively constant.

A different form of rhythmical variety as a means of intensifying the "meaning" behind the words was already detected in the opening lines of the "Schwanenlied":

> Wenn die Augen brechen,
> Wenn die Lippen nicht mehr sprechen,
> Wenn das pochende Herz sich stillet
> Und der warme Blutstrom nicht mehr quillet:
> O dann . . .

(W I 245)

The anxiety of the speaker at the warning signs of death's approach is conveyed not only by the "what" of these verses, but also by the "how." The anaphoral "wenn" clauses would be sufficient in themselves to express the feeling of tension and terror because of the unknown adventure confronting the speaker. The rhythmical variety of these basically trochaic lines adds a dimension of meaning to the poem, which the words themselves do not—and perhaps, could not—articulate. The gradually increasing length of the dependent syntactical units culminates in the third and fourth lines, which are to be considered together as a single "wenn" unit with a double nominative referent. The hypertension aroused under these conditions is only released by the following "O dann." A comparable musical illustration of rhythmical variety as a method of undergirding the "meaning" of a highly charged passage can be found in the opening measures of Wagner's "Prelude" to *Tristan und Isolde* in which the initial motif of longing recurs several times in succession, on each occasion with slight but significant alterations in the rhythmic pattern of the original.

There is obviously a high degree of subjectivity involved in such interpretations as the above, and this aspect of the problem of rhythm represents the greatest handicap to a strict systematization in either music or literature. Whereas the reader may appreciate a poem and remain oblivious to its artistic complexity (especially any musico-poetic form parallels), metrical considerations do compel him to follow certain standard stress patterns when reciting lyric poetry. However, reading metrically is not reading rhythmically. The latter demands sensitivity and receptivity for a complex nexus of forces including meter, lyrical syntax, semantic connotations and denotations, in addition to a wide range of "intangibles." The criteria for a "correct" rhythmical reading of a given text transcend any single faculty of aesthetic apperception and appreciation. For that reason, rhythm remains not only the most elusive element in the poet's repertoire, but also the most rewarding. When author and audience find themselves in intimate rapport, this stems most likely from the rhythm of the poem more than from any other factor, since the rhythm imparts to the reader what words cannot say.

THE SOUND STRATA OF POETRY AND MUSIC

Music has been defined in the broadest terms as "the science or art of incorporating pleasing, expressive, or intelligible combinations of vocal or instrumental tones into a composition having definite structure and continuity."[72] If one regards the human voice as a vocal instrument, then the above definition might also be applied to certain manifestations of spoken language, especially of lyric poetry when read aloud. Just as the composer selects and arranges the tones and timbres at his disposal, so, too, does the acoustically conscious poet such as Brentano take pains with the sound patterns of his lyric line. To be sure, not all poets of all ages have aimed at producing lyrics that were musical in their acoustical properties.[73] However, the writers of Brentano's generation were definitely of this persuasion, and they eagerly seized upon the idea that the spoken idiom was a kind of musical instrument with which one might construct a variety of tonal configurations rivaling those of music.[74] In their zeal to find correspondences between tones and words, however, the Romanticists too often

---

[72] *Webster's Third New International Dictionary*, p. 1490.

[73] With the advent of printing, of course, poetry lost much of its "oral" quality and became more closely allied with the eye than with the ear. In addition, since musicality of verse is so intimately associated with nineteenth-century trends of Romanticism and Symbolism, many modern poets have turned away from any attempt to achieve euphonious tone configurations in verse.

[74] Note, for example, Novalis' assertion in *Werke*, I, 353: "Language is a musical instrument of ideas. The poet, rhetorician, and philosopher play and compose grammatically. A fugue is completely logical or scientific. It can also be treated poetically."

minimized obvious differences. When, for example, Tieck and A. W. Schlegel contended that rhyme represented the poetic counterpart to musical harmony,[75] they failed to recognize certain elementary distinctions between the sound configurations that constitute the life's blood of the respective arts. First of all, musical tones have definite pitch, duration, dynamic range, and timbre, all of which can be indicated accurately by the composer in his score. The sounds of spoken words, on the other hand, have varying pitch, duration, dynamics, and timbre, depending upon a complex number of variables, including the emotional attitude of the reader toward the denotative impact of the words he encounters, or such subsidiary factors as the pitch of his voice, his age, his sex, and even his dialect idiosyncracies. The poet has only very limited means at his disposal to specify his wishes with regard to the manner in which the verbal artifact is to be "performed" (punctuation, for instance), and almost no control at all over the variables. In rebuttal of Tieck and Schlegel, therefore, one need only point out that harmony in the sense of the simultaneous sounding of several tones of different pitch to form a chord—a fundamental and indispensable aspect of homophonic music—has no direct parallel at all in lyric poetry, where there can only be solo "melody" or, at best, "Harmonia" in the original sense of the balanced fusion of relatively equal parts into a well-proportioned totality. Of course, the strongest argument against a blanket comparison stems from the fact that words remain forever tied to a semantic function, from which the tones of music are totally divorced from the beginning.

In view of these very rudimentary differences between the "tones" of the two arts, it is obvious that the poet should not or could not compete on any kind of equal basis with the composer in either the richness or the variety of sound. A comparative analysis of the two media in this regard, therefore, can—like the earlier investigation of form and rhythm—yield at best similarities of method, but, under no circumstances, identity of means. Poetry which "aspires toward the condition of music"[76] on the level of sound alone, invariably proves to be inferior music and usually poor literature. Nevertheless, the contention of one twentieth-century critic that "Orpheus long ago laid down his

---

[75] Eva Tiegel, *Das Musikalische in der romantischen Prosa*, Diss. Erlangen (Coburg: Tageblatt-Haus, 1934), p. 19.

[76] Walter Pater, "The School of Giorgione" in *The Renaissance: Studies in Art and Poetry* (London: Macmillan, 1925), p. 135, states categorically: "*All art constantly aspires towards the condition of music.*"

lute in favor of a typewriter"[77] does not quite apply to Brentano and
his contemporaries, even though it may be valid for a majority of the
"moderns." To be sure, Brentano and his generation also felt that they
were living in a prosaic age, an epoch that was more inclined to lament
an Orpheus *absconditus* than to celebrate an Orpheus *redivivus*. And
yet the Romantic writers did not slacken in the attempt to devise for
the lyric an idiom that would produce a musicality sui generis. This
modified *mousiké* would not be as universally appreciated as that of
Orpheus nor as sonorous as the acoustical world fashioned by the
composer; but it would certainly offer a richer musicality than the
lackluster verses of some of the eighteenth-century rhymesters and
occasional poets.

The evolution of such a unique tonal cosmos in the lyric poetry of
Brentano will be traced through three—not necessarily chronological
—stages: (1) "Klangmalerei," or onomatopoeia; (2) "Klangspiel," or
tone play; (3) "Klangsymbolik," or sound symbolism. The first of
these terms refers to the effort of the poet to capture in the medium of
his verse sounds resembling those stemming from the external sphere
that he describes. The second concept denotes verbal virtuosity and
mastery of the language, exhibited by various manipulations of vowels, consonants, and other tone clusters. The third designation indicates the concentration on a few key tonal complexes which, owing to
a variety of contributory factors, acquire special significance for the
poet, so that he may eventually utilize them more for their suggestive
"sound" values rather than their denotative function (even though the
latter factor may, at the outset, have been decisive in the establishment
of such sound symbolism and, as will be indicated later, can never
be totally disregarded in spite of all attempts to minimize the importance of "meaning").

"Klangmalerei"

The proclivity of Romantic poets to emulate the timbres of particular musical instruments in their works is a phenomenon that most
likely stems from the homage paid by them to the art of music as the
apex of aesthetic expression. However, whereas a facile writer such as
Tieck produced a rash of poetry in which vowel and consonant group-
ings were intended to reproduce the tonal qualities of specific orchestral

[77] Douglas Newton, "The Composer and the Music of Poetry," *The Score*,
1 (1948): 13.

instruments, it is doubtful whether the reader would ever have discovered this intention had he not been influenced by suggestive titles and subtitles, such as "Schalmeiklang" and "Waldhornmelodie."[78] The same might be said with regard to Brentano's "scoring" of his lyric "Phantasie" for diverse instruments. Even though critics have commented on the "rather dark clarinet" and the "sonorous bassoon,"[79] such appraisals seem to be based more on preconceived notions of what the timbres of these instruments sound like rather than on any intrinsic tone quality of the stanzas in which the soloists "perform." One wonders, for example, if the following verses ascribed to the bassoon are particularly "sonorous" in their own right, or whether they are described as such because the instrument in question produces such tones: "Wer den eignen Ton nicht hört, / Lausche, bis er wiederkehrt" (W I 28).[80]

The majority of onomatopoetic devices employed by Brentano in approximating the timbres of orchestral instruments are restricted to that branch of the orchestra which produces noise rather than music: the percussion family. In addition to the drum rolls and cymbal crashing to be found in the eleven repetitions of the refrain of the merry minstrels ("brauset und sauset," "prasseln und rasseln"), there are scattered throughout his poetry isolated verses that seem to suggest the hollow thumping or the shrill rataplan so characteristic of the drum. The din of battle during the Wars of Liberation, for instance, seems to have been particularly conducive to producing such sounds in his poetry. The line from "Die Gottesmauer" that tells of the onslaught of hostile troops also brings the music to these contingents in our ears: "Trommeln rommdidomm rings prasseln" (W I 327).[81] The many trilled or uvular r's together with the resonant o and u vowels in this line undergird the description acoustically. In the chauvinistic pageant *Viktoria und ihre Geschwister* the incessant rolling of drums together with the roar of the cannons seem to infiltrate the speech patterns of the characters, so that Lippel, the lost son of the camp-follower Liese Trommelklippel, can lament:

> Von dem Kümmel werd ich dumm,
> Vom Verstummen werd' ich stumm,

[78] Brown, *Tones into Words*, pp. 21 ff.
[79] *Clemens Brentano: Gedichte*, ed. Paul Requadt (Stuttgart: Reclam, 1968), "Nachwort," p. 71.
[80] "He who does not hear his own tone, / Let him listen, until it returns."
[81] "Drums round about rumble rum-dee-dum."

Von dem Sitzen werd' ich krumm,
Von dem Studium krumm, stumm, dumm
Rundum, rundum, rundumherum,
Ist halt nichts als ein Gebrumm![82]

(GS VII 389)

Aside from these few excursions into onomatopoetic rendition of the percussion family, Brentano does not utilize this technique in a conspicuous manner for any other branch of the orchestra, but rather has recourse to verbal description, as in the lines of 1806: "Die süßen Pfeifen drumher schleifen, / Trompeten scharf in die Nacht eingreifen" (W I 176).[83] Finally, it should be mentioned in passing that a work like *Viktoria*, in which the onomatopoetic technique reaches its high point (at least in frequency of application), represents, from the standpoint of aesthetic quality and artistic subtlety, the nadir of Brentano's literary output.

A form of onomatopoeia standing at the crossroads between music and noise comes to the fore in those instances where the poet attempts to render the sounds of nature's song—the chirping of birds, the rustling of trees, and the rippling of brooks—audibly in verses. Poets themselves—including Brentano's contemporaries—were not in accord as to whether the spontaneous and unrehearsed tones emanating from the bucolic milieu were to be regarded as superior to or inferior to man-made music.[84] In general, however, the aesthetic evaluation of these sounds was overshadowed by their ethical import for the listener. Consequently, by echoing even imperfectly the sounds of nature in his verses, the Romantic poet moved a step closer to regaining the paradise from which time and his consciousness had alienated him.

Even though Brentano does resort on occasion to what seems to be obvious poetic imitation of avian singers,[85] his unique forte lay not

[82] "From the kümmel I grow stupid, / From silence I become mute, / From sitting I am bent, / From my studies bent, mute, stupid, / Round about, round about, all around / Is nothing but grumbling!"

[83] "The sweet fifes banter about, / Trumpets pierce sharply through the night."

[84] Tieck, for example, in *Franz Sternbalds Wanderungen*, lauded nature's organ music and placed it high above the "feeble" art of man—in his *Schriften* (Berlin: G. Reimer, 1843), XVI, 274. Wackenroder, on the other hand, a friend and contemporary of Tieck's, called the unadulterated music of nature "incomprehensible and coarse" in comparison with instrumental sounds—see his *Werke und Briefe*, ed. Friedrich von der Leyen (Jena: E. Diederichs, 1910), II, 294–295.

[85] For example, in the song of the swallow from *Das Märchen vom Murmeltier* one reads: "I, wie ziehn die Winde / So geschwinde durch die Linde" (W III 239).

so much in this superficial mode of emulation but rather in the more subtle manifestations of the interplay of music in the extrapersonal and intrapersonal spheres. One can, for instance, point to examples of what might be called expressive and impressive correlatives. The first of these is seen in "Auf dem Rhein" when the narrator, under the delusion that he has just spent the night in the embrace of his beloved, awakens to the effusive song of the birds:

> Es rauscht der grüne Wald,
> Vor wildentbrannten Weisen,
> Der Vogelsang erschallt.[86]
> (W I 100)

The unusual adjectival compound "wildentbrannt" reflects, as was indicated earlier, the elation of the speaker, which he then projects into the singing of the birds. Brentano undergirds this tacit *expression* of innermost hopes by acoustical devices. An elective empathy between the speaker's state of mind ("wildentbrannt") and the world outside the perceiving subject is suggested by the bonds of alliteration and assonance. The concepts "Wald," "Weisen," "-sang," "erschallt" establish subtle tonal links between the subject and object. This procedure is, for all practical purposes, reversed in "O kühler Wald," where the forest milieu gradually *impresses* itself upon a receptive subject:

> O kühler Wald
> Wo rauschest Du,
> In dem mein Liebchen geht,
> O Widerhall
> Wo lauschest Du
> Der gern mein Lied versteht.

> O Widerhall,
> O sängst Du ihr
> Die süßen Träume vor,
> Die Lieder all,
> O bring' sie ihr,
> Die ich so früh verlor.

> Im Herzen tief,
> Da rauscht der Wald
> In dem mein Liebchen geht,

[86] "The verdant forest rustles, / From the passionately enkindled melodies, / The song of the birds resounds."

>   Im Schmerzen schlief
>   Der Widerhall,
>   Die Lieder sind verweht.[87]
>
>   (W I 125–126)

The opening three stanzas of the poem illustrate the process of gradual
"interiorization" insofar as the first, with its rhetorical question, sets
the general tone by announcing four central concepts: "Wald-Liebchen-
Widerhall-Lied." The forest, as the *locus amoenus*, must resound with
the echoed love song of the speaker—a sign that his plea has struck a
responsive chord. The *"Lied"* for his *"Liebchen"* in the *"Wald"* is
present both explicitly (the Melos-Eros theme) and implicitly (acoustical echo) in the *"Widerhall."* Stanza three marks the transition
from an unresponsive forest in the external sphere to an inner realm
where a faint echo lingers ("Wald-Liebchen-Widerhall-Lieder") even
though the music of love is over. The concluding stanza introduces an
ambivalent note insofar as the "Wald," in which the speaker now wan-
ders faithfully singing "Lieder" in spite of "Liebchen's" silent indifference (the term "Widerhall" is missing here), lies somewhere between the forest as an objective landscape and a *locus amoenus* as a
subjective "soulscape":

>   Im Walde bin
>   Ich so allein,
>   O Liebchen wandre hier,
>   Verschallet auch
>   Manch Lied so rein,
>   Ich singe andre Dir.[88]
>
>   (W I 126)

"Klangspiel"

If the "musicality" of Brentano's lyrics were limited to his occasional imitation of orchestral timbres or to the onomatopoetic reciprocity between nature's domain and the inner world of the speaker,
then the significance of his contribution to lyric musicality would not

---

[87] "O woodland cool, / Where rustlest thou / Wherein my love doth stray?
/ O echo, tell / Where listenest thou / Who understands my lay? // O echoing
sound, / O singst thou her / The dreams I like the most, / The ballads all / O,
bring them her / Whom I so early lost! // Deep in my heart / The rustling wood
/ Wherein my love doth stray; / In sorrows slept / The echoing sound, / The
tunes have blown away." Translated by Mabel Cotterell in *An Anthology of
German Poetry from Hölderlin to Rilke*, p. 92.

[88] "In woodland am / I so alone, / O dearest, come to me; / Though many
a song / Away has flown, / Others I'll sing to thee!"

exceed that of Tieck or some of the lesser talents of the Romantic period. A similar assertion could be made with regard to another of Brentano's predilections—the addiction to "Klangspiel," or tone play and tonal interplay. The extent to which Brentano emulated and excelled his mentor Tieck during his apprenticeship in the workshop of lyric poetry reveals the manner in which Brentano paved the way for later developments in the field of "Klangsymbolik."

The practice of "Klangspiel" could be regarded as an attempt to emancipate the sound stratum of words from their semantic ties by organizing them into semi-autonomous acoustical configurations. This technique of arranging verbal sound patterns may have been what Schiller had in mind when he spoke of "whatever is music in poetry actually and in relation to its material."[89] Modern critics, however, are loath to claim that words in a literary context can be considered for their tonal value alone. This, of course, is the verdict of a post-Romantic—and in many respects, anti-Romantic—age, an era which has witnessed the extreme distortions to which hypotheses about beautiful-sounding but meaningless word-juggling can lead. Whereas Brentano's "Klangspiel" may, on occasion, seem contrived and ostentatious, it seldom runs rampant to the extent of submerging the sense completely beneath a flood of euphonious sound. On the contrary, his manipulations of vowel and consonant combinations are generally dexterous and deliberate, ranging in scope from simple alternation of sounds at regular intervals to juxtapositions involving more subtle techniques. Neither the simple nor the more refined versions of "Klangspiel" that will be outlined on the following pages occur in isolation; rather, they are interwoven to form a delicate tonal fabric. Whereas it would be misleading to claim that every one of these techniques had been carefully calculated by the poet, the frequency and persistence of occurrence seems to preclude their being either purely accidental or mere figments of an interpreter's imagination.

Proceeding from the simpler to the more complex modes of sound patterning, one might begin with an illustration of Brentano's favorite device, the regular alternation of consonants or vowels:

> *Aller Himmel bald verschwindet* (a-i-a-i) (b-v)
> *Alle Sterne bald vergehen* (a-e-a-e) (b-v)
>
> (W I 33)

---

[89] Friedrich Schiller, *Werke*, ed. Lieselotte Blumental and Benno von Wiese, XX (Weimar: Hermann Böhlaus Nachfolger, 1962), 456.

A further development of the above is interlocking alliteration and assonance (sometimes referred to as acrostic scrambling or tonal chiasmus).[90] Brentano was fond of using this rhetorically effective scheme in the opening lines of his poems:

> *W*este *s*äuseln; *s*ilbern *w*allen (w-s-s-w)
> (W I 42)
> Wie sich auch die Zeit *will wenden, enden*
> *Will* sich nimmer doch (will-enden-enden-will)[91]
> (W I 123)

However, tonal chiasmus can also be found in the body of a poem, especially in verses that contain important ideas:

> O *w*ähnend *L*ieben, *L*iebes*w*ahn (w-l-l-w)
> (W I 128)
> *R*osse *w*iehern, *W*agen *r*asseln (r-w-w-r)
> (W I 526)
> *Wellington* in *Tones Welle* (*Well-ton-Ton-Well*)
> (W I 311)

The above techniques are modified by what has been called phonetic syzygy or concealed alliteration, whereby the poet links together sounds requiring similar labial or tongue positions, but which are not identical in sound:[92]

> Es *lacht* und *klagt* der süße Schall (acht-agt)
> (GS II 426)

The oft repeated refrain of the poem "Die Gottesmauer" shows phonetic syzygy in a dual capacity: "Eine *Mauer um uns bau*e" (mau-u-u bau) (W I 327 ff.). Here one realizes that "Klangspiel" can actually enhance the sense of a poem. The plea for God's protection from the invading hordes is not only heard by the ear, but also seen by the eye. The wall ("Mauer") erected ("bauen") around ("um") the beleaguered populace ("uns") for protection forms a counterpart to the acoustical-visual descriptions of the enemy troops surrounding the city: "*R*osse *w*iehern, *W*agen *r*asseln."

[90] Kenneth Burke, "On Musicality in Verse," in *The Philosophy of Literary Form*, 2nd ed. (New York: Vintage Books, 1961), p. 298.

[91] "However time may wend, end / Will never, however, . . ."

Of course, this poem is not original with Brentano, but rather is based on the lines of the medieval poet Walther von Klingen: "Swie diu zît sich wil verkêren Sêren / Muoz das sende herze mîn . . . (W I 1054).

[92] Burke, p. 296.

The principle of regular alternation of similar tonal configurations can also be developed by employing the composer's devices of augmentation and diminution. In augmentation, the interval between the recurrent sounds is increased, thereby breaking the pattern of metric regularity:

> Von den Saiten schwingen (s-t)
> Sich die Töne (s—t)

Augmentation combined with interlocking alliteration is seen in the following lines:

> Wo der Schwan im Wellenspiegel
> In sein Sternbild niedertaucht (er-i) (ie-au)
> Bricht der Schmerz auch mir das Siegel (i—er) (au——ie)
> (W I 392)

Diminution, on the other hand, entails the shortening of the interval between the parallel sounds or acrostic scramblings:

> Daß mein Leid im Liede (m—l) (m-l)

> Stille Liebe, süße Blicke (l—b) (b-l)

> Wo ist die Liebe geblieben (l—b) (b-l)

Brentano's "Klangspiel" also includes the utilization of vowel gradation and the "Ablaut" series, as the following examples will attest:

> O wähnend Liebe, Liebeswahn
> (W I 128)
> Gärtnerlied im Liedergarten der Liebe
> (GS II 276)
> O klinge nicht du Widerklang
> (GS II 121)
> Um Kling und um Klang,
> Um Sing und um Sang
> (W II 396 ff.)

In spite of the virtual emancipation of some sound configurations in the above examples from semantic obligations, "Klangspiel" is most effective, not when it exists on its own, but rather when it supports the meaning of the poem. For example, in the following excerpt from "Die lustigen Musikanten," interlocking consonants (or tonal chiasmus) combines with a striking form of vowel gradation to underscore acoustically the "message" which the stanza delivers—the intrusion of the merry minstrels' music into the bridal chamber:

> Wenn in des goldnen *Bettes Kissen*
> Sich *küssen Bräutigam* und Braut
> Und glaubens ganz allein zu wissen,
> Macht bald es unser Singen laut.[93]
>
> (W II 398)

The sounds emanating from the external world, the realm of the "outsiders," betray by their "tonal embrace" (B-K—k-B) the intimate secrets which the newlyweds harbor in the innermost recesses of their hearts (Kissen-küssen). Finally, a similar constellation of rhythmical and acoustical factors in close proximity contributes to the fascination which the following lines have always exerted on readers:

> Singt ein Lied so süß gelinde,
> (s-l-s-l [regular alternation])
> (i-ie-ü-i [tonal chiasmus])
> Wie die Quellen auf den Kieseln,
> (ie-q[k]-el-n-n-kie-eln [diminution])
> Wie die Bienen um die Linde
> Summen, murmeln, flüstern, rieseln.
> (um-mu) (r-ln-l-rn-r-ln)

"Klangsymbolik"

Whereas "Klangspiel" could be compared with poetic meter to the extent that it represents an aspect of the craft of "making" lyric poetry, "Klangsymbolik" is more akin to rhythm insofar as it enables the verbal signs on the printed page to convey more than the factual "content" of the word indicates. In addition, "Klangspiel" was basically indifferent to meaning: "Klangsymbolik," on the other hand, uncovers a deep primordial relationship between the sound properties of words and their cognitive function. Therefore, if "Klangsymbolik" is successful, the ultimate significance of a particular text will be underscored each time the tonal complex or acoustical configuration occurs—just as rhythm, in its subtle fashion, gave a heightened dimension of meaning to lyric line. Sound symbolism in poetry might, in view of the above criteria, be likened in its function to the Wagnerian leitmotif:

[93] "When on the pillow of the golden bed / Bride and groom are kissing, / Thinking they alone must know it, / Soon our singing makes it public."

it triggers in the mind of the listener an emotional reaction based on repeated exposure to similar tonal constellations in certain specific contexts.

During the epoch when Brentano began to write, there was already a growing desire on the part of poets and philologists to establish what might be termed "emotional coefficients" for specific verbal sounds, especially for the vowels.[94] Such an attempt to standardize the reactions to be elicited in the reader by different vowel combinations is analogous to the system of "Ethos" propounded by the Greeks for the musical modes, or to the "Affektenlehre" (doctrine of the affections) for various intervals of the musical scale formulated in the seventeenth and early eighteenth centuries. The drawbacks to all such musico-verbal schematizations, however, is that they are seldom in accord with one another and too often contradictory in their basic premises. Not only do the emotional equivalents ascribed to vowels and other tonal stimuli vary from epoch to epoch, but it can also happen that the feelings and psychic responses attributed to a specific sound differ from poet to poet in the same given period. Not even the original Greek aestheticians, for instance, were in complete agreement with regard to what response was provoked by the Dorian mode.[95] Similar conflicts of opinion can be discovered in the tables of emotional correspondences for the vowels set up by Brentano's contemporaries.

A basic fallacy, then, in dealing with "Klangsymbolik" lies in the attempt to arbitrarily impose the pattern of correspondences devised by one author on the works of another. Within certain prescribed limits, however, the isolation and analysis of recurrent "tonalities" can provide valuable insight into the creative process of a particular poet. In Brentano's work, for example, one could illustrate the dominant role played by the *a-ei* vowel combination (also called "Grundvokale" or "Grundtöne")[96] in his lyric poetry. It should be made clear from the outset, however, that any symbolic significance accruing to this vowel pair does not necessarily result from the intrinsic acoustical qualities of the tonal components themselves, but stems rather—as Wilhelm

[94] For an extensive tabulation of the various scales of emotional coefficients for vowels, see Mittenzwei, *Das Musikalische in der Literatur*, pp. 491–492.

[95] Curt Sachs, *The Rise of Music in the Ancient World* (New York: Norton 1943), p. 248, points out that whereas Aristotle felt the Dorian mode was suitable for producing a settled temper in the listener, one of his contemporaries classified the same mode as "bellicose."

[96] These terms have been taken from Hans Jaeger, *Clemens Brentanos Frühlyrik* (Frankfurt am Main: M. Diesterweg, 1926), p. 158.

Schneider has noted in his *Ausdruckswerte der deutschen Sprache*—from the fact "that the reader, seduced by the contextual significance of words and by the inflection of speech created in the mind or actually heard, imparts an emotional value to the sounds which is not due them intrinsically."[97] With this caveat in mind, therefore, the following analysis will trace the growth and development of this basic tonality in some of its most significant manifestations and variations.

Turning again to the "Symphonie" in *Gustav Wasa* (1799), one notes that the *a-ei* tones function in two capacities: structural and thematic. The original hypothesis of a "sonata" form for this poem, although rejected in favor of the overture, might be defended on the basis of key (tonic-dominant) relationships. The tonic key, in this case *ei*, is used to introduce the principal theme (the movements of the "Geister" under the tacit aegis of the "Meister") in the exposition section. There are, however, appropriate excursions into the dominant —"Tanz-Glanz-Kranz"—to instill the desire on the part of the listener for a return to the primary key (*ei*). The interplay of the two is also counterbalanced by brief "modulations" to related keys in the development section, but the fundamental tonality hovers constantly on the periphery ("Geister Gesang," "Geistertanz," "Alle in einem erstanden," "einzeln verbanden") and celebrates a triumphant return in the recapitulation: "Fesselt der Meister das Sein," "Handelnd durcheilet die Reihn / Das Ganze im einzelnen Schein." With regard to the thematic role of the *a-ei* combination, some informative conclusions can already be drawn in this early poem concerning its "existential" significance and its application to the Orphean situation. For Brentano, who often felt alone and alienated from family and friends, the concepts "all(e)," "das Ganze," and "verbanden" evoked the sense of companionship, the impression of a communal spirit. On the other hand, terms such as "einzeln," "eigen," and "ein jeder" implied individuation and isolation. However, as was noted previously regarding social harmony, Brentano and his literary spokesmen both seek and eschew a binding commitment to the established community. This reciprocity of centrifugal and centripetal forces is evident on the acoustical plane through the persistent interplay and interdependence of the *a-ei* vowels. The fact that the actions ("Tanz," "im eigenen Glanz," and so forth) of the ostensibly independent tonal spirits ("Geister")

---

[97] *Ausdruckswerte der deutschen Sprache* (1931; reprinted, Darmstadt: Wissenschaftliche Buchgesellschaft, 1968), p. 204.

are, in the final analysis, determined by the maestro ("Meister"), reveals that the latter, by curtailing the freedom of these forces, makes
an inevitable—but, in the long run, beneficial—infringement upon the
prerogatives of the individual in the interest of the entire group. Existence ("Dasein") is and remains a fusion of individual liberty
("Tanz") and social conformity ("die Reihn"). The verses following
the "Symphonie" in *Wasa* that describe an incipient storm likewise
stress the ultimate contingency of autonomous forces by means of the
a-ei tonality: "Will und Tat wird einerlei, / Und das Ganze glaubt
sich frei" (W IV 61).[98] A comparable thematic tonality occurs in the
poem "Phantasie" in which not individual notes, but rather individual
instruments perform; after completing their solo passages, however,
they join in a "tutti" section in which the *a-ei* constellations pre-
dominate:

> Es eilet jed Leben die eigene Bahn;
>
> .   .   .   .
>
> Und reißet vom Ganzen nicht einer sich los;
> Doch blüht einem jeden das Ganze im Schoß.
>
> (W I 29)

> Im eigenem Busen muß alles erklingen,
> Und daß der Sinn leicht finden es kann,
> Hat's viele buntfarbige Kleider an,
> Und Hülle und Geist sich zum Leben verschlingen.[99]
>
> (W I 30)

A poem which illustrates the symbolic significance of the *a-ei*
combination on an even more extensive level is "Der Spinnerin Nachtlied" of 1802. Here the odd and the even stanzas can be juxtaposed,
not only in accordance with the previously outlined technique of literary theme and variations, but also with reference to the consistent
application of key vowels:

Stanzas 1, 3, 5 (*a* tone)	Stanzas 2, 4, 6 (*ei* tone)
Es sang vor langen Jahren	Ich sing' und kann nicht weinen,
Wohl auch die Nachtigall,	Und spinne so allein

---

[98] "Will and deed becomes [sic] one, / And the whole believes itself free."
[99] "Each life rushes along its own path; / ... And not a single one tears itself loose from the whole; / Yet the whole blossoms in the heart of each. // In
one's own heart all things must resound; / And so that the mind can easily find
it, / It wears many brightly-colored clothes, / And spirit and covering embrace
for life."

Das war wohl süßer Schall,	Den Faden klar und rein
Da wir zusammen waren.	So lang der Mond wird scheinen.

Als wir zusammen waren	So oft der Mond mag scheinen,
Da sang die Nachtigall	Denk' ich wohl dein allein,
Nun mahnet mich ihr Schall	Mein Herz ist klar und rein,
Daß du von mir gefahren.	Gott wolle uns vereinen.

Seit du von mir gefahren,	Gott wolle uns vereinen
Singt stets die Nachtigall,	Hier spinn' ich so allein,
Ich denk' bei ihrem Schall,	Der Mond scheint klar und rein,
Wie wir zusammen waren.	Ich sing' und möchte weinen.[100]

(W I 131)

The odd stanzas relate the events of a happy past in a predominantly *a* tonality; the even strophes, on the other hand, tell of the painful present in which only the elegiac memory of former joy remains. However, whereas the odd stanzas are, acoustically speaking, devoid of any traces of the sorrows to come (except for "seit"), the even group has a balance of *a-ei* in virtually every line: "kann-weinen," "allein," "klar und rein," "lang-scheinen," and so forth, indicative of the acknowledgment that pure happiness (unmitigated *a*) can be possible only in a remote past, a paradise that may be recalled but not regained. In addition to the *a-ei* "Grundvokale," Brentano employs a subsidiary acoustical device in order to further set apart the blissful "then" from the mournful "now." In the odd stanzas he speaks of "wir" and undergirds the initial *w* of the plural pronoun with a number of alliterating terms ("wohl . . . war . . . waren, . . . wie . . ."); the even stanzas, in contrast to this, stress the isolation of the "ich" and tell of two activities that are repeated in cyclical fashion as an attempt to fill the

---

[100] In other time long gone
    Here caroled the nightingale.
    It told a sweeter tale
    When our two hearts were one.

When our two hearts were one,
    Of joy sang the nightingale;
    Now all its changeful tale
    Is but that thou art gone.

Since thou from me art gone,
    The ceaseless nightingale sings
    And restless memories brings
    Of how two hearts made one.

I sing; I cannot weep;
    I turn my wheel, and there
    The strand gleams pure and clear
    While moonbeams vigil keep.

While moons wax bright or wane
    I think of thee, most dear,
    My heart's truth pure and clear.
    God yield us joy again!

God yield us joy! No sleep
    Is mine; I spin while here
    Moonlight streams pure and clear.
    I sing; I fain would weep.

Translated by Wyatt A. Surrey in *Anthology of German Poetry from Hölderlin to Rilke*, pp. 95–96.

void in the speaker's life now that she is alone: "*singen*" and "*spinnen*."

If one were to examine the *a* component in the above poem with reference to the tables of emotional equivalents for vowel sounds set up by Brentano and his contemporaries, it would become apparent that there was some degree of correlation between literary theory and poetic practice. For instance, A. W. Schlegel's contention that the vowel *a* is to be associated with "youth, joy, and splendor"[101] is corroborated insofar as this sound is reserved for reporting the happy events of the past. Bernhardi's theory of the *a* as an expression of "feeling without passion" is also applicable,[102] since the spinner—albeit in a distraught state—speaks in resigned and dispassionate tones. Finally, Brentano's claim "In dem A den Schall zu suchen"—"To seek in the A a resonance" (W I 763)—is also affirmed, since the sonorous tones of the "Nachtigall" not only provided the background music for the erstwhile lovers, but also intrude incessantly and almost imperceptibly into the lonely present (the *a* component of the even stanzas), reminding us and the speaker that life is not meant to be a sequence of joy and sorrow, but rather a coincidence of the two.

The symbolic overtones of the *a-ei* vowel combination established in the early poetry remained fairly constant and consistent throughout Brentano's entire lifetime. That the *ei* component became further entrenched as the acoustical counterpart for painful or unpleasant experiences (in spite of the positive attributes of such terms as "heilig," "leise," "rein," the suffix "-lein," and homonyms such as "Weise," "weise," but not "Waise") can be seen in the following excerpts from his later poetry:

> Es grüßte mich kein Sänger in dem Hain;
> Auch aus dem Tal schallt keines Hirten Flöte.
>
> (W I 163 [1803])
>
> Du freches lüderliches Weib!
>
> .   .   .   .
>
> Fluch über deinen feilen geilen Leib.
>
> (W I 264 [1812])

---

[101] Mittenzwei, p. 120.

[102] A. F. Bernhardi in his *Sprachlehre* of 1803 wrote under the topic "Language as Tone and as Constituent Element of Tone Rows" that the vowels form a "natural scale" and provide the "first traces of genuine and true music" which is then made a reality by rhyme and assonance. To illustrate this thesis, Bernhardi postulates the following emotional correspondences for vowels: A = feeling without passion; O = grandeur and harmonious completeness; U = unpleasantness.

> O schweig nur Herz! Die rächende Sibille
> Die über deiner Zukunft, Wehe! kreischt,
> Den gier'gen Geier, der dich lang zerfleischt
> Bannt ein gottselig Kind ...
>
> (W I 362 [1817])

> Daß das heil'ge hohe Lied
> Mir konnt Sinnentaumel scheinen,
> Muß, der durch den Spiegel sieht,
> Himmeltrunken ich beweinen.
>
> (W I 453 [1821–1822])

> Du nötigst mich, ich soll nur schreiben;
> Was weiß ich denn, das nicht ein jeder weiß,
> Nicht jeder sucht von Stirn und Blatt zu reiben?
> Denn alles, was wir wissen macht uns heiß.[103]
>
> (W I 492 [1827])

Whereas some of the *ei* concepts in this representative sampling indicate activities or aspects of life that are distasteful to mankind in general (kreischen, zerfleischen, beweinen), others apply to situations that were disturbing to the author in particular (Weib, deinen feilen geilen Leib, scheinen, schreiben, weiß [wissen]). Usually, however, Brentano persisted in his habit of mitigating the harshness of these events or experiences by including an *a* component in the proximity of the *ei* tone (as noted in his "Symphonie"). The *a* complement can be found in the very same word or it may occur within the surrounding context. In either case, it serves as the force which counteracts—and in most cases, counterbalances—the implications of the *ei* complex on the acoustical level. Note, for instance, the following key concepts:

Einsamkeit. This term is used to imply not only existential isolation (W I 389), but also—with regard to Beethoven—necessary crea-

---

[103] "No singer sent me greetings in the grove; / Also from the valley no shepherd's flute sounds."

"You bold and lewd hag; / ... / A curse upon your prostituted lascivious body."

"O heart, be still! Avenging sibyl, / Who shrieks 'Woe!' over your future, / The greedy vulture which has mangled you so long / Is banished by a godly child."

"Looking through the mirror, enchanted with heaven / I must bewail the fact / That the sacred, sublime song / Could appear to me as sensual frenzy."

"You impose upon me that I just write; / What do I really know, that not every one knows, / Every one seeks to wipe from his brow or his page? / For everything we know makes us agitated."

tive seclusion (W I 308). (Compare also the use of "allein" in this sense.)

Baßgeige. Even though this instrument unceremoniously announced life's bitter disappointments ("all the prophetic sounds of experience in the hollow bass viol" [F 311]), it also served as the sobering voice of truth which, as Brentano grudgingly admitted to Luise Hensel in 1816, interrupted the surface melody of the words he spoke: "The conversation then cheerily begins to socialize on its own while my soul lies in fear, grief and longing, and only now and then, while cutting through the impetuous and lilting melody, the bass viol of contemplation organizes and classifies" (S II 183).

Phantasei. On the one hand, "Phantasei" represents the domain of art and imagination in which one might seek refuge from personal sorrow; but this solution remained, in the final analysis, a surrogate for true existence and consequently, to use a modern term, an inauthentic approach to the problem (W I 587).

Heiland and *Weihnacht*. Whereas Christ's birth promised deliverance from the burden of original sin ("In Heilands Heilhand Heil"— "In salvation from the Savior's saving hand" [W I 412]), this salvation also necessitated His suffering and death on the Cross.

Examples of verses in which the *a-ei* complex is extended over a larger span may also be cited:

> Um Sing und um Sang
> Schweifen die Pfeifen, und greifen
> Ans Herz,
> Mit Freud und mit Schmerz.
> (W II 396 [1801])

> Und wenn ich glühend weinte,
> Verzweiflung mich zu singen zwang
> (W I 385 [1817])

> Weh' aus meiner Harfe Saiten

> Von dem weiten Babylon
> Klang wie Leiden, Meiden, Scheiden,
> Mir durch's Herz ein Klageton.
> (GS I 50 [1838])

The *a-ei* tonality and its concomitant symbolism may very well have provided the basis for the names which Brentano gave to several of his major fairy tale figures: Ameleya, Gackeleia, and Amey. In the first two, the sequence of the tonal components would correspond to the triadic course of the story itself: $a=$ initial happiness; $ei=$ forfeiture of joy; $a=$ happiness regained. For instance, the good fortune enjoyed by both Ameleya (rescued by and promised to Radlauf) and Gackeleia (childhood innocence in a happy household) is lost, either because of personal guilt (in the latter's addiction to dolls) or because of the interference of evil forces in the life of the former. As Ameleya descends into the waters of the *Rhein* river with the other children of *Mainz* to the frenzied tones of the "Pfeife," for instance, their desperate plea for mercy contains a preponderance of *ei* sounds counterbalanced by an equal number of *a*'s (unknown to them, they will ultimately dwell in safety under the waters of "V*a*ter Rh*ei*n"):

> Die Pfeife bläst du gar zu mild,
> Die Pfeife bläst du gar zu wild;
> Die Erde weicht, das Wasser schwillt
> Und uns mit Nacht die Augen füllt,
> Ach Pfeife! Pfeife! Pfeife!
>
> (W III 47)

Finally, the third stage in their respective fates—Ameleya's union with Radlauf and Gackeleia's atonement for her sin—and the generally happy resolution of all difficulties could be correlated with the last tonal element in each of their names: the *a*. When Gackeleia twists Solomon's ring at the close of the "Märchen" and recites those accompanying verses which announce one of Brentano's most important themes, we again find that a balance is struck between the two key tonalities:

> Laß die Engel bei uns wachen,
> Daß wir wie die Kinder lachen,
> Daß wir wie die Kinder weinen,
> Laß uns alles sein, nichts scheinen.
> Mache uns zu Kindern alle,
> Jedes sei nach seiner Art,
> Wie's dem lieben Gott gefalle,
> Einsam oder treu gepaart.[104]
>
> (W III 822)

---

[104] "Let the angels stand guard with us, / That we might laugh like children, / That we might weep like children, / Let us be everything, appear to be nothing. / Let each be in accordance with his nature, / As it pleases God above, / Alone or faithfully paired."

The sequel to the *Gockelmärchen, Die Blätter aus dem Tagebuch der Ahnfrau* (which actually traces the origins of the Gockel line), represents what in many respects is the culmination of the *a-ei* tone complex. First of all, the name of the protagonist, Amey, is significant since it does not, in contrast to Ameleya or Gackeleia, contain within its tonal orbit that neat triadic resolution (*a-ei-a*) but rather suggests the coexistence of two forces between which man is and remains suspended. The ancestress, then, does not follow the same line of development that characterized the other two figures, and consequently we do not have in the *Tagebuch* a fairy tale resolution but rather one more in keeping with the realities of life as Brentano came to understand them and with the Orphean situation as he had always known it.

The major musical instrument in the *Tagebuch*—the "Schalmei"— should also be regarded as an integral part of Amey's world. It is the blaring ("schreien") of the shawm in the darkness of the night which reminds Amey how basically alone and lonely she is ("einsam," "allein"). When, at one point in the narrative, the "Schalmeienklang" together with the "Pfeifen" and torchlights ("Fackeln") combine to exert a particularly unnerving effect on her, Amey's companion, Klareta, intones verses telling of the perennial danger to the dream castles that man erects somewhere between yesterday and tomorrow—visions of happiness, which are dispelled by the harsh sights and sounds of "naked" truth ("Kömmt dann Wahrheit mutternackt gelaufen" [W III 866]):[105]

> Horch! die Fackel lacht, horch! Schmerz-Schalmeien
> Der erwachten Nacht ins Herz all schreien;
> Weh, ohn Opfer gehn die süßen Wunder,
> Gehn die armen Herzen einsam unter![106]
>
> (W III 867)

Even though the "Schmerz-Schalmeien" also penetrate to the core of Amey's being and echo in her innermost soul ("Herz all schreien"), she insists on hearing them: "Be quiet, that I might hear the shawms; indeed, tomorrow is too late; this fact they seem to bemoan, and therefore overpower me" (W III 867). Her plea is expressed in terms of three *ei* concepts that were critical in Brentano's life because of their

---

[105] "If truth then comes running along stark naked."
[106] "Hark! the torch is laughing, hark! Pain-shawms / Of the awakened night all scream at the heart. / Woe, without sacrifice the sweet miracles, / And the poor hearts perish alone!"

dual potential: "schweigen" (which, as an alternative to "schreiben,"
was not always amenable to the poet); "scheinen" (the distinction
between true essence—Sein—and surface appearance proved to be a
thorn in Brentano's side); "hinreißen" (this experience entailed both
positive effects—the power to transcend the bonds of routine existence
—and negative side effects—complete loss of control). Amey becomes
acquainted with the latter condition vicariously when she listens to
Klareta singing "the song of the Weaver Jürgo with its confused melody
into the night" (W III 867). This song tells of the loss of spiritual
equilibrium:

> Die Fackeln und Schalmeien,
> Sie brennen, reißen, schreien
> Mir tief durch Mark und Bein.
>
> . . . .
>
> Das Seelchen springet trunken
> Von Tönen, Farben, Funken
> Zur roten Lust hinein.
> Wenn Tön und Farben starben,
> Kömmt Nacht und bittres Darben,
> Arm, bloß, allein; allein;[107]
>
> (W III 868)

The perspective of the Weaver Jürgo has become so distorted because
of his mental breakdown that even the tonality in which his words are
set reverses the standard pattern. Darkness ("Farben starben") and
death ("Darben") converge in the night and nightmare of Jürgo's mind,
a jumbled universe in which man stands exposed and alone. But yet
no man—not even the insane Jürgo—is an island; the "continent" of
which he forms a part is represented by the tonal cosmos in which
he communicates his tragic vision. Amey subsequently shares a similar
moment of ominous portent when she enters the devastated Gock-
elsruh and hears "das Wehgeschrei der Todesmahnerinnen, der Eulen,
und die wildentbrannten Weisen der Waldvögelein, über deren Brut
die Geier drohend kreisten"—"the cries of lamentation from the ad-
monishers of death, the owls, and the passionately enkindled melodies
of the forest birds, above whose brood vultures circled threateningly"
(W III 915). The "wildentbrannten Weisen" of the birds, at one time

---

[107] "The torches and the shawms / Are burning, ripping, shrieking / Deeply
through my very marrow and bone. / ... / Little Soul leaps intoxicated / By
tones, colors, sparks, / Into ardent desire. / When tones and colors died, / Night
and bitter want then come, / Poor, naked, alone; alone!"

the deceptive harbinger of love (1801) and later (1812) the meta-morphosed "wildentbrannten Psalmen" performed in response to angelic choirs in the temple of nature (whereby, from the standpoint of sound symbolism, the painful *ei* element has been replaced by the propitious *a*), are now threatened by signs (and sounds) of evil portent: the "Wehgeschrei" of the predators ("Geier") circling menacingly overhead ("kreisen"). But even though the world of the nightingale ("Nachtigall") cedes precedence to that of the "Geier," there are even here sufficient positive overtones to counteract the negative tonality ("-mahnerinnen," "-entbrannt," "Wald-") and restore the feeling of equilibrium.

Neither unmitigated happiness (*a*), nor unrelenting sadness (*ei*)—and certainly not Jürgo's inversion of the two—is meant to be the lot of man during his tenure on earth, but rather a complex reciprocity of both. This condition is embodied in the fate of the mysterious "Büblein" (young lad) at the conclusion of the *Gockel* tale. After all the adults have been miraculously transformed into children, only the status of the "Büblein" remains in doubt:

> "Amey," sprach die [Vrenli], "dicht am Grüblein
> Schläft es [das Büblein], o daß Gott sein walte!
> Seine Sache hats vollbracht,
> Und daß, wenn der Tag erwacht,
> In der Ernte es nicht darbe,
> Leg ihm milde in den Arm
> Eine kleine feine Garbe,
> Hart liegts jetzt, daß Gott erbarm!"[108]
>
> (W III 830)

Such a wish (with its heavy concentration of *a* sounds) represents the quest for a complete security and is "unrealistic" in terms of human experience. Even though the "Büblein" has satisfactorily fulfilled the condition of atonement ("Sache . . . vollbracht"), he knows there is no absolute assurance of deliverance ("nicht darbe"); his own words affirm that basic human condition to which man remains bound from the darkness of finite existence ("Nacht") to the dawn of eternity ("Tag erwacht"):

[108] " 'Amey,' she [Vrenli] said, 'close by the ditch / He sleeps, oh, may God preserve him! / He has finished his task, / And so that he might not be wanting on the day of harvest, / Lay gently into his arm / A small sheaf, / He now lies on hard ground, may God have mercy!' "

Morgentau rührt mir die Wange
Weckend, bald zerrinnt der Wahn;
Und der erste Hahnenschrei,
Wenn die Kinder auferstehen,
Bricht den lieben Traum entzwei;

. . . .

Dann wird alles vorgelesen
Und wird das, was er gewesen,
Tretend aus dem trüben Schein
Auch in vollem Lichte sein;
Ja dann ist selbst auf ein Härchen
Dieses Märchen mehr kein Märchen;
Und bis so das Märchen aus,
Sing ich in die Nacht hinaus:
"O Stern und Blume, Geist und Kleid,
Lieb, Leid und Zeit und Ewigkeit!"[109]

(W III 831)

Certainly the awakening of the "Büblein" from the deceptive dream of life is less abrupt than the shock caused by the "Schalmeien" earlier, and his attitude toward this experience is more conciliatory. Instead of lamenting how "die armen Herzen [gehn] einsam unter," the "Büblein" celebrates his threshold condition in song: to sing affirmatively about an existence between matter and spirit ("Geist und Kleid"), between the finite and the eternal ("Zeit und Ewigkeit") in awareness of the fact that the night in which he now finds himself ("Nacht") forms a necessary transition to the dawn ("Tag erwacht") which is to come.

IMAGINATION AND IMAGERY:
THE EVOCATIVE POWER OF MUSIC AND POETRY

The final phase of the discussion concerning the musicality of Brentano's lyric verse represents both the summation and consummation of the techniques elaborated up to this point. The problem to be broached here is: Can the poet through the verbal medium stir the

[109] "Morning dew touches my cheek / Awakening me, soon the madness will pass away; / And the first crowing of the cock, / When the children are resurrected, / Breaks the lovely dream in two; / ... / Then everything will be read aloud / And it will be what it once was, / Emerging then from the gloomy sheen. / It will be in full radiance; / Then indeed even this fairy tale will be, / In its minutest detail no fairy tale any longer; / And until the fairy tale thus is over, / I sing out into the night: 'O star and blossom,' ..."

imagination and emotions of his audience in a manner comparable to that of the composer with his "pure," nonrepresentational tones? The clearest formulation of this hypothesis was given by Schiller when he distinguished between what he termed plastic and musical poetry:

> I say *musical* to recall here the dual relationship of poetry with music and plastic art. According as poetry either imitates a given *object* as the plastic arts do, or whether, like music, simply produces a given *state of mind*, without requiring a given object for the purpose, it can be called plastic or musical. The latter expression, therefore, does not refer exclusively to whatever is music in poetry actually and in relation to its material, but rather in general to all those effects which it is able to produce without subordinating the imagination to a given object; and in this sense I call Klopstock a musical poet above all.[110]

Two important and interrelated criteria are enumerated here by Schiller for musical poetry: it produces a "state of mind" in the listener (or reader), and it activates his imagination without reference to a specific object from the phenomenal world. Brentano expresses a similar thought when writing to Arnim in 1803 concerning the nature of the latter's correspondence: "I really do not know how one should answer such letters, but I do believe one must take them as a complete piece of music which expresses the condition of the other person and which then also resounds itself" (S I 170). The manner in which lyric poetry might produce a particular "state of mind" (or reproduce the "condition of the other person") without enlisting the aid of specific objects or concepts from the empirical sphere is touched upon by Schiller in the essay "Über Matthisons Gedichte":

> To be sure, feelings are capable of no representation *as to their content*; but *as to their form*, they are indeed capable of it, and there actually exists a generally popular and effective art that has no other object than precisely this form of feelings. This art is music. . . . Actually, we also view each pictorial and poetic composition as a type of musical work and, to a degree, make them subject to the same laws. . . . In every poem we separate thinking from feeling, the musical attitude from the logical one; in short, we demand that every poetic composition, besides what its content expresses, be at the same time the imitation and expression of feelings and that it affect us as does music. . . .

[110] From the essay "Über naive und sentimentalische Dichtung" as translated by Julias Elias in *Friedrich von Schiller: Naive and Sentimental Poetry and On the Sublime* (New York: Frederick Ungar, 1966), p. 133.

> Now the full effect of music . . . consists of accompanying and sym-
> bolizing the inner motions of the spirit through analogical external
> ones.[111]

Of course, the crux of the matter remains obscure: how does poetry render the "form of feelings" rather than their content? The response to this question has perplexed poets and critics alike; one possible approach to the problem was offered in the twentieth century by Erich Jenisch:

> The greater the emotional content of a word, the more its objective con-
> tent dissolves in feeling, the more intimately that word is related to the
> tone as the expression of feeling per se. The spirit of music is at work
> in literature when the emotional content of language far outweighs
> its conceptual significance. Then poetry approaches music, for now the
> objective validity of the image is assimilated in feeling to such a degree
> that it can scarcely be considered objective any longer.[112]

Yet if musicalization is achieved by diminishing the "objective content" of words in favor of their "emotional" value, the question remains: How is this process of reduction or minimization of objectivity to be accomplished? Some scholars feel that for an acoustically dominated poet of Brentano's caliber, this process involves the unique manipulation of verbal sounds: "Brentano is able to suggest feelings through a select sequence of sounds. In the inwardness of the tone, language and that which language expresses become one. . . . The sound coloration of the tone becomes the bearer of expression, and it alone is able to reproduce the attitude of mind."[113] Others maintain that the "emotional" value of the verbal elements in a poetic utterance is intensified to the extent that the function of these words to designate actual conditions or phenomena in the external world decreases. For instance, Günther Müller states in connection with the "Lied" genre:

> The relationship of the experience to the word here is similar to the re-
> lationship of the tone in Romantic music. A logically conceptual mid-
> dle ground has been eliminated, the objective *meaning* of the word re-
> duced to the lowest degree, and at the same time the emotional or mood

[111] Schiller, *Werke*, XXII, 271–272.
[112] Erich Jenisch, *Die Entfaltung des Subjektivismus: Von der Aufklärung zur Romantik* (Königsberg: Gräfe and Unzer, 1929), pp. 16–17.
[113] Hans Rupprich, *Brentano, Luise Hensel und Ludwig Gerlach* (Vienna, 1927) pp. 12–13.

value of the word, its tonal, rhythmical and indeed cognitive value of expression in the sense of a direct embodiment of the spiritual impulse, has been developed to the fullest.[114]

Emil Staiger in *Grundbegriffe der Poetik* traces, as was indicated earlier, the essence of pure lyricism to what he calls "music, fluidity, interpenetration" whereby inner and outer worlds coalesce and are—if only for a fleeting moment—undifferentiated. In his *Wandlungen des lyrischen Bildes*, Walter Killy detects in Brentano the ability to create images that have a minimal mimetic aim and that recede markedly from verbal portrayals aimed at a precise depiction of the world of concrete phenomena.[115] In spite of the claims for a musicality deriving from the fact that poetry becomes more musical to the degree that the language and the concepts behind it recede from those customarily employed to denote aspects of external reality, one cannot maintain that such linguistic utterances ever reach the "zero point" of correspondence, the nonmimetic and pure tonal center at which music begins its unique form of communication. Again it is Wilhelm Schneider who makes an important qualification:

> In contrast to music, language, insofar as it deals in words which express something concrete, cannot avoid evoking tangible perceptions. . . . Tangible perceptions are evoked even by musical style; but they are weak and do not fuse into vivid, inner conceptions; they are not there for their own sake, but because of their effect on our feelings. They arouse moods and do not intend to do anything else, and to this extent they resemble the expressive modes of music, which are tones.[116]

The Brentano studies of Hans Magnus Enzensberger and, more recently, of Wolfgang Frühwald make possible an attempt at a more satisfactory resolution of the problem of poetic imagery and musical imagination. In essence, the concept of "musicalization" could be brought into alignment with the central discoveries of these respective critics: "Entstellung" (distorting) and "Verschlüsselung" (encoding).[117]

---

[114] *Geschichte des deutschen Liedes* (1925; reprinted, Munich: Wissenschaftliche Buchgesellschaft, 1959), p. 291.

[115] In *Wandlungen des lyrischen Bildes*, p. 55, Killy speaks of "imagelets" ("Bildchen") and maintains that "the sensuous side of language changed into music dominates completely."

[116] Schneider, *Ausdruckswerte*, p. 190.

[117] On the process of "Entstellung" Enzensberger states that "words lose their conventional clarity. This phenomenon signifies a turning away from the pre-formed and established language to previously unused possibilities of the

Although neither of these interpreters employs his technique to a probe of a specifically musical quality of Brentano's poetry, their designations could be applied in this manner. The premise on which they build their arguments is that, in certain literary works, the poet creates, through the medium of the spoken word alone, a self-contained, hermetically sealed universe.[118] For instance, in his study *Brentanos Poetik*, Enzensberger examines the extent to which words are torn from their traditional environment and usage in the process of "Entstellung," or distortion, so that they may serve as "Chiffren," or ciphers, with which the artist constructs a private cosmos existing apart from—and yet constituting a part of—the world of everyday reality. Whereas Paul Böckmann had once spoken of an "interiorized imagery" with reference to Brentano's appropriation of images from the realm of nature, Enzensberger alludes to "an inner world, whose boundaries to the outer world are the boundaries of the poem."[119] The laws governing this

---

word. This procedure is called 'distortion' (Entstellung), because it tears the word from its accustomed context in order to make it poetically amenable" (*Brentanos Poetik*, p. 28).

In "Das verlorene Paradies" Frühwald employs the term "Verschlüsselung" (pp. 116 ff.) together with the concepts of "verrätselte Konfession" (obscure confession [p. 114]), "Chiffrierung" (enciphering [p. 125]) and "das uneigentliche Sprechen" (nonliteral speech [p. 125]) to characterize the unique idiom devised by the poet to simultaneously conceal and convey his innermost thoughts. In the Postscript to his edition of Brentano's correspondence with Emilie Linder, Frühwald augments his terminology with "Schmerz-Stenogramm" or "Stenogram seines Innersten" (shorthand for pain / shorthand of his innermost being [p. 314]) and, finally, in his Brentano study for *Deutsche Dichter der Romantik*, he adds "Hieroglyphensprache" (hieroglyphic language [p. 293]) and "Sehnsuchtsstenogramm" (shorthand of yearning [p. 300]).

[118] The ideas which Enzensberger and Frühwald were later to develop with reference to Brentano had been anticipated on a very general level by other critics. For instance, the *Reallexikon* under the heading "Musik und Literatur," contains the following statement, p. 162: "The final goal sought consists of effects which in spite of links to words, seek to be 'absolute,' that is, independent of the normal communicative character of language and its relation to reality and which come about through free poetic association and are to become similar to the sister art of music not only thematically, but also in their deeper meaning." Ronald Peacock, in a brilliant essay, "Probleme des Musikalischen in der Sprache," *Weltliteratur: Festgabe für Fritz Strich zum 70. Geburtstag*, ed. Walter Henzen, et al. (Bern: Francke, 1952), pp. 92–93, writes: "The language of music is a secret one, because it has its own vocabulary and its own syntax which cannot be translated into our ordinary language and which, while bypassing conceptual thinking, addresses itself directly to our imagination. When a poem relies to an extreme degree on metaphorical and symbolical associations and, in this manner, replaces the ordinary use of language with one which is formalized, it affects our being in the same, mysterious fashion as music does. One should add that rhythm, the sounds of language also play a role in this, but in comparison with the earlier examples, this is a subordinate role."

[119] Enzensberger, p. 12.

interiorized universe are autonomous (as in music) and divorced from the principles of logical causality, which hold sway in the empirical sphere:

> The laws of the inner world, ... their indifference to the realm of the concrete and the spacio-temporal, their inclination toward the paradoxical, toward identification [of subject and object], toward multiplicity of meaning, and their hermetic nature are, at the same time, poetic principles of the lyric. Just as the life of the heart is not comparable to all conventions of outer reality, so the language of this lyric poem is not to be compared with that of any prescribed and pre-formed idiom.[120]

If the poet were to succeed in giving expression to the "life of the heart" by means of a mode of articulation that was removed from "all conventions of outer reality," then he would, in essence, attain that condition of musical poetry postulated by Schiller in 1795, a type of lyricism that communicates "a given *state of mind*, without requiring a given object for the purpose." Just as the composer excites the imaginative faculties of the listener by means of a musical texture that has no direct correlation with the phenomenal world but which is sui generis and divorced from mimesis, so the poet, by creating a verbal cosmos whose imagery is as independent of any ties with the empirical sphere as possible, might approximate, if not duplicate, the success of the former. The lines that Brentano once directed to Beethoven could stand as both a tribute to that composer and a word of encouragement to the literary artist who would attempt similar ends in his own medium: "... dem Gott gleich, / Selbst sich nur wissend und dichtend / Schafft er die Welt, die er selbst ist" (W I 309).[121]

With regard to Brentano's own poetry, three stages in the evolution of a mode of lyric expression which might rival music in the evocation of a "state of mind ... without subordinating the imagination to a given object" could be postulated. Whereas in his early poetry the ideal is sketched hypothetically (in such poems as "Symphonie" and "Als hohe in sich selbst verwandte Mächte"), in the second or middle stage it is realized in theory but not in practice ("Schwanenlied" and "Nachklänge Beethovenscher Musik"), while in the third it is achieved

---

[120] Enzensberger, pp. 33–34.
[121] "... like God, / Knowing and composing only himself / He creates the world which he himself is."

in practice but denied in theory ("Wenn der lahme Weber träumt" and "Traum der Wüste").

The preliminary step on the artist's journey to a hermetically sealed, inner world of the creative subject is taken in "Symphonie" where one reads: "But in the inner life / The maestro fetters their being." The route leading to an "inner life" is then further delineated by the *Godwi* poem, "Als hohe, in sich selbst verwandte Mächte." The elements constituting this magical no-man's-land (or, perhaps, every-man's-land) stand in close correlation (internally) with each other, but do not necessarily have ties with the universe outside themselves. Nevertheless, the keys to unlock this secret chamber are ubiquitous, provided that we are able to recognize them: "The tones take you there . . . "; "The colors spread out their nets and beckon." The goal to which all these diverse channels are directed in this early period (1797–1803) is felt to lie close at hand: "Let poetry arise in my soul."

Two poems from the middle years of Brentano's career (1803–1817) take the reader into the innermost worlds of contrasting "singers": the "Dichterin Schwanenlied" and the composer Beethoven. Whereas the former had been content during its entire lifetime to listen to the music of other avian performers as a nonparticipant ("Birds . . . / Which sang such wildly fervent psalms"), and then, just prior to its death, to heed a form of inspirational music from above ("And I hear the songs of angels once again"), it is only when the swan is caught in the throes of death that there emanates from the depths of its soul that single song representing the culmination point of its existence: "The sum of life sings from my heart." On the other hand, it is incumbent upon the composer-singer Beethoven to create a personalized tonal universe that is forever accessible to all mankind. The first three poems of the five which make up the "Nachklänge" cycle delineate the origins of that private and interiorized tonal cosmos which inspires Beethoven:

> Einsamkeit, du Geisterbronnen,
> Mutter aller heil'gen Quellen,
> Zauberspiegel innrer Sonnen,
> Die berauschet überschwellen,
> Seit ich durft' in deine Wonnen
> Das betrübte Leben stellen,
> Seit du ganz mich überronnen
> Mit den dunklen Wunderwellen,

Hab' zu tönen ich begonnen,
Und nun klingen all die hellen
Sternenchöre meiner Seele,
Deren Takt ein Gott mir zähle,
Alle Sonnen meines Herzens,
Die Planeten meiner Lust,
Die Kometen meines Schmerzens,
Klingen hoch in meiner Brust.[122]

(W I 308–309)

The "loneliness" referred to here subsumes the painful alienation
which the composer experienced in his dealings with society as well as
the self-imposed isolation to which every artist withdraws in order to
probe to the source of creativity, the "Seele" (which, as was indicated
earlier, was the homeland of "Poesie"). Since any and all normal channels of communication would be inadequate in conveying an impression of this unique moment of introspection, the poet appropriates a
familiar *topos* from the literary repertoire (the music of the spheres)
and develops it in a highly unconventional fashion: "inner suns,"
"star choruses of my soul," "suns of my heart," "planets . . . comets . . .
Resound loftily in my breast." This storehouse of inspiration
("Schätze[ ] meines Innern" [W I 309]),[123] however, before which
even the singer—aware of its divine origin—humbles himself, does
not, as yet, extend beyond the confines of the composer's innermost
being.

The second poem of the series takes the reader a step further on
the odyssey leading from the point of conception to the moment of
articulation: "Klänge, die die alte Nacht ersonnen / Tönest du, den
jüngsten Tag zu grüßen" (W I 309).[124] In the third poem we set foot
on that promised land to which—as the previous poem had intimated—
many are summoned, but few are chosen for entry.[125] Therefore, those
who gain access to this aesthetic paradise do so by circumventing the

---

[122] "Solitude, you source of spirits, / Mother of all sacred fountains, / Magic
mirror of inner suns, / Which well over with intoxication, / Since I have been
permitted to place / My gloomy life in your glories, / Since you have inundated
me completely / With your dark waves of wonder, / I have begun to emit tones,
/ And now all the bright / Astral choirs of my soul / Whose rhythm may be set
for me by a God, / All suns of my heart, / The planets of my desire, / The comets
of my pain, / Resound sublimely in my breast."
[123] "Treasures of my inner self."
[124] "Tones, which the past night conceived / You play to greet the new day."
[125] One might mention at this point that the protagonist of E. T. A. Hoffmann's tale *Ritter Gluck* was privileged to have access to the "realm of dreams."

normal avenues of accessibility: "Selig, wer ohne Sinne / Schwebt, wie ein Geist auf dem Wasser" . . . (W I 309).[126] Since the ordinary sense perceptions are of little avail ("ohne Sinne") the "sym-syndrome," which had been so prominent in "Als hohe, in sich selbst verwandte Mächte," is no longer called into play. However, the self-contained universe represented by Beethoven's music is immediately subjected to misinterpretation by petty minds, to distortion by those who lack his all-encompassing perspective and thus hunt for what seem—because of their shortsighted perspective—flaws and weaknesses:

> Nein ohne Sinne, dem Gott gleich,
> Selbst sich nur wissend und dichtend
> Schafft er die Welt, die er selbst ist,
> Und es sündigt der Mensch drauf,
> Und es war nicht sein Wille!
> Aber geteilt ist alles.
> Keinem ward alles, denn jedes
> Hat einen Herrn, nur der Herr nicht;[127]
>
>   (W I 309–310)

The sanctity of the originally pure conception from the singer's inner world is not contaminated by the transgressions of the mob, however. In the final analysis, the composer towers above any such aberrations of the ultimate artistic truth just as the Creator of all mankind remains untouched by mortal sinfulness: "Einsam ist er [der Herr] und dient nicht, / So auch der Sänger!" (W I 310).[128]

The repetition of the central concept of "Einsamkeit" at the conclusion of this poem is doubly significant. On the one hand, it recapitulates the opening theme of the cycle ("Einsamkeit") while, on the other, it simultaneously seals off poetically that hermetic world which must remain free of the desecration befalling the work of art (and which actually did befall the composition that provided the impetus for Brentano's lyric cycle: "Die Schlacht bei Vittoria").[129] Ironically, one might point out that Beethoven himself "sinned" against the canons of absolute music, in the "programmatic" format of the work which Brentano lauds so highly. And indirectly Brentano repeats this blunder in his

[126] "Blessed is he who, senseless / Hovers, like a spirit, over the waters."
[127] "Not with recourse to the senses, but like a god, / Knowing and composing only himself / He creates the world, which he himself is. / And man sins upon it, / And it was not his will! / But everything is divided. / To no one was granted everything, for each one / Has a lord, only not the Lord."
[128] "He is alone and does not serve, / So, too, the singer!"
[129] Fetzer, "Clemens Brentano on Music and Musicians," pp. 224–226.

"Nachklänge" insofar as the remaining poems of the cycle constitute a break in both thematic continuity and aesthetic quality. Even though one might regard Brentano's subsequent panegyric to England—the "Eiland, vom Meere gegürtet" (W I 310), the virgin territory untouched by the tides of the "Sündflut,"[130] and the birthplace of the Duke of Wellington whose name lingers on "in Tones Welle" (W I 311)[131]— as a geographic counterpart to the idealized realm of creative isolation by the composer, the analogy is not very fortuitous. The closing verses of the final poem reveal how Brentano infringed upon precepts of genuine lyric musicality by falling prey to a cumbersome and noisy "Klangspiel" in order to link the heroic composer with the conqueror of Napoleon:

> Er spannt dir das Roß aus dem Wagen,
> Und zieht dich mit Wunderakkorden
> Durch ewig tönende Pforten.
> Triumph, auf Klängen getragen!
> Wellington, Viktoria!
> Beethoven, Gloria![132]

(W I 311)

Whereas at least the first three poems of the "Nachklänge" cycle succeeded in presenting an account of the exclusive sphere to which the supreme creative artist must ascend in order to produce great music (by implication, the "Sänger" alluded to at the close includes the singer-poet as well), the final two poems disrupt the symmetry by interjecting banal elements into what was otherwise a tight-knit artistic universe. This same form of destruction or dissolution of the illusion also comes to the fore in two lyrics of the later years (1817–1842) in which the poet succeeds momentarily in creating a verbal idiom that gives expression to a "state of mind" by emancipating words from their traditional context. This process of "Entstellung" (and "Verschlüsselung," to a

---

[130] "Island, girded by the sea;" "the Flood."
[131] "In the tonal waves." For a recent interpretation of the cycle which, aside from illustrating Brentano's "genius of adaptiveness" and his ability to assimilate sources into his own writings (the fourth poem in the group with its praise of England is traced to Shakespeare's *Richard II*), examines passages such as this from the standpoint of "nomen est omen," see Gerhard Friesen, "Clemens Brentano's 'Nachklänge Beethovenscher Musik'" in *Traditions and Transitions: Studies in Honor of Harold Jantz*, ed. Liselotte E. Kurth, William H. McClain, and Holger Homan (Munich: Delp'sche Verlagsbuchhandlung, 1972), pp. 194–209.
[132] "He unhitches the steed from your chariot, / And takes you with wondrous chords / Through eternally resounding portals. / Triumph, borne on tones! / Wellington, Victoria! / Beethoven, Gloria!"

lesser extent) results in a mode of poetic expression which is more akin to musicality than that of the other lyrics discussed thus far.

The poems from Brentano's last years selected to illustrate both the construction and the destruction of a hermetically sealed "inner world" are "Wenn der lahme Weber träumt" and "Traum der Wüste." It is significant that both deal with dreams and dreaming, for when one is asleep, one is actually "removed" from the sphere of everyday reality and transported to a domain of existence divorced from the commonplace. In addition, the first poem is sung by the mentally deranged Klareta; a person suffering such a psychic breakdown also lives in a "private" realm that has minimal ties with reality and rational causality. The word "träumen" runs (explicitly or implicitly) through the incantory lines recited by Klareta and helps to conjure up the surrealistic universe in which the encumbrances of life are invalidated. The first ten verses of the eighteen-line poem enumerate the elements that form the dream world; the progression (the numbering and the tripartite division are mine) is from the rationally conceivable (1) to the logically more remote, "Entstellung" (2), and finally to the esoteric, "Chiffren" (3):

> (1) Wenn der lahme Weber träumt, er webe,
> Träumt die kranke Lerche auch, sie schwebe,
> Träumt die stumme Nachtigall, sie singe,
> Daß das Herz des Widerhalls zerspringe,
>
> (2) Träumt das blinde Huhn, es zähl' die Kerne,
> Und der drei je zählte kaum, die Sterne,
> Träumt das starre Erz, gar linde tau' es,
> Und das Eisenherz, ein Kind vertrau' es,
>
> (3) Träumt die taube Nüchternheit, sie lausche,
> Wie der Traube Schüchternheit berausche;[133]
>
> (W I 611)

The movement away from a generalized to a personalized comprehensibility and communicability begins in section two with the "Entstell-

---

[133] (1) "When the lame weaver dreams, that he might be weaving, / The sickly lark also dreams, she might be soaring, / The silent nightingale dreams, she might be singing, / So that the heart would burst from the echo, (2) The blind hen dreams it might be counting the kernels, / And he who never could count to three, the stars, / The rigid metal dreams, it might gently melt, / And the heart of iron dreams that a child might trust it, (3) Deaf sobriety dreams it might be listening / How the timidity of the grape intoxicates."

ung" of the idioms "Ein blindes Huhn findet auch einmal ein Korn," "weißt du, wieviel Sternlein stehen," and "er kann nicht bis drei zählen."[134] This tendency is then further developed by the next two verses consisting of images that have a very personal application to the poet's relationship to Emilie Linder and belong to a kind of private mythology which he advocated ("Verschlüsselung") in order to simultaneously reveal and conceal his personal dilemma. The extensive use of multiple rhyme in the phrases "das starre Erz, gar linde tau' es" and "das Eisenherz, ein Kind vertrau' es" suggests some esoteric ties or identity between the two. The adverb "linde" is, as are many other of Brentano's derivatives from the name Linder, a fairly transparent concept; its tonal counterpart "Kind" is somewhat more elusive, although it was not an uncommon practice for Brentano to refer to himself or the Swiss paintress by this term. Whereas the concept of "das starre Erz" that melts in the realm of reverie is an image that can be readily understood, its tonal and conceptual equivalent—the neologism "Eisenherz," which, under such ideal conditions, "even a child could trust"—prepares the way for those lines that constitute the fulcrum or pivotal section of the poem, the point at which the language becomes most esoteric, most magical, and—because it forms the climax of the "impossible dream"—the most elusive in terms of rational comprehensibility. In the phrases "die taube Nüchternheit, sie lausche" and "Wie der Traube Schüchternheit berausche," the "heart" of the hermetically sealed world of introversion is reached; here words function as ciphers or sounds devoid of logical ties to the rational world. The fact that they nevertheless "communicate" something to the reader— an emotion or a "state of mind"—without the aid of objects or even objective correlatives from "real" life or "real" language, brings them into close proximity to the unique and inimitable idiom in which music always speaks to the listener.

At this midway point in the poem, therefore, the apex of lyrical musicality has been attained. But like so many of the other elements of "musicality," such a condition cannot be maintained or sustained for any length of time. The approach to the goal is—as Orpheus discovered—intimately bound with its loss. Consequently, Brentano's poem deals not only with the "journey of the artist into the interior,"[135]

---

[134] Enzensberger, pp. 46 ff.
[135] Erich Heller, *The Artist's Journey into the Interior* (New York: Random House, 1965).

but also with his banishment from this exclusive domain. The verses following this culminating point report the intrusion of harsh reality into the dream world:

> Kömmt dann Wahrheit mutternackt gelaufen,
> Führt der hellen Töne Glanzgefunkel
> Und der grellen Lichter Tanz durchs Dunkel,
> Rennt den Traum sie schmerzlich übern Haufen,
> Horch! die Fackel lacht, horch! Schmerz-Schalmeien
> Der erwachten Nacht ins Herz all schreien;
> Weh, ohn' Opfer gehn die süßen Wunder,
> Gehn die armen Herzen einsam unter![136]
>
> (W I 611)

Noteworthy, however, is the fact that his rude awakening is presented by means of the same devices used previously to evoke the unique inner world of the heart. There is, first of all, distortion ("Entstellung") of a standard cliché or proverb ("die nackte Wahrheit," "über den Haufen werfen") which "regenerates" the language insofar as it imparts a new dimension of meaning to a time-worn phrase.[137] Second, there is a further instance of abundant multiple rhyme ("der hellen Töne Glanz-gefunkel" "der grellen Lichter Tanz durchs Dunkel") even though here the level of comprehension is not as difficult as before, especially if one takes into account the surrounding prose context. A word should also be said at this point about Brentano's use of variation in the re-currence of some of the devices mentioned above; whereas on the first occasion, the double "Entstellung" of proverbial expression was com-pressed into two successive verses, the same situation does not obtain later, since the distorted clichés are separated by two intervening lines. In addition, the double use of quadruple rhyme in the first half of the poem occurs in four successive lines; in the second part this pattern is also broken.

With the destruction of the realm of an introverted world of the heart, the "impossible dream" of poetry is replaced by the nightmare of reality. The sweet delusion is followed by the bitter truth that the lame weaver remains impaired, the sick lark cannot fly, the silent night-ingale will never sing again, and, most important for the speaker, all hope of melting the "Eisenherz" of an Emilie Linder will fade as "Ein-samkeit" returns. This "loneliness" is not the creative isolation that

---

[136] All sections of the poem have been translated previously.
[137] Enzensberger, pp. 46–47.

enabled Beethoven to produce great music from the depths of his soul, but rather an existential "Einsamkeit," which condemns even the sweetest miracles to go to their death unheralded and unheeded ("ohn' Opfer"). Brentano had already experienced this tragedy in his youth with regard to the paradisiacal never-never land of fantasy, "Vadutz," to which he so often took refuge. This realm, like the musico-poetic dream world in the poem of the "Lame Weaver," is also severely undermined by the intrusion of "naked truth," when Brentano was informed that Vadutz was not a product of his creative imagination but rather an actual geographical location.[138]

The second hermetically sealed sphere is the desert dream "Traum der Wüste" or "Wüstentraum" of 1838, which owes its existence and its essence to the incantory power of language. Whereas the land of dreams in "Wenn der lahme Weber träumt" was created and demolished in chronological sequence, the dominant feature of the relationship between the dream and reality here is that of simultaneity. From the very outset there are both contextual and acoustical clues that a desert vision remains what it has always been: a mirage. The last line of the first stanza, for instance, begins with one of those rare causatives in Brentano's lyric poetry: "Weil sich unendlich Nahes ewig fern" (W I 624).[139] The painful overtones of this particular conjunction are clear: even that which seems infinitely near proves to be perpetually distant. The desert dream of love is accompanied not by the song of nightingales but by the flight of vultures: "O Traum, wo der Geliebten Schleier rauschet, / Wenn Geierflug im Sandmeer Schlangen fischt" (W I 624).[140] Even in this state of reverie, there can be no respite: "Da geißelt wach, verhöhnt halb, ganz verlassen / Ihr Herz, der Wüste Geißel, glüher Sand" (W I 624).[141] The "Sehnsuchtspalme" in this milieu do not extend their lush foliage heavenward, but rather "die blütenlos Gezweig" (W I 624).[142] In view of such disappointments, the speaker asks rhetorically: "Steigt nie ein Weiherauch aus dir

[138] Frühwald, "Das verlorene Paradies," p. 174, notes: "The story of Vaduz ... represents a series of unsuccessful attempts on the part of the poet to bridge the gap between ideal and reality, fantasy and life." Later in this same article, Frühwald traces the collapse of this dreamland.

[139] "Because the infinitely near is eternally far."

[140] "O dream, where the veil of the beloved rustles, / When the swarm of vultures fishes serpents in the desert."

[141] "Then the lash of the desert, glowing sand, / Whips awake her forsaken heart, half mocks it."

[142] "The blossomless limbs."

empor?" and "Geht duftend . . . / Nie meine Seele heil aus dir her-
vor?" (W I 625).[143] The "Heimatkranke[ ]" (W I 625) for whom "kein
Quell" (W I 626) flows amidst the hot sand, who is helpless prey for
thieves ("gastfrei" [W I 626]), seems to find a hint of relief in the last
half line: "und Gott findet dich!" (W I 626).[144] But in view of the
severe debunking to which all previous mirages and images in the poem
have been subjected, one wonders whether this final ray of hope—
desirable though it may sound—might simply be another *fata morgana*.

In his discussion of this poem, Hans Magnus Enzensberger claims
that such concepts as "vulture" (Geier) are no longer to be regarded
as "real beings belonging to the outer world" but rather as "figures of
the inner world."[145] To the extent that this holds true, Brentano can
be said to evoke a "state of mind" by creating and combining images
devoid of manifest ties to external reality. Nevertheless, Enzensberger
also feels that this particular poem exhausts and overstrains the powers
of language to accomplish this aim, owing to a lack of "artistic economy."[146] One result of this failing in the case of "Entstellung," for
example, is "that their effectiveness is questioned; that they, instead of
releasing the powers of language, block these forces."[147] Focusing his
attention on the last stanza, Enzensberger believes that the concluding
half-line represents not an organically integrated finale but rather a
"breaking off of the circling movement of variation which had become
ever more cumulative."[148] However correct Enzensberger may be in
his aesthetic evaluation, one might also regard this last half-line from
a different perspective. The entire poem has lamented the fate of those
who, in the desert of life, look for mirages and miracles. They are wast-
ing their time; there is only one hope for salvation, and Brentano had
acknowledged this as early as 1816 in the famous outcry from the depth
of despair: "Meister, ohne dein Erbarmen / Muß im Abgrund ich
verzagen" (W I 329).[149] The possibility of absolute art ascribed to the
"Meister" in "Symphonie" and then to the "Sänger" of the "Nachklänge Beethovenscher Musik" (creating under the aegis of "ein Gott"

[143] "Will incense ever rise from you?" "Will my soul ever go forth / From
you, fragrant and whole?".
[144] "The person sick with yearning for a homeland (Heimatkranke) / . . . no
spring / . . . and God finds you!"
[145] Enzensberger, p. 62.
[146] Ibid., p. 63.
[147] Ibid., p. 62.
[148] Ibid., p. 70.
[149] "Master, without thy mercy / I must despair in the depths."

and the "Ew'ge[e]) is rejected both in theory and in practice in "Traum der Wüste." By so doing, Brentano once more illustrates the Orphean quality of his work. It had been the tragic greatness of the mythical singer-poet to forge a link in the chain leading from a realm that transcends men's powers of comprehension and, at the same time, to forfeit what his art had attained, because of a basic human weakness. Brentano, on the threshold of creating a new form, which would be able to voice adequately the needs and emotions of his innermost being, likewise faltered because of an all too human failing. His enterprise was new and daring, literally a "Wagnis der Sprache,"[150] and it might have enjoyed greater success had he shared the conviction of a twentieth-century lyric poet who, in his own *Sonette an Orpheus*, articulated that condition which Brentano experienced a century earlier, but never expressed so tellingly: "Hier, unter Schwindenden, sei, im Reiche der Neige, / sei ein klingendes Glas, das sich im Klang schon zerschlug."

[150] "Venture of language." The phrase comes from Fritz Martini's book *Das Wagnis der Sprache* (Stuttgart: E. Klett, 1954).

5. Chandos-Brentano: The Crisis of Communication

THE chapter on the musicalization of literature has shown that Brentano occasionally approached the periphery of what one today would call "absolute art," but that these high points were immediately followed by the demise of the ideal through the intrusion of "reality" in the form of the "naked truth," against which the "Innenwelt" could offer no substantial resistance but simply collapsed like a house of cards. The reasons for this tragic flaw in the superstructure of the aesthetic universe are manifold, but two of the primary causes can be traced to intrinsic weaknesses: the discreditation of art and the artist, and the breakdown of the verbal medium as an effective means of communication.

One tangible result of these two factors was the growing suspicion that silence might be preferable to song. The vehicles of expression—language and literature—were not commensurate with the demands placed on them. This "discovery" by Brentano puts him into another Orphean threshold situation: he straddles the fence, as it were, between the "inexpressibility topoi" of the past[1] and the full-fledged crisis in communication (and skepticism concerning the validity of any mode of verbal intercourse) which bursts onto the modern literary scene with Hugo von Hofmannsthal's letter of Lord Chandos (1901)[2] bequeathing a legacy of silent despair to many a poet in the twentieth century. There remains for that verbal artist for whom the medium as well as the means of self-expression has become highly suspect only one choice: renunciation of the spoken word. However, it is characteristic of Brentano—and also of his modern heirs in the

---

[1] Ernst Robert Curtius, *Europäische Literatur und lateinisches Mittelalter*, 4th ed. (1948; reprinted, Bern: Francke, 1963), pp. 168–171 ("Unsagbarkeitstopoi").

[2] Hugo von Hofmannsthal, *Gesammelte Werke in Einzelausgaben*, ed. Herbert Steiner, IV, 2 (Frankfurt am Main: S. Fischer, 1951): 7–22. Hofmannsthal writes, on p. 13 of this essay, that "abstract words ... crumbled in my mouth like rotten mushrooms."

communication crisis—that some of his most eloquent and memorable lines of poetry deal with the impossibility of writing or with the impropriety of creating lyric verse. Whereas it is customary to regard Brentano's provocative statements concerning the inadequacy of words, language, and literature as the sentiments of the aging poet—especially of the staunch defender of the faith who could declare a short time before his official re-entry into the Catholic church: "For a considerable time I have had a certain dread of all poetry which reflects itself and not God" (S II 165), or who spoke in 1815 of "poetry's final year" (W I 318)—it can be shown that this skepticism began early in his career and intensified toward the conclusion of his life.

Since Brentano's remorse with regard to his participation in the "Toilettensünden" ("dressing-table sins") of secular art, and his guilt complex about having an overdose of poetic imagination, have been examined extensively in critical literature, the findings of these investigations will not be repeated here.[3] Instead, the discussion focuses on those remarks which, in some way, relate the crisis in the domain of literature to the problem of musicalization. For instance, one might draw attention to the following two statements separated by almost forty years, but uttered in a similar spirit of despair at the basic insubstantiality and frivolity of prosody: "However, now such a singsong and such Romanticizing ("Romantismus"?) have made inroads," Brentano complained to Arnim in 1803, "so that one is ashamed to contribute; what disheartens me most, however, is the poetic poverty, or rather parsimony" (S I 220). Although the negative inferences here seem to suggest a temporary situation which, Brentano hopes, might be alleviated, a similar tone of disdain for poetry can be detected in a remark he allegedly made to Emma Niendorf as late as 1841: "All that indefinite poetic life which I led earlier is only a music making in the air."[4]

The attributes "such a singsong" and "music making in the air" certainly do not characterize art of a very high caliber. In a similar

---

[3] For example, Wolfgang Frühwald in his Brentano essay in *Deutsche Dichter der Romantik*, p. 294, notes the paradox in *Kasperl und Annerl* "that in a work of art the justification of the work of art is questioned, that in a narrative which has as its object the poetic process per se, . . . the questionable nature of the 'professional' poet is depicted and in an artistically perfect creation the validity of such artistry is denied."

[4] Clemens Brentano: *Dichter über ihre Dichtungen*, ed. Werner Vordtriede and Gabriele Bartenschlager (Munich: Heimeran, 1970), p. 277.

vein, Brentano is fond of using the derogatory term "Bänkelsänger" to refer to himself or his poetic activity. For instance, he states to Arnim in 1802: "I taught you to love by singing to you my own story like an itinerant balladeer" (S I 148). The transfer of "Bänkelsänger" from the poet to his poetry occurs in a letter fragment (1834), which contains one of Brentano's strongest denunciations of his craft:

> And that is the sad thing on earth: that eternal hunger which de-
> vours itself, that thirst which intoxicates itself, and wretched, pitiful,
> ragged poetry, half naked, half berouged, half red with shame, half
> innocent, steps up to the banquet table like an itinerant street singer
> who has escaped from the police, offers toasts and decorates the goblets
> with immortelles [or: artificial flowers], the greatest part of which have
> been strewn about for her as chaff. (GS IX 295)

The importance of this concept for Brentano can be inferred from the fact that he incorporates a much expanded and intensified version of this image in a letter to Emilie Linder from the same year (1834).[5]

One of the prime reasons for the decline of poetry to the status of a half-naked street singer fleeing from the police was the alarming rate at which its medium—words and language—became discredited in Brentano's eyes. There are at least five contributing factors to the mistrust which Brentano came to harbor against the verbal idiom: the inadequacy of words; the facility of words; the fragility of words; the duplicity of words; the musicality of words.

The inadequacy of words—what in *Godwi* was referred to as "the wretched fragment of my language"—springs from the awareness that the verbal medium is incapable of rendering certain emotional states or experiences—especially those bordering on the ineffable. In an occasional poem of 1800 Brentano formulated this insight into the shortcomings of language as follows: "Erstorben ist die Sprache, wenige Worte / Durchirren, sich verspätend, meine Welt" (W I 59).[6] The two versions of the concluding stanza from the poem "Lieb und Leid im leichten Leben" (1802) both contain a plea for silence, but the impact of each is quite different. Whereas one is playful, the other shows early signs of a tragic shroud of silence about to descend upon the speaker:

[5] EL 26.
[6] "Language is dead, few words / Tardily stray through my world."

Wasser fallen um zu springen.	Wasser fallen um zu springen,
Um zu klingen, um zu singen,	Um zu klingen um zu singen
Muß ich schweigen. Wie und wo?	Schweig' ich stille, denn zu sagen
Trüb und froh? nur so, so.	Wäre wagen und entsagen.[7]
(W I 131)	(W I 130)

Brentano's later poetry—whether occasional or confessional—bears traces of the dilemma of being taciturn as opposed to voicing half-truths or untruths:

> Ich soll dir singen,
> Doch ich schweig' still,
> 's möcht' übel klingen.[8]
>
> (W I 335 [1816])

So laßt mich denn und nötigt nicht zum Singen . . .[9]

> O wär' aus mir, was ich gesungen
> Wär's nicht in meinen Mund gelegt.[10]
>
> (W I 562 [1834])

Of course, one paradox implicit in Brentano's particular crisis of language ("Sprachkrise") or his skepticism of the reliability of the verbal medium ("Sprachskepsis") is the fact that he often told of his loss of communicability in lines of moving lyric beauty. In addition, the extreme length of some of the poems in which the problem is presented would seem to belie the credibility of the issue: in the *Romanzen*, for example, following a lengthy description of Älila Lälia Crispis, there occurs the famous omission of the fourth verse of the quatrain following the statement: "Ich erschrecke und muß schweigen," but up to this point his language has been very graphic in its portrayal. On other occasions, however, the crisis in verbal communication manifests itself not so much in the paucity of words as in an overabundance of verbiage. Instead of renouncing words, the poet, like a drowning man, grasps for any and every possible object of articulation in the hope that one of these will insure survival. This tendency leads to

---

[7] "Waters fall in order to rise up. / In order to ring, in order to sing, / I must be silent. How and where?. / Sad and gay? just so, so." "Waters fall in order to rise up, / In order to ring, in order to sing / I am silent, for to speak / Would be daring and renouncing."

[8] "I am to sing to you, / Yet I am silent, / It might sound bad."

[9] "So leave me then and don't force me to sing."

[10] "Oh, had I never sung what I did, / Had it never been put into my mouth."

what has been termed the "facility" of words, a mode of the communication crisis in which quantity replaces quality.

Brentano was afflicted with the "Midas" gift for words insofar as whatever he touched or whatever touched him—even the inexpressibility theme—turned into "golden" verses. Whereas critics today no longer accept without qualification Emil Staiger's view that Brentano did not control language, but rather, language controlled him,[11] it is obvious when one examines his entire oeuvre that on numerous occasions, words and word associations simply ran away with him. Brentano himself recognized—but seemed unable to remedy—this affliction: "Unfortunately I am so old that my words flow from my lips carrying my feelings not as legitimate inhabitants but as mice, beasts of prey, thieves, paramours, refugees and the like" (S II 164). In 1818, about two years after he addressed the above words to E. T. A. Hoffmann, a writer with whom he felt such an affinity, Brentano confessed to Luise Hensel that his often acrid comments on life were the result of his inability to keep silent. His penance, he adds a short time later, is to endure in silence a sense of sorrow—the punishment of silence being commensurate with his crime of having too often dared to "express the inexpressible" (GS VIII 441). Yet it appears that moments of emotional upheaval and inner turmoil were particularly conducive to eliciting from Brentano prose or poetic passages in which excess and exaggeration rather than reticence came to the fore. Writing to Luise in 1831, for instance, long after their romance had become a faded memory of the past, Brentano inserts into his letter a poem which, although not addressed to her directly, nevertheless reflects by certain syntactical and semantic peculiarities the inner agitation of the writer:

> Meine Irrtümer in diesem Liede
> Wecken meine, so wie deine
> Schmerzen tief im Herzen
> Immer wieder, wieder
> Auf;
> Aber leider, leider, leider!
> Tränen, Sehnen, Gähnen
> Löschen, wäschen
> Sie im Fließpapier, Siegspanier
> Unsrer Wehmut, Demut

---

[11] *Die Zeit als Einbildungskraft des Dichters*, p. 41.

Immer wieder wieder
Aus.
Denn wir lachen, machen Sachen
Solche Dinger für die Singer,
Lieder draus,
Vor den Mieder einen Strauß![12]
(W I 524–525)

Language out of control reflects a life no longer under control. Symptoms of this condition characterize some of the poetry and letters to Emilie Linder during the middle 1830s. The poem "Ein Becher voll süßer Huld" (1834), for example, represents for Enzensberger the destructive extreme to which the otherwise productive device of "Entstellung" can lead when it is driven beyond the limits of artistic economy: such a "fetish" of words lames rather than liberates, becomes destructive rather than constructive and, in the final analysis, contributes to the "suicide of the poem" in which such overuse occurs.[13] The suicidal tendencies of another Linder poem can be detected in the concluding stanzas of "Blumen, still blühende!" when words run rampant and, cancer-like, destroy the very organism which sustains them:

Quellen, ihr rinnenden,	Liebe, die leibt und lebt,
Sterne, ihr sinnenden;	Liebe, die treibt und webt,
Von Minn zu Minnenden,	Liebe, die rankt und rebt,
Strahlen hin spinnenden,	Lieb', die verlangt und strebt,
Um so begrüßter mir,	Kind mit der Binde, ich,
Als Freud-Geschwister ihr,	Find bei der Linde dich,
In's Lindendüster hier	Bind', daß erblinde ich,
Webt das Geflüster mir,	Lindernd entzünde mich
Zu Frühlingsmuth!	In Maies Gluth.[14]

(GS II 228)

Similar linguistic excesses are to be found in Brentano's correspondence with Emilie, as the following passage from a letter of 1841 illustrates in both its style and its content:

[12] "My mistakes in this song / Awaken my, as well as your / Pains deep in the heart / Again and again, / Again; But sadly, sadly, sadly! / Tears, yearning, yawning / Quenching, they rinse / In blotting paper, victory banner / Of our melancholy, humility / again and again / Again. For we laugh, make things, / Such trivia for the singers, / Make songs from them, / A bouquet to be put before the bodice."

[13] Hans Magnus Enzensberger, *Brentanos Poetik* (Munich, 1961), p. 78.

[14] This song, like so many others by Brentano, defies translation. And since the purpose of including it is to illustrate the tendencies of exaggeration and excess in certain devices and linguistic play, it will not be translated.

Vergib und habe Geduld mit dem armen Bruder?!?!, wenn er wirr und unbestimmt schreibt, schrieb, schreiben wird, schreiben soll ich Dir ja, Du hast es selbst verlangt, gibst mir auch wohl Aufträge, so ertrage es dann mit Geduld ... wenn Dein armer, tief betrübter, und zerschmetterter Diener nicht zu Dir springen und in klarer ungebundener, oder, weil unbändiger, gebundener Rede sprechen oder singen kann. (EL 151)[15]

Such excerpts—to which hundreds more could be added—may serve to undergird the contention that an important phase of Brentano's personal crises in life and language is represented by an affluence and abundance of verbiage and not, as one might suspect, by reticence or abstinence from the spoken word.

A third aspect of Brentano's crisis of communication stems from what has been labeled the fragility of words. The problem here centers around the extent to which words wear out in the course of time; they lose their vitality and impact through overuse, or they are reduced to hollow formulae of social intercourse as the original force behind the concept or its verbal sign weakens. In certain respects, Brentano himself may be said to have contributed his share to the exhaustion of the German language. On the one hand, his proclivity for verbal pyrotechnics—whereby the significance of individual words is lost behind layers of homonym, synonym, and antonym play—results in a devaluation of the individual linguistic utterance; on the other hand, it was noted in conjunction with the evolution of lyric musicality that extensive use of such devices as refrain or other means of verbatim repetition tends to reduce words to the status of tonal complexes and minimizes their function as bearers of explicit meaning.

Because of his great concern for words, Brentano became acutely aware of their loss of stamina. Especially in the years after 1817 he reacted almost like a seismograph in recording the fluctuations of potency with regard to key terms in the life and liturgy of the Church— as the following comment, which Brentano attributes to one of the ubiquitous detractors from orthodox faith, will attest: "All form in religion nowadays is exceedingly empty and ridiculous; the word is so worn out generally, that it has become completely useless" (W II 1044).

---

[15] "Forgive and have patience with your poor brother?!?! when he writes confusedly and indistinctly, wrote, will write, I am supposed to write you, you requested it yourself, you give me mandates and so endure this with patience ... when your poor, deeply troubled, and shattered servant cannot leap to you and speak or sing in clear, unbridled or, because it is unruly, verse discourse."

Brentano was particularly appalled by the way in which periodicals and journals, together with other "mass media" of the "paper age" (GS IX 247), watered down many concepts and, by employing them in slogans and other jargonistic contexts, converted them into what he once called "wasted words":

> Wasted, however, is every word to which we do not impart the intention of fruitful harvest.... It occurs to me that one could compare with them compliments, figures of speech, the lying chit-chat of pseudo-friendship, and a large part of all social discourse.... Words which bear no fruit are slain words, wasted words. (GS IX 263)

Aside from the obvious religious implications in these lines, one can also perceive the fundamental discomfort of an individual who has devoted his entire life to the spoken word and who now finds it necessary to speak out against his chosen métier. This uneasiness becomes more apparent as he develops the theme further, moving from the area of fructification to that of utilization:

> Those wasted words which I mean are good words which, however, are used by people who do not understand the inner essence of words and have only gathered for themselves a goodly supply of nice, pious idioms with which they overwhelm others.... They are like ... people who cannot bake bread but who utilize all wheat grain to make overly rich pastries, layer cakes and other baked goods which upset one's stomach to such an extent, that one can no longer eat cake or bread and turns completely to meat. (GS IX 264–265)

This very passage—and innumerable others like it—reveal that Brentano often fell victim to the very situation he deplored; to use his own image from the culinary sphere, he overindulged in "rich pastries, layer cakes and other baked goods." Hugo von Hofmannsthal, who drew the attention of the twentieth century to various manifestations of the crisis of verbal communication, also pinpointed Brentano's problem in a succinct comment from the essay *Ad me ipsum*: "We are dealing with a 'too much' in speaking, an exaggeration—and in this 'too much' is a dichotomy—one part of the 'I' does what the other part does not want —and this is viewing diagonally across the exaggerated, bizarre, clever talk which the 'other person' in us engages in (Clemens Brentano)."[16]

Brentano's reference to "lying chit-chat" in a passage quoted ear-

---

[16] Hugo von Hofmannsthal, "Ad me ipsum," *Neue Rundschau*, 65 (1954): 371.

lier touches upon the fourth aspect of the crisis in communication which manifested itself in his work: the duplicity of language. The fact that words operate in different capacities (denotation and connotation) or have different inferences on various levels of usage (social milieu, formal, or informal context) is a facet of the verbal medium which poets like Brentano have long exploited. Furthermore, this area has always proved fertile for puns, double entendre, or other plays on words, as well as a source of neologisms and the creation of word composites. In Brentano's case, he was not averse to deliberately hiding behind the mask of language by devising a mode of expression that both revealed what he could not refrain from imparting and yet concealed all too personal information which he preferred to keep from public consumption. This practice has been given various designations by different Brentano scholars—encoding, mystification, interiorization, and enciphering—but what has not been stressed sufficiently is the fact that even though Brentano may have consciously pursued this style of writing, he also foresaw its dangerous consequences. The cleft between what was uttered and what was understood, for example, could result in both comedy or tragedy. Particularly distressing, however, was the awareness that virtually every poetic statement was deceptive: "In verse," Brentano noted in 1816, "almost everything becomes a lie or a sham; artistic form steals from possession that which belongs to it and makes of it common property" (S II 179).

Yet it was the skillful use of the multivalent potential of words which also enabled Brentano to devise his unique brand of poetic musicality, to construct the introverted world of the heart by converting what had previously been public domain (everyday vocabulary, clichés, commonplace speech patterns, and proverbial phrases) into private property. With such verbal building blocks and the mortar of his mind, Brentano helped lay the foundation for a lyricism which later in his century was to be called "absolute," which, on the surface at least, maintained a link to the phenomenal sphere by using a common vocabulary, but which, in its essential layers of meaning, created a cosmos far removed from that in which the reader lived and breathed. This sui generis idiom could thus rival that of music, that art which, utilizing no words borrowed from language, nevertheless made the ultimate statement, comprehensible to all even though enigmatic in its means. But here, too, doubts arose and gave rise to the suspicion that instead of constituting a breakthrough to a new mode of communication, this esoteric medium might have inaugurated the break-down of all channels of communication. Instead of making the ultimate statement, the musical poetry of a hermetically sealed world may remain just that, hermetically sealed off and inaccessible except to an elite group of privileged initiates. T. S. Eliot may have suspected this when he cautioned: "I think it might be possible for a poet to work too closely to musical analogies: the result might be an effect of artificiality."[17] The author of *Das Musikalische in der Literatur*, Johannes Mittenzwei, in spite of his polemical Marxism, is not entirely wide of the mark of truth when he notes: "The increase in musicality of language together with a content which is becoming ever more abstract is the sign of a more and more aggravated opposition of the artist to bourgeois society."[18] However, the most astute analysis of the aesthetic risks involved in the musicalization of literature was offered by a contemporary of Brentano's, a poet who over the course of the last century has been lauded for the musicality of his own verse and who, nevertheless, recognized the dubious distinction of this accolade: Heinrich Heine. Heine had already put his finger on one vulnerable facet of Brentano's language when he commented in 1832 concerning *Ponce de Leon*: "And it dances and hops and twirls and rattles, and above it ring out the trumpets of a bacchanalian delight in destruction."[19] Finally, in 1841, one year before Brentano's death, Heine hazarded the following theory on music in general (and, by implication, on those art media which aspire toward the condition of music): "The increased spirituality, the abstract thought, these grasp for sounds and tones in order to express a stammering exuberance which is perhaps nothing other than the dissolution of the entire material world; music is perhaps the last word of art, just as death is the last word of life."[20]

Brentano's chronological status as an heir of the "inexpressibility topos" of the past and as precursor of the genuine crisis of communication at the end of the nineteenth century was not the only Orphean—or threshold—aspect to his relationship to language. The various other factors enumerated in this chapter—the facility, fragility, and duplicity of words—placed him in his approach to the verbal art somewhere between Tasso's conviction that his type of poet was the most eloquent, divinely elected spokesman for all mankind and that "propriety of si-

[17] *On Poetry and Poets* (New York: Farrar, Straus and Cudahy, 1957), p. 32.
[18] Mittenzwei, *Das Musikalische*, p. 121.
[19] Heine, V, 309.
[20] Heine, VI, 259.

lence" prescribed by Hofmannsthal for all those who, like the writer of the Lord Chandos letter, find that words crumble on their lips like rotten mushrooms. Brentano will indeed be remembered as the creator of a number of works which, to use Wolfgang Kayser's term, represent "the verbal artifact" ("das sprachliche Kunstwerk") in its purest form. On the other hand, he cannot be forgotten as the sorcerer's apprentice among Romantic poets, as the man who produced a bulk of verse that would have to be ranked as "artificial verbiage" ("das künstliche Sprachwerk") had Kayser ever seen fit to establish such a category.

Retrospect

THE preceding five chapters of this investigation have examined the career, the creative writings, and autobiographical documents of Clemens Brentano with reference to the role played in each of these three facets of his life and works by music, musicianship, and musicality in order to substantiate the contention that this singer-poet deserves the accolade of Germany's Romantic Orpheus. Instead of merely recapitulating in a more or less mechanical fashion the evidence adduced in support of this claim throughout the study, this final phase of the analysis will summarize the major topics covered previously by regarding them from a radically altered viewpoint— from the perspective of that ubiquitous figure in Bretano's literary repertoire who serves as the antipode of all that Orpheus was and did: the philistine.[1]

A statement by Shakespeare in *The Merchant of Venice* strikes at the very heart of the philistine temperament and talent:

> The man that hath no music in himself,
> Nor is not mov'd with concord of sweet sounds,
> Is fit for treasons, stratagems, and spoils;
> The motions of his spirit are dull as night,
> And his affections dark as Erebus.
> Let no such man be trusted. Mark the music.
>
> (Act 5, scene 1)

The fact that this type of unmusical and, in many cases, antimusical individual occupied such a prominent place in Brentano's writings says something significant about the author and his attitudes. Therefore, by investigating the negative components of those facets of music which, up to this point, have been treated in a fundamentally positive light, this closing phase of the discussion will not only recall what has gone before, but also make manifest yet another "threshold" straddled by Orpheus-Brentano.

---

[1] A comprehensive analysis of the philistine both in Brentano's works and in the writings of late eighteenth-century authors can be found in Ulrich Westerkamp's unpublished dissertation "Beitrag zur Geschichte des literarischen Philister-

In contrast to chapter 1 ("Proteus-Brentano: The Crisis of Continuity"), in which it was discovered, after an analysis of available primary sources and statements by contemporaries of Brentano's as well as later scholars, that the poet's skill as a composer and his abilities as a music critic fall into the range of adequate to mediocre, no comparable difficulty arises in assessing these talents in the philistine. If the full extent of Brentano's accomplishments in practical music remain a "book with seven seals," those of his sworn enemy, the "Philister" are forever an "open book." The pedestrian core and restricted intellectual horizon of the latter preclude any serious contributions to the field of music from the outset, since this medium is the least tangible and most ethereal of the arts from the standpoint of creation and appreciation. The bureaucratic minister, Tartaglia, for instance, from *Die lustigen Musikanten*, expresses the philistine ethic when he explains how he remains so impervious to the poignant music of the morose troupe: "I have an astonishing ear, to be sure, particularly at key holes, but for music I have no retentive powers at all" (W IV 294). On those rare occasions when some philistine figure is seen composing music of his own, his composition betrays the hallmark of dilettante art: emotionalism in excess of the fact—like the member of the "bureau d'esprit" in *Godwi* whose rendition of a simple song "lifts him to the heights, he turns his eyes fancifully toward heaven and tenderly raises his head, taking delight in his own resonant, full voice, God knows in the embrace of what higher life, love, or art" (W II 196). The critical response of the philistine mentality to music of higher caliber is, as was indicated in conjunction with Brentano's comments on Reichardt, summarized most tellingly in the remark from the poet's trenchant satire of 1811, *Der Philister vor, in und nach der Geschichte*: "The philistines have a feeling only for music that is insipid, frivolous, or stiff-as-a-board; they consider Beethoven to be completely insane" (W II 998). Whereas Brentano's own musical muse may, on occasion, have deserted him in either his original compositions or his reviews of absolute music or operatic works, there were enough highlights and sidelights in each to regard his achievements in the fields of practical and speculative music with a forgiving smile; his fictitious philistine, on the other hand, remains in musical matters as

typus mit besonderer Berücksichtigung von Brentanos Philisterabhandlung," Munich, 1941.

Shakespeare had delineated him—"dull as night" in his spirit and "dark as Erebus" in his affections.

The "crisis of conscience" which plagued the various Orphean figures discussed in chapter 2—most notably, Rosadora-Biondette from the *Romanzen vom Rosenkranz*—and led them to the threshold of doubt, the limbo of ambivalence or the gray of relativity, likewise remains excluded from the province of the philistine, who operates on the solid ground of certainty, plodding along the path of complacent absolutes and "always," preferring the dichotomy of day and night to the twilight zone of relativity. Any musical talents which the philistine might display are more likely to be verbal than actual—as is indicated by Alonso, the spokesman for a group of such performers in *Ponce de Leon* who are more adept at "pausing together" than "playing together" (W IV 249). One member of this ensemble, a corpulent piper, reveals in a kind of linguistic cadenza based on the homonyms "Fuge" (fugue) and "Fuge" (joint, seam) and the German idiom "aus den Fugen" (out of joint, disrupted) that his confreres are too concerned with the state of their gastronomy to bother about the standards of their artistry (a common philistine trait): "You know the scrawny fiddler is strong in his fugues but hollow in his ribs. He could rip a few ribs from the cold roast, then we would have to rest, playing pizzicato on the bones" (W IV 258). And whereas Brentano's Orphean singers braved the hazards of Hades to rescue a loved one, their philistine counterparts are unmitigated cowards who use music as an excuse not to be daring. Thus the royal musicians in the *Rheinmärchen*, for example, when faced with the challenge of saving the drowning Princess Ameleya from certain death in the waters of the river, refuse their aid on very specious grounds: "Water spoils one's auditory faculty," they protest, "puts fiddles out of tune, is much too far below concert-pitch, finds no resonance and, in the low notes one could easily lose the proper beat" (W III 16). At best, such philistine performers are exponents of shallow showmanship—as can be inferred from the following passage in *Godwi* which juxtaposes Mozart as the superior artist of high purpose with a third-rate fiddler catering to the whims of the crowd:

> The whole affair . . . appears to me to be that which would have marked a Mozart who, as a lark or at the request of some powerful but taste-less individual, conjured up a miserable tune on his violin. It was . . .

the self-reliance of a beer fiddler who, after having compelled his listeners to dance long enough to his street ballad, still appends to the end of the last beat a final, enticing morsel for the ears—gratis. (W II 31–32)

The high-water mark in Brentano's portrayal of philistine performers is reached in his account in *Briefe über das neue Theater* (1818) where he writes, tongue in cheek, about the concert hall antics of Kapellmeister Krumpipen: "He began to fantasize, cast his gaze to heaven and dabbled wretchedly on the piano. You poets would be quite fortunate if you could patch up your empty drivel as easily as the musicians do with a bit of euphony" (W II 1155). Krumpipen, whose name links him etymologically with chirping barnyard fowl, surrounds himself with extraneous accoutrements to sustain audience interest: a goldfinch caged beneath the piano sits in abject silence—the emaciated bird, even though it has access to a bass fiddle case filled with ham and sausage (rather than with the instrument), starves as any true artist would in a prosaic environment offering no spiritual nourishment; a corpulent turkey-cock, however, an unmusical bird, thrives in the milieu provided by Krumpipen's kith and kin,

> the stomach enthusiasts and bacon fanatics . . . who think they are making splendid music when they direct toward heaven like an amorous, snorting bull their bland, self-indulgent stew-countenance,[2] while they squeeze out wretched, meaningless, hackneyed passages on the pianoforte and, in the process, press and tremble their fingers as if the keys were alternately soft as butter or glowing hot; usually a tear hangs in their eye, a touch of perspiration clings to their brow, and a drop of sweat lies on their nose—and they call this dissolving away in lofty, infinite longing. (W II 1163–1164)

Exposed to such trivia, the discerning audience instead of sitting spellbound or being wafted away "on wings of song" as with Biondette, the female Orpheus, is more likely to be lulled to sleep in the arms of Morpheus.

In view of the deterioration in the caliber of performer and performance in those areas in which philistine hegemony holds sway,

---

[2] In his essay of 1811 *Der Philister vor, in und nach der Geschichte* Brentano employs a variation of the term "Schmorgesicht" (translated as "stew-countenance") when he writes: "die dichtenden Philister, welche man auch Schmorer nennen kann" (W II 1009), which may be translated as "the poeticizing philistines whom one could also call stewers."

it is to be expected that the pace at which the "musicalization of life" discussed in chapter 3 from several vantage points would also slacken, if not cease altogether. Brentano's anecdotal parable of 1817 entitled "Lieblingslied der Geizigen" clearly illustrates this development as well as the decline in the stature of the poet-singer. The protagonist of this tale in prose and verse is a lutist who enters the court of a prospective patron intent upon winning a handsome reward for his playing. The comparison which Brentano uses in the opening paragraph, however, should serve as a warning that we are now encountering an anti-Orphean world: "It would have been easier for him, as it was for Orpheus, to entice a soul from Hades than to pry a single cent from the pocket of this lord" (W II 856). Throughout the remainder of this brief story, one illusion after another concerning the power of music to exert beneficial effects on the human soul or psyche is unmasked in an avalanche of double entendre and punning word play. For instance, the tightfisted prince is impressed not in the slightest by musical modes that are martial (the Phrygian) or even sensual (Lydian) but rather by those that are financial (Dorian—especially if it is "louis d'orian" or the like). His favorite composers are those whose surnames suggest, not giving ("Schenkendorf"), but receiving ("Brinville" who in German becomes "Bringviel," the bringer of much); and since the ruler is not moved by "concord of sweet sounds," he finds it difficult ("hart") to be generous ("reichen") with his patronage and, consequently, will listen only to the sounds of Reichardt (Brentano takes final vengeance on his old nemesis, the now deceased composer). Realizing that his efforts have been a miserable failure, the lutist, a far cry from his mythical prototype or his predecessors in Brentano's world, stands on the threshold of the castle, not seized by the pangs of doubt and despair, but acknowledging the victory of the utilitarian and pragmatic way of life over the aesthetic:

> So nackt und kahl geh ich von eurer Schwelle,
> So nüchtern, bar und blank in voller Klarheit,
> Als wär ich, der ich singe, selbst die Wahrheit,
> Denn nur *Reale* sind bei euch's Reelle![3]
>
> (W II 858)

[3] "So naked and bare I pass from your threshold, / So sober, destitute and empty-handed, in full clarity, / As if I, the one singing, were truth itself, / For only realia are real to you!"

Having varied in these lines Hölderlin's famous lament "Wozu Dichter in dürftiger Zeit?"[4] (which one might paraphrase in this context as: "Wozu musikalischer Dichter in a-musischer Zeit?"—"Why be a musical poet in an age alienated from the Muses?") the lutist becomes the victim of a world in which practical concerns hold sway and his instrument—which symbolized the aesthetic and, consequently intangible values of life—is unceremoniously destroyed in the name of absolute truth:

> When the poor lutist had thus sung the truth to the courtiers in this fashion, they inquired angrily why he handled so argumentatively ["Händel"]. He answered, however, that his song was not by Händel, but his own. Whereupon they, wanting argument, handled things in their own way, took the lute from him and smashed it in two over his head in order to affirm the proverb "He who fiddles the truth will have the fiddle broken over his head." (W II 858)

One of the prime functions attributed to Orphean music was the ability either to induce a state of spiritual harmony in the individual and in his interrelations with society, or to express by analogy the existence of such intra- or interpersonal accord and equilibrium. Since the philistine lives in a one-dimensional world with narrow horizons and clearly defined boundaries, he never runs the risk of being out of harmony—or perhaps "monotony" would be more appropriate—with himself or his environment. Immune to the "concord of sweet sounds," the philistine can, nevertheless, be kept on even keel or even cured of physical maladies by suitable music; for example, one scene in *Fanferlieschen Schönefüßchen* tells of the potential disruption of the harmonious "body politic" because of the illness which threatens the regent. In lieu of David's exalted psalms, which soothed Saul's furrowed brow, a preposterous group of singers attempts a cure by transcribing the medical prescription directly into musical tones: ". . . the artistic accomplishments of the Ce-Celery Glee Club . . . which presented a cantata in the form of a sixteen and three-eighths part fugue, performed while they circled around the city in a very scrambled and yet surprisingly unscrambled fashion, a fugue in which the prescription

---

[4] This line from Hölderlin's poem "Brod und Wein, *Sämtliche Werke*, II:1 94, can be translated: "What is the sense of being a poet in a barren age?" The same thought is expressed by Brentano in his famous letter of 1810 to Runge in which the poet sought to enlist the painter's aid for his *Romanzen:* "I do not believe that a single artist in difficult times ["in spröder Zeit"] will ever further art with serious works" (S II 13).

recommended by the distinguished medical practitioners for the ailing first lady were adequately sung" (W III 974). Lest one overlook the humorous exaggeration in which these events are reported or the pedestrian framework in which the episode is set (and thereby run the risk of missing the satiric barbs), Brentano augments the performance of the choraleers with a descant provided by a host of partially singed suckling pigs "which punctuated the musical presentation with their "grunting" (W III 975). Not only does the philistine music displace the Orphean tones, but the former is itself disenfranchised by even more pedestrian, more "earthy" sounds. Brentano, in typical Romantic fashion, raises his satiric debunking procedures "to a higher power."

The most devastating exposé of the inability of the philistine mind to musicalize life and make it aesthetically more appealing can be observed with reference to the "pathos of love" in the context of the Melos-Eros-Thanatos constellation. Strangely enough, the novel *Godwi*—which concludes by heralding the coming age of Orphean domination—opens with one of the most candid debunkings of the music of love in Brentano's entire oeuvre:

> When cats sing songs of courtly love at the doors and when at the window a screech-owl sings the death dirge of honest burghers—who, without the affinity of the swan for breathing out its last breath of life in melody but who do not care to die without singing—then indeed woman approaches man with trepidation, fear becomes love, love which dissolves everything, and everything becomes united in this lovely moment. (W II 18)

The tacit juxtaposition of highly controlled human emotions (the Minnelied) with the unrestricted mating call of the animal kingdom is reiterated in a later context when the month of March is hailed as that joyous time of year "when cats are acknowledged singers of courtly love" (W II 1020).

Even the sexual inadequacies of certain philistine types can become the source of witty musico-erotic double entendre as, for example, in *Die lustigen Musikanten*, when the entrepreneur Alonso alludes to the amorous shortcomings of one of his instrumentalists using the homonyms "E-Saite" (E-string) and "Eh'Saite" (or "Ehe-Seite" meaning the "institution of marriage"):

> ALONSO: ... then I have a fiddler who is somewhat emaciated and not entirely capable at consort playing on the E-string ["E-Saite"].
> VALERIO: God grant then that he is not married!

ALONSO: Or may God take his wife from him, for she alone is responsible; she has ruined his consorts on the E-string [implied is "Eh'-
Saite"] often enough. (W IV 248)

Melodic-erotic repartee is also characteristic of a work that exemplifies
the alliance of love and music from the Orphean as well as the philistine
standpoint: *Aloys und Imelde*. The culprit here is the blind grand
seigneur, Benavides, who, although totally a-musical (SW IX:2 449)
himself, nevertheless knows how to marshal his musical forces for a
veritable onslaught on the citadel of Imelde's tender emotions. Benavides' "affections dark as Erebus" hardly conceal themselves behind
the instructions he imparts to the serenaders whose aid he enlists to
carry out his "stratagems and spoils":

> Die Mauer Jerichos neigt sich den Zinken,
> Ein Unterrock wird ihnen auch wohl sinken.
> Ist erst die Bresche da, dann hilft kein Schirmen;
> Von Kunst und Lüge, Religion und Schwüren
> Will ich Faschinen so ironisch schnüren,
> Daß Pauke und Trompet hinüber stürmen,
> Und in die Himmelsluft von allen Thürmen
> Paniere meiner Liebe triumphieren.
> > (SW IX:2 451–452)
> Nun, meine Freunde, greift die besten Noten,
> Die ihr auf eurer Töne Leiter finden mögt,
> Laßt sie die Leiter eines Buhlers sein,
> An seiner Liebsten Kammer angelegt;
>
> . . . .
>
> So schwing Musik sich kühnlich auch hinan,
> Mit heißem Kuß die Angst ihr zu ersticken
> Und trag sie dann herab auf luftger Bahn;[5]
> > (SW IX:2 464–465)

An aside by Forcas, a member of the musical contingent assembled by
Aloys to compete with Benavides, unmasks the underlying impetus
behind the philistine's elaborate rhetoric—animal instinct:

[5] "The walls of Jericho fell before the horns, / A petticoat will no doubt also
sink for them. / Once the breach is there, no defense will help; / Of art and
falsehood, religion and oaths / I shall bind fascines together so ironically / That
drum and trumpet will storm over, / And in the skies of heaven, from all towers
/ Will wave triumphantly banners of my love."
  "Now, my friends, play the best notes / That you can find on your scale
[ladder] of tones, / Let them be the ladder of a lover / To scale the chamber
of his beloved; // . . . Thus may music boldly leap upwards / To stifle with
fervent kiss her fear / And then carry her down on airy path."

Die Katzen mauen schier
Vor der guten Leute Thür
Verliebte Arien
Mit Pausen und Suspir!⁶
(SW IX:2 465)

With regard to the music of nature, which the Orphean singer either reproduced in his own inimitable fashion as "musica naturata" or emulated as a process of creativity ("musica naturans"), the philistine seems intent upon destroying instead of enjoying the euphonious symphony of sound that echoes in his environment. For example, instead of merely contenting himself with the song of the nightingale, the philistine would prefer to consume the songstress—perhaps under the delusion that such an act of consumption would become the source of actual inspiration. The demise of so lofty a singer in an age "which eats nightingale tongue in a pâté and cultivates only the great bagpipe —the stomach" (W II 896) may be Brentano's method of signaling the death of Romanticism, and the following lines of 1818, which literally contain more truth than poetry, are indeed prophetic of developments on the aesthetic scene a few years later:

Die liebliche November-Nachtigall
Muß drum seitdem zum Halsgerichte hin.
Beim Bratenwenden singt im hohen Ton
Die Köchin nun; . . .⁷
(GS II 598)

Such a scene would certainly have warmed the cockles of every philistine heart. The quasi-humorous suggestion posed in the *Gockel* fairy tale of 1838 was the harbinger of a terrible truth, which had already come about in the age of the *poeta absconditus*: "The friendly songbirds which make our home into a heart-warming place of refuge with

---

⁶ "The cats are meowing / Before the doors of respectable people / Almost nothing but amorous arias, / With rests and sighs!" These lines are an adaptation from Abraham a Santa Clara's poem of the late seventeenth century "Nachtmusikanten" (from the *Narren-Meß*, or *Fools' Fair*), a work which Brentano and Arnim had incorporated into *Des Knaben Wunderhorn*, ed. Willi Koch (Munich: Winkler, 1957), p. 21, as follows:

Da fängt man alsbald an
Vor der Geliebten Tür
Verliebte Arien
Mit Pausen und Suspir.

⁷ "The lovely November nightingale / Must therefore since that time submit to capital punishment. / While roasting it on the spit the cook / Now sings in lofty tone."

their innocent chirping, do you want to hear them sing or eat them broiled?" (W III 630). The philistine pragmatist would most certainly espouse the latter cause, since to his mind, nature's songbirds, like any other mode of aesthetic expression, are a form of consumer goods, and the purpose of such items is, of course, to be consumed. But Brentano has his revenge on those for whom artistic taste and the taste buds are undifferentiated: "They slurp down some Mathissonian or Ossianic punch dregs, then they go strolling into the Kosegarten and declare with disgustingly sweet countenance: 'Listen how the aeolian harp of creation gurgles and roars,' when actually only their bellies are gurgling and roaring, unable to tolerate the nauseous spicy mixture" (W II 1009).

The polarity between cosmic order and chaotic disorder which marked the dance image throughout Brentano's writings contains certain inherent features—namely, conformity and confusion—which made it especially amenable to the philistine's *modus vivendi*. The imposition of restrictions and regulations in the name of social decorum or law and order had constituted one of the less propitious aspects of the dance concept in its Apollinian framework of control—self- or otherwise. The philistine, however, thrives on the observance of long-standing, stereotyped patterns, formulae which have been retained not necessarily because of their intrinsic validity but simply through longevity; it is to such a fossilized and petrified attitude that Brentano directs the following admonition:

> Ach! im Sarge erlahmt selbst des Tanzmeisters Fuß,
> Ach! im Backofen singen selbst die erfrorenen Äpfel.
> Sollen die Kuchen aufgehn, ach! so erhitze die Formen,
> Ist dir dein Elend Gesang, ach! so pfeife dein Lied![8]
>
> (S I 279)

The dialectical interplay inherent in the dance concept—between the arbitrary imposition of regulatory systems and the complete loss of control under the liberating influence of music which serves as an invitation to the dance—leads, in the case of one particular philistine figure to a very interesting development: a marked incongruity between factual statement about life and the facts of life. The individual

---

[8] "Alas! in the coffin even the dance master's foot grows lame, / Alas! in the oven even frozen apples sing. / If you want the cakes to rise, alas! then heat the pans, / If your misery is song to you, alas! then whistle your tune!"

in question is Watchmaker BOGS, the composite creation of *Brentano* (BO-) and his close friend, Joseph *Görres* (-GS) who appears in a narrative the very title of which reveals a fundamental dualism resulting from dual authorship as well as the dual personality of the protagonist: *Entweder wunderbare Geschichte von BOGS dem Uhrmacher . . . , oder die über die Ufer der badischen Wochenschrift als Beilage ausgetretene Konzert-Anzeige* (1807). On the surface, BOGS is a paragon of order, a person whose life should proceed with the same monotonous regularity as the precision-tooled watches he makes. Emphatically BOGS decries any force that disrupts the preestablished laws of his life—for instance, the music of the dance: "And it is now so easy to dance to you, you plucking, jolting, flirtatious dance music, you who have sent your composer and your dancing master to school on the Witches' Peak (Blocksberg) and the Mount of Venus (Venusberg)— it is so easy to love with you, lusty musical lechery, sweet, wanton aria which tosses and catches the seductive apples of Paradise like a juggler in a thousand lascivious ways" (W II 881). Yet BOGS protests too much and too well; in spite of his vehement denunciation of the dance as a source of morally reprehensible behavior, the language of his tirade is as seductive in its gyrations as the object he attacks, and the only one who falls victim to this disruptive force of chaos is, in the final analysis, BOGS himself. And this is the point of the entire satire, a treatise which presents BOGS's attempt to prove to the arch-philistine organization to which he desires membership, the Most Revered Society of Marksmen, that he is well qualified for admittance, especially in view of the fact that he has remained immune to the powers which music can exert on the imagination. The wild phantasmagoria which he submits as proof of his immunity to music's charms that "soothe the savage breast" are the most self-contradictory and self-incriminatory documents possible. Watchmaker BOGS, ostensibly a philistine to the core, proves instead to be a melomaniac, an individual whose reactions to the slightest musical stimulus border on the pathological.

One passage from the "Paralipomenon" to the story illustrates with reference to the dance the two souls dwelling within his breast; in this description, the dual potentials of the dance—its cosmic and chaotic powers—are shown to be complementary rather than contradictory. In such passages as this the language of the tale reads no longer like the bureaucratic jargon of the philistine or the disjointed ramblings of a madman, but rather like the prose of an Orphean poet:

Up and down the gentle waves tossed, and rose more and more from the sea's clear surface, and the ringlets wove together as in tonal configurations, they were swallowed up again and broke away from each other gracefully and tenderly, and there was a harmonious rising and falling, as if dainty maidens were exercising their well-formed, slender wave-limbs in a floating dance, and more and more water-nymphs seemed to rise up from the depths, and the turbulence of the waves became greater, but all was still clear and harmonious, and the movement grew faster and faster until it finally became the raging dance of Maenads. (W II 925)

The succeeding pages of this account expand the details of the wave dance, but retain the interplay of precise and calculated movement with wild, reckless abandon:

Then melodies poured from heavenly harp and the dance became music of the spheres ... a charming dragon-fly danced the fandango harmoniously on its delicate web with the waves (W II 926); ... Harlequin danced the war- and sword dance and armed youths leaped up like lightning from the swirling, whirling sounds and wrestled boldly with each other... The contours rose and sank as in a snake dance, and there was in these factions lively vitality and a harmonious bustling, in these groups which, continually changing in form and motion, interpenetrated one another in manifold fashion. (W II 926–927)

The comic—or tragic—aspect to this whole procedure is that neither BOGS, the narrator, nor his audience, the members of the Most Revered Society of Marksmen, has any conception of the full scope of the experience that transpires before their (inner) eyes and ears respectively. BOGS bravely reports under the misapprehension that what he tells will gain him admission to the organization; the members of that organization, however, after "reasoning about what they had seen" (W II 929), will have to refuse to admit him because of what he has told.

The account of Watchmaker BOGS also elucidates the final phase of the Orphean musicalization of life discussed—"singen-lobsingen"—from a basically philistine perspective but with significant insights. BOGS begins by lamenting the downfall of liturgical music, that sublime church song which was the "abyss and apex of all tones, in and on which man might prostrate himself before God or elevate himself to God" (W II 880). BOGS then delineates those musical forms which have usurped the prerogatives of ecclesiastical music—including the aforementioned dance tunes, together with the "eternally contrasting opera, flitting to and fro, running about helter-skelter in order to establish roots, taking root in order to soar upwards, soaring upwards in order to descend below, descending below in order to touch our emotions, touching our emotions in order to make us laugh" (W II 881). Once again BOGS ironically misses the main thrust of his own statements. What he condemns as contrary and apparently contradictory motion in the secular opera, making it unacceptable and actually reprehensible when compared with the single-minded aims of liturgical music (which, incidentally, could humiliate as well as elevate—a point which he likewise glosses over), constitutes the very essence of the human condition, perched as it is on the precarious intersection of forces which, in his later life, Brentano was to circumscribe as "star and blossom" (celestial and terrestrial), "spirit and garment" (essence and appearance), "love and sorrow" (pleasure and pain), "time and eternity" (limit and delimitation). BOGS's vitriolic condemnation of secular music articulates the paradox that those very same tones which once were so divine in spirit have been reconstituted in such a way as to make them serve "sensual desire and sinful reveries":

> And all you other secular tone-configurations, sonatas, symphonies, or whatever you may be called, spiced confections of virtue and vice, Karl Moor, etc., you have unfortunately gained much ground from the angels of God, angels who used to carry buckets of water up and down God's tone ladder and who filled and emptied them in the breast of the slumbering Jacob. Now the tone ladder lies against the scaffolding for some fireworks that will be ignited on the day of the devil's christening and his birth and on his grandmother's silver, golden and paper wedding anniversary. One must come to such despairing thoughts when one is compelled to think about you [secular tone-configurations], for tones are of such a divine, pure nature that they, no matter how exploited, no matter how joined together for the purpose of worldly lust and sinful dreams—as I call it—still smile through to us in ghost-like, frightening fashion, like the heads of angels and of saints buried alive in walls of earthly pleasure. (W II 881)

In the final analysis, therefore, Watchmaker BOGS could be considered the prosaic counterpart to the poetic Orpheus; a nonperformer himself (having renounced the playing of various instruments in his youth), BOGS nevertheless evokes or recreates in powerful verbal images the private universe of his psyche which music sparks and sustains, even though he does so under the delusion that these reports will confirm his a-musicality. And if Orpheus enjoyed dual citizenship in two worlds and was condemned to falter on the threshold between upper and lower realms, so BOGS also is a man of split affinities, existing somewhere between the domain of watches, with its mathematically measured time, and the weird and wonderful world opened to his alter ego in its full and infinite dimension not by the regular ticking of the clock but by the rhythmic tones of the concert hall.

In contrast to BOGS, the dyed-in-the-wool philistine, having no music in himself and being unmoved by the "concord of sweet sounds," resisted the musicalization of life just as he opposed the "musicalization of literature"—the topic of chapter 4. The prerequisites to literary musicalization—the ability to exchange or interchange sense impressions (synaesthesia), or the faculty of appreciating in a composite work of art stimuli from various avenues of access (visual, auditory, tactile) and of synthesizing them into a total work of art (the syn-aesthetic), were too overwhelming for the philistine mentality. One might recall the difficulties encountered by Godwi and Maria in communicating their ideas in this vein to Haber. In the same novel, the *philistus primus inter pares* is Jost von Eichenwehen, a son of the enlightened eighteenth century and heir to the view that the genres of literature as well as all modes of artistic expression must be carefully segregated and clearly categorized. Characteristically, he cannot tolerate opera (W II 109) and becomes totally confused when he finds himself accidentally at a performance: "O God," he moans, "what misery down there in front; it was as if the entire world were being created around me in fiddling, thundering and singing" (W II 109). Aesthetic inflexibility and the refusal to appreciate art forms that traverse established boundaries and traditions are condemned rather harshly by Brentano in the poem in which he celebrates Schinkel as an innovator and as the chief exponent of the theory that architecture is frozen music (W I 342)—an enigmatic concept for small minds ("at which the philistines laughed stupidly") (W I 342), since such Orphean daring transcends their one-dimensional thought processes:

> Indessen ein Philister stolz verblüfft
> Durch aufgesteiften Leichnam des *Vitruv*,
> Von seines ausgestopften Schulpferds Huf

Sich *Hippokrene* leckt, *Karnieschen* knifft,
Bist Du mit *Orpheus* glaubend eingeschifft.[9]

(W I 341)

In the realm of the "musicalization of literature" BOGS also serves
as the intermediary figure hovering between the philistine nightmare
on the one hand and the Orphean dream on the other. For example, his
receptivity and capacity for sensual interchange are exaggerated almost
to the point of becoming ludicrous: "Through my ears flowed a whirlpool of music tasting just like fiery alcohol which has been distilled
ten times" (W II 884); "the flutes poured streams of sweet almond
oil" (W II 885); "a thousand flames gushed from the violins" (W II
885); "I felt as though the musical magic were lifting me up with both
hands by the temples, as my grandfather used to do when I was a little
boy to show me the angels" (W II 887). The manner in which the narrator conveys what might be termed the "Nachklänge BOGS'scher
Musik" (in analogy to the Beethoven poem) in the prose renditions
of the extraordinary visions makes them a kind of "verbal music,"
which offers the reader a syn-aesthetic experience of sight, sound, motion, color, and so forth. Whereas the lyric "echoes" of Beethoven's
music made the interiorized universe of creative isolation the springboard from which to project the tonal cosmos into the public domain,
the course pursued by BOGS is, as might be expected, more zigzag in
its path, beginning with the musical stimuli from without, being immediately appropriated in the inner recesses of the listener's brain, and
interrupted periodically by prosaic reality. Note this progression in
the following passage:

> Out of all instruments a hurricane of tones broke forth, I closed my
> eyes . . . my two hands held the watches in my pockets, good-bye,
> world! The tempest of a heathen symphony seized my thinning hair,
> my brain with all its capacities slipped out of my ears and opened up
> like a twin sail, which the wind then caught hold of and bore me
> through heaven and earth, water and fire, sometimes tossing me against
> the cliffs—alas, my watches! (W II 883–884).

What follows this introduction are extensive psychic abberations trig-
gered by the music and only feasible in a hermetically sealed world

---

[9] "While a philistine haughtily dumbfounded / By the stiffened corpse of
Vitruvius / Licks from the hoof of his stuffed, trained horse / Hippocrene [the
fountain on Mount Helikon sacred to the Muses and said to be a source of poetic
inspiration], dodges cornices [?], / You, full of faith, have set sail with Orpheus."

removed from rational causality—as the first of the visionary land-
scapes illustrates:

> I was at the bottom of an ocean, all people were fishes, I myself a type
> of herring; I saw myself a thousand times, then music resounded power-
> fully, a whale rose up, fantasies of death leaped from its nostrils, a
> clap from its tail, a flood, we were all washed down its gullet; there sat
> Jonah, singing and praising God. (W II 884)

Lyric musicality, it will be recalled, entailed not only the verbal
evocation of a universe divorced from the exigencies of the real world,
but also the manipulation of vowel and consonant configurations. Re-
turning once more to the anecdotal parable "Lieblingslied der Geizigen"
with which the recapitulation of the findings of chapter 3 began, it
can also be shown that this rather unassuming tale contains, on a very
rudimentary level, the seeds of that technique of sequential construction and destruction of a hermetically sealed world of poetry analyzed
previously with reference to "Wenn der lahme Weber träumt." For
instance, following his initial disappointment, the lutist improvises
some verses in which the bitter truth of his discovery is couched behind
a veil of puns and other verbal pyrotechnics:

> Sing ich Sonette euch auch noch so nette:
> Ihr werdet nimmer Speise mir und Bette,
> Statt Geld für Verse Fersengeld nur geben.[10]
> (W II 857)

One is subsequently reminded of the opening section of Weaver Jürgo's
wish-dream sequence in which the lame weaver wove, the lame lark
flew, the sick nightingale sang, and so forth, when the singer next
evokes a world through the power of the spoken word, an idealized
realm in which musical feats enjoy their proper reward:

> Ein Duca ist mir lieb, doch mit Dukaten!
> Souv'rainen pflege ich für Severinen,
> Baronen ohne Bares nie zu dienen—
> Und kann mit Ahnen keine Hahnen braten![11]
> (W II 858)

---

[10] "No matter how nicely I sing you sonnets: / You will never give me bed
and board, / Instead of money for verses, you will give me only my walking
papers."

[11] "I like a duke, but one with ducats! / Sovereigns I serve for severence pay,
/ I never serve a baron who does not bare his cash—/ And with my ancestors I
can roast no roosters!"

The concluding verse of the above stanza is reminiscent of the cryptic, logically "meaningless," but poetically significant lines "die taube Nüchternheit, sie lausche" and "der Traube Schüchternheit berausche" from the "Weber" poem, concepts which represented the low point of rational comprehensibility but the high point of lyric evocation through tonal configuration and association.

The subsequent undermining and eventual collapse of this fragile verbal paradise which marked "Wenn der lahme Weber träumt" likewise has a counterpart in the present context as the singer departs from this parsimonious threshold with empty pockets but with full knowledge of the "naked truth" of the situation ("bar und blank in voller Klarheit," "die Wahrheit" [W II 858]). But this truth is that facticity which always holds sway in the philistine world, a realm without access to a higher echelon of existence: "Denn nur *Reale* sind bei euch's Reelle"—in modern terms, only "realia" are "real." The lutist, for having dared expose the "truth," is finally rewarded by having his instrument smashed over his head by the irate populace. In keeping with the philistine framework, the destruction wrought by the intrusion of "naked truth" operates not only on the mental and aesthetic levels, but also on the physical.

One final observation might be made concerning the sound symbolism in the lines and words used to relate these events: "entzwei," "Wahrheit geigt . . . Geige . . . zerschlagen." It was noted previously that the vowel configuration "*a-ei*" was of prime importance in Brentano's poetic tonality and that the "*ei*" component was usually suggestive of anguish or some other form of psychic malaise, whereas the "*a*" vowel tended to denote positive or beneficial factors. Thus the proverb with which the tale closes, conveys by means of its arrangement of fundamental tones in stressed syllables (*a-ei-ei-a*) either the restoration of balance (truth—Wahrheit—returns when the illusion of art—"geigen," "Geige"—is destroyed—"zerschlagen") or, if one recalls the tonal sequence in the names of key fairy tale figures (*Ameleya, Gackeleia*) the familiar triadic rhythm so prevalent in Romantic thought and art, whereby the state of an original golden age of innocence in Paradise is superceded by a period of painful consciousness (in which man is keenly aware of what he has lost), to be followed in some unspecified future by the restoration of the primordial condition of bliss transposed, as it were, to a "new key," insofar as pristine innocence has been heightened by the dimension of knowledge. Viewed in this light, even the simple song form of a work like "Guitarre und Lied" (A-B-A¹) could be regarded as symbolic of the mystical, magical tripartite complex.

Considering the complacency of the arch-philistine toward the ineffables of life, and his insensitive approach to the aesthetic world, it seems virtually inconceivable that this type of individual could experience the breakdown of language and the "crisis of communication" which Brentano underwent and which served as the focal point of chapter 5. In fact, the philistines in Brentano's works share the sense of distrust for the verbal medium which the poet himself came to harbor. For example, one stipulation made by the Society of Marksmen for BOGS's possible admission at some future date is that the Watchmaker renounce all undesirable elements in society such as "Bänkelsänger," or street singers, a term which Brentano had used in derogatory fashion to refer to poetry per se. BOGS, on the other hand, had expressed some qualms about the shortcomings of language, but certainly not in terms calculated to placate the Society: "We no longer pray out of reverence, love and enthusiasm, because for us the word suffices and we no longer need pure, eternal music which makes the ultimate statement in order to delineate the soul, and the soul no longer loves what is inexpressibly inexpressible" (W II 880). Remarks such as these certainly ally BOGS closer with the Orphean camp and reveal a break with the philistine faction. The latter, even though they are unaware of the collapse of words and language, certainly contributed to these developments.

In his critique of 1811, Brentano points out how the ancestors of the present-day philistines—the builders of the tower of Babel—tarnished the aboriginal language of mankind, so that "the confused babbling of the philistines today echoes the linguistic hodgepodge from Babylon" (W II 975). In order to illustrate this thesis, Brentano cites the speech pecularities of a philistine whom he recently met and whose mode of articulation almost deprives language of its fundamental purpose: communication. The following compendium of philistine terms together with their "translation" by the narrator into comprehensible German may illustrate the disenfranchisement process: "die Zusammenstimmung" becomes "das Konzert"; "klangschallend" becomes "musikalisch"; "Schallwerkzeuge" becomes "Instrumente," and so forth.

Not only does such gibberish undermine the role of language as

a means of communication, it also deprives the object spoken about—
in this case, music—of its verbal existence. The next stage in the
process of deterioration would be to dispense with the creator of music,
the composer; and this development can be seen in the poem "Der Musikanten schwere Weinzunge," written in the same year as the satire
on the philistine (1811). In this occasional poem, "Mozart ein Wunder-
thier" becomes confused with "O zartes Wunderbier" (after what has
been ascertained concerning the philistine, it is no surprise to find
Mozart the prodigy mistaken for an alcoholic beverage) while Beethoven, in his esoteric late works ("Ja, auf *Beethovens* Spur / Fängt's oft
zu dunkeln an!" [GS II 555]) is relegated to a place of artistic insignifi-
cance: "Bet hinter'm Ofen nur / Deine Karfunkeln an!" (GS II
555).[12]

Admittedly, lines such as the above are found in an occasional
poem written for a boisterous occasion and are not the product of a
rare moment of genuine lyric inspiration. By the same token, the story
of BOGS, the essay on the *Philister*, and the "Lieblingslied der Geizigen" are by no means literary works of first magnitude; rather they are
momentary flashes of the kaleidoscopic fantasy that characterized
Brentano's productivity. Were his barbs and broadsides against the
philistine restricted to these polemical writings, then the battle lines
between the Orphean contingent and their philistine opponents would
be clearly discernible. However, as has been shown in *Godwi* and
Aloys und Imelde, this is not always true. The spheres of influence
ascribed to Orphean genius and its antipode are often inextricably enmeshed, and whereas they may be disentangled for the purposes of
critical analysis, they exist only as an integrated totality. The suspicion
also persists that in order to have scrutinized the philistine temperament so astutely and presented it so convincingly, Brentano may have
actually experienced it first-hand in his own person. In support of this
view one might cite the report that upon hearing Brentano read aloud
his treatise of 1811 (*Der Philister vor, in und nach der Geschichte*)
for an elite coterie in Berlin, Fichte, a member of the audience, is reputed to have characterized the author as the greatest philistine of
them all.[13]

The above assertion becomes even more convincing when one re-

---

[12] "Lonely Beethoven, / Darkness brings the nights!"
  "Only behind the oven / Worship your almandites!
[13] Rudolf Köpke, *Ludwig Tieck* (Leipzig: Brockhaus, 1855), I, 250–251.

calls how often in Brentano's major works lines of great poetic and lyric beauty vie with the most pedestrian verses. In the *Rheinmärchen*, for instance, one encounters not only the incomparable lullaby "Singet leise, leise, leise" with all its verbal magic, but also stanzas such as the following, which bear many of the earmarks of philistine artistry (exaggeration, lack of restraint):

> Wie wird mir? Wer wollte wohl weinen,
> Wenn winkend aus wiegendem See
> Süß sinnend Sternelein scheinen,
> Werd' heiter, weich' weiter du wildwundes Herz.
>
> Komm Kühle, komm küsse den Kummer,
> Süß säuselnd von sinnender Stirn,
> Schlaf schleiche, umschleire mit Schlummer
> Die Schmerzen, die schwül mir die Seele umschwirren.
>
> Flöß' flehend du Flötengeflüster
> Mir Himmel und Heimat ans Herz,
> Leucht' lieblich und lispele düster
> Und fächle, daß lächle im Schlummer der Schmerz.[14]

(W I 244–245)

After comparing and contrasting the lilting cradle song with this cumbersome lullaby, one must conclude that Brentano shared both the Orphean blessing and the philistine curse. Yet does this not place him on still another threshold—between the ultimate poetic idiom and the idiosyncrasies of the bungling amateur? If so, then it would seem that in the process of writing the kind of poetry which anticipated Rilke's challenge of being, amidst the transitory, in the realm of decline, a resonant glass that shattered while yet ringing, Clemens Brentano produced a select number of lyrics that illustrate musicality in the best sense of the term, as well as a fair amount of writing in which the language no longer can be considered the means to an end, but rather the end of a means.

[14] No attempt is made in the following translation to render completely the flood of alliteration that marks all three stanzas: "What's happening to me? Who would wish to weep / When from the surging sea, little stars shine, / Waving and meditating sweetly, / Grow gay, mellow more, wildly wounded heart! // Come cool, come kiss care / From pensive brow, sighing sweetly, / May slumber slink in, screen with sleep / The sorrows which encircle my soul in so sultry fashion. // Float fervently, you whispering flute, / Holding heaven and homeland to my heart, / Lighten lovingly and lisp dismally / And fan breezes, so that suffering might smile in slumber."

Chronology of the Life and Major Writings of Clemens Brentano

1778　Born in Ehrenbreitstein near Coblenz.

1784　After spending his early childhood in Frankfurt am Main, Brentano is sent to his Aunt Luise Möhn in Coblenz.

1797　Begins his study at various universities, including Halle and Jena.

1798　Meets the writer Sophie Mereau, wife of Jena professor of law.

1799　Acquaintance with Minna Reichenbach.

1800　The fairy tale fragment *Die Rose* (The Rose) is published. Estranged from Sophie Mereau.

The satire *Gustav Wasa* appears under the pseudonym "Maria."

1801　The novel *Godwi oder Das steinerne Bild der Mutter. Ein verwildeter Roman von Maria* (*Godwi or the Statue of the Mother. A Novel Run Wild by Maria*).

Der Sänger (*The Singer*), a fragmentary narrative.

Friendship with Achim von Arnim begins.

Comedy of intrigue *Ponce de Leon*.

1802　Rhine journey with Arnim. Brentano meets and falls in love with Benedikte Korbach and Hannchen Kraus (he calls the latter "my new Arnim").

Libretto or text for an opera, *Die lustigen Musikanten* (*The Merry Musicians*).

Resumption of contact with Sophie Mereau.

1803　Reconciliation with Sophie Mereau, marriage in Marburg.

1805　Volume I of *Des Knaben Wunderhorn* (*The Boy's Magic Horn*).

1806　Death of Sophie Mereau Brentano.

1807　*Entweder wunderbare Geschichte von BOGS dem Uhrmacher ..., oder die über die Ufer der badischen Wochenschrift als Beilage ausgetretene Konzert-Anzeige* (*Either the Strange Story of BOGS the Watchmaker ..., or the Concert Review*

Which, Although a Supplement, Has Overflowed the Banks of the Baden Weekly), a satiric prose fantasy.

Marriage to Auguste Bußmann.

1808 Publication with Arnim of the *Zeitung für Einsiedler* (*Newspaper for Hermits*).

1809 Flight from Auguste to Munich and other parts of Bavaria (divorced 1812).

1810 Partial copy of the epic *Romanzen vom Rosenkranz* (*Romances of the Rosary*), begun in 1803, sent to the painter Philipp Otto Runge.

1811 Fragments of the novel *Der schiffbrüchige Galeerensklave vom Todten Meer* (*The Shipwrecked Galley Slave from the Dead Sea*).

Der Philister vor, in und nach der Geschichte (*The Philistine in pre-, present-, and post-History*), a satiric essay.

1812 The tragedy *Aloys und Imelde*.

1813 The patriotic spectacle *Viktoria und ihre Geschwister mit fliegenden Fahnen und brennender Lunte* (*Victoria and Her Siblings with Flying Colors and Burning Fuse*).

1814 Theatrical reviews for the *Dramaturgischer Beobachter* in Vienna. *Die Gründung Prags. Ein historisch-romantisches Drama* (*The Founding of Prague. A Historic-Romantic Drama*).

1815 Review of Beethoven's *Fidelio* and other operas in the *Berlinische Nachrichten von Staats- und gelehrten Sachen*.

The novella *Die Schachtel mit der Friedenspuppe* (*The Case with the Doll of Peace*).

1816 First meeting with Luise Hensel.

1817 Brentano's universal confession (marking his official "return" to Catholicism).

First report of the stigmatized nun Anna Katharina Emmerick (or Emmerich) in Dülmen.

The novella *Geschichte vom braven Kasperl und dem schönen Annerl* (*The Story of Honest Kaspar and Fair Anna*).

The narrative tale *Die mehreren Wehmüller und ungarischen Nationalgesichter* (*The Several Mr. Wehmüllers and Hungarian National Physiognomies*).

1818 *Aus der Chronika eines fahrenden Schülers* (*From the Chronicle of a Wandering Student*), the original version begun in 1801/1802.

1819 Brentano puts up his entire library for auction—except for theological books.

1824 Death of Anna Katharina Emmerick and the end of Brentano's service as the recording secretary of her visions.

1825 Brentano devotes his time and efforts to charitable organizations of the Catholic church.

1833 *Das bittere Leiden unsers Herrn Jesu Christi* (*The Bitter Passion of Our Lord Jesus Christ*), based on the visions of Anna Katharina Emmerick.

Encounter with and love for Emilie Linder, the Swiss artist.

1835 Revisions of *Das Märchen von Gockel und Hinkel* (*The Fairy Tale of Gockel and Hinkel*), which had been begun in 1815/1816. Final version appears in 1837 as *Das Märchen von Gockel, Hinkel und Gackeleia*.

Begins work on the supplement to the *Gockel* tale, called *Blätter aus dem Tagebuch der Ahnfrau* (*Pages from the Diary of the Ancestress*).

Revisions begun on *Das Märchen von Fanferlieschen Schönefüßchen* (*The Fairy Tale of Fanferlieschen Schönefüßchen*) and completed 1838.

1841 "Die Marina-Legende" ("The Legend of Marina").

1842 Death of Brentano in Aschaffenburg.

1846–1847

Appearance of *Die Märchen des Clemens Brentano* containing, among others: the so-called "Rheinmärchen" of *Müller Radlauf* (*Miller Radlauf*), *Von dem Hause Starenberg und den Ahnen des Müllers Radlauf* (*Of the House of Starenberg and the Ancestors of Miller Radlauf*), and of *Schneider Siebentot* (*Tailor Siebentot*).

Selected Bibliography

I. Brentano Editions and Translations

An Anthology of German Poetry from Hölderlin to Rilke in English Translation. Ed. Angel Flores. Gloucester, Mass.: Peter Smith, 1965.

Anthology of German Poetry. Ed. Alexander Gode and Frederick Ungar. New York: Frederick Ungar, 1964.

Arnim, Ludwig Achim von, and Clemens Brentano. *Des Knaben Wunderhorn.* Ed. Willi Koch. Munich: Winkler, 1957.

Brentano, Clemens. *Briefwechsel zwischen Clemens Brentano und Sophie Mereau.* Ed. Heinz Amelung. 2 vols. Leipzig: Insel, 1908.

————. *Clemens Brentano: Briefe.* Ed. Friedrich Seebaß. 2 vols. Nürnberg: Hans Carl, 1951.

————. *Clemens Brentano: Briefe an Emilie Linder.* Ed. Wolfgang Frühwald. Bad Homburg: Gehlen, 1969.

————. *Clemens Brentano: Briefwechsel mit Heinrich Remigius Sauerländer.* Ed. Anton Krättli. Zurich: Artemis, 1962.

————. *Clemens Brentano: Dichter über ihre Dichtung.* Ed. Werner Vordtriede and Gabriele Bartenschlager. Munich: Heimeran, 1970.

————. *Clemens Brentano: Gedichte.* Ed. Werner Vordtriede. Frankfurt am Main: Insel, 1963.

————. *Clemens Brentano: Gedichte.* Ed. Paul Requadt. Stuttgart: Reclam, 1968.

————. *Clemens Brentano und Apollonia Diepenbrock: Eine Seelenfreundschaft in Briefen.* Ed. Ewald Reinhard. Munich: Parcus, 1924.

————. *Clemens Brentano und Luise Hensel.* Ed. Hubert Schiel. Aschaffenburg: Paul Pattloch, 1956.

Brentano, Clemens. *Clemens Brentano und Minna Reichenbach: Ungedruckte Briefe des Dichters.* Ed. W. Limburger. Leipzig: Insel, 1921.

————. *Clemens Brentanos Frühlingskranz.* Ed. Heinz Amelung. Leipzig: Insel, 1921.

————. *Clemens Brentanos Liebesleben.* Ed. Lujo Brentano. Frankfurt am Main: Frankfurter Verlags-Anstalt, 1921.

————. *Clemens Brentanos Romanfragment 'Der schiffbrüchige Galeerensklave vom Todten Meer.'* In *Abhandlungen der Deutschen Akademie der Wissenschaft.* Philosophisch-historische Klasse, No. 4 (1948), "Nachwort" by Walther Rehm, pp. 15–54.

————. *Das Leben unseres Herrn und Heilandes Jesu Christi. Nach den Gesichten der gottseligen Anna Katharina Emmerich aufgeschrieben von Clemens Brentano.* 3 vols. Regensburg: Friedrich Pustet, 1858–1860.

———. *Das unsterbliche Leben: Unbekannte Briefe von Clemens Brentano.* Ed. Wilhelm Schellberg and Friedrich Fuchs. Jena: Eugen Diederichs, 1939.

———. *Die Chronika des fahrenden Schülers: Urfassung.* Stuttgart: Philipp Reclam, 1971. "Nachwort" by Elisabeth Stopp, pp. 112–136.

———. *Gedichte.* Ed. Wolfgang Frühwald. Munich: Rowohlt, 1968.

———. *Gesammelte Schriften.* 9 vols. Frankfurt am Main: J. D. Sauerländer, 1852–1855.

———. *Sämtliche Werke.* Ed. Carl Schüddekopf et al. 10 vols. Munich and Leipzig: Georg Müller, 1909–1917.

———. *Viktoria und ihre Geschwister.* Berlin: Maurersche Buchhandlung, 1817.

———. *Werke.* Ed. Max Preitz. 3 vols. Leipzig and Vienna: Bibliographisches Institut, 1914.

———. *Werke.* Ed. Wolfgang Frühwald, Bernhard Gajek and Friedhelm Kemp. 4 vols. Munich: Hanser, 1963–1968.

German Stories and Tales. Ed. Robert Pick. New York: Washington Square Press, 1954.

Niendorf, Emma von. *Aus der Gegenwart.* Berlin: Duncker, 1844.

II. *Critical Studies of Brentano and Romanticism*

Adam, Joseph. *Clemens Brentanos Emmerick-Erlebnis.* Freiburg im Breisgau: Herder, 1956.

Arntzen, Helmut. *Die ernste Komödie.* Munich: Nymphenburger Verlagshandlung, 1968.

Behrens, Jürgen, Wolfgang Frühwald, and Detlev Lüders. "Zum Stand der Arbeiten an der Frankfurter Brentano-Ausgabe." *Jahrbuch des Freien Deutschen Hochstifts* (1969), 398–426.

Boetius, Henning. "Zur Entstehung und Textqualität von Clemens Brentanos 'Gesammelten Schriften.'" *Jahrbuch des Freien Deutschen Hochstifts* (1967), 406–457.

Dellers, Walter. *Clemens Brentano: Der Versuch eines kindlichen Lebens.* Diss. Basel, 1955. Basel: Druckerei Cratander, 1960.

Diel, Johannes B., and Wilhelm Kreiten. *Clemens Brentano: Ein Lebensbild nach gedruckten und ungedruckten Quellen.* 2 vols. Freiburg im Breisgau: Herder'sche Verlagshandlung, 1877–1878.

Enzensberger, Hans Magnus. *Brentanos Poetik.* Munich: Hanser, 1961.

Ewald, Reingard. "Das Bild des Kindes bei Clemens Brentano." Diss. Graz, 1966.

Fetzer, John F. "Clemens Brentano on Music and Musicians." *Studies in Romanticism,* 7 (1968): 218–230.

———. "Old and New Directions in Clemens Brentano Research (1931–1968)." *Literaturwissenschaftliches Jahrbuch* (im Auftrag der Görres-Gesellschaft), 11 (1970): 87–119; 12 (1971): 113–203.

————. "Clemens Brentano's *Godwi*: Variations on the Melos-Eros Theme," *Germanic Review*, 42 (1967): 108–123.

Friesen, Gerhard. "Clemens Brentano's 'Nachklänge Beethovenscher Musik.'" In *Traditions and Transitions: Studies in Honor of Harold Jantz*. Ed. Liselotte E. Kurth, William McClain, and Holger Homan. Munich: Delp'sche Verlagsbuchhandlung, 1972, Pp. 194–209.

Frühwald, Wolfgang. "Clemens Brentano." In *Deutsche Dichter der Romantik*. Ed. Benno von Wiese. Berlin: Erich Schmidt, 1971. Pp. 280–309.

Frühwald, Wolfgang. "Das verlorene Paradies. Zur Deutung von Clemens Brentanos *Herzliche Zueignung* des Märchens *Gockel, Hinkel und Gackalia* (1838)." *Literaturwissenschaftliches Jahrbuch*, 3 (1962): 113–192.

————. "Frankfurter Brentano-Ausgabe." *Jahrbuch für Internationale Germanistik*, 1, No. 2 (1969): 70–80.

————. "Zu neueren Brentano-Ausgaben." *Literaturwissenschaftliches Jahrbuch*, 5 (1964): 361–380.

Gajek, Bernhard. *Homo poeta: Zur Kontinuität der Problematik bei Clemens Brentano*. Frankfurt am Main: Athenäum, 1971.

Glöckner, Karl. *Brentano als Märchenerzähler*. Deutsche Arbeiten der Universität Köln, 3. Jena: Diederich, 1937.

Guignard, René. *Un poète romantique allemand. Clemens Brentano (1778–1842)*. Diss. Paris, 1933. Paris: Les Belles Lettres, 1933.

Gundolf, Friedrich. *Romantiker I*. Berlin: H. Keller, 1930.

Hilton, Ian. "Clemens Brentano." In *German Men of Letters*. Ed. Alex Natan. London: O. Wolff, 1969. V, 51–74.

Hofe, Gerhard vom. *Die Romantikkritik Sören Kierkegaards*. Frankfurt am Main: Athenäum, 1972.

Hoffmann, Werner. *Clemens Brentano: Leben und Werk*. Bern and Munich: Francke, 1966.

Hunter, Rosemarie. "Clemens Brentanos 'Wenn der lahme Weber träumt' und das Problem der Sprachverfremdung." *Germanisch-Romanische Monatsschrift*, 50 (1969): 144–152.

Immerwahr, Raymond. "Romanticism." In *The Challenge of German Literature*. Ed. Horst S. Daemmrich and Diether H. Haenicke. Detroit: Wayne State University Press, 1971. Pp. 183–231.

Jaeger, Hans. *Clemens Brentanos Frühlyrik*. Frankfurt am Main: M. Diesterweg, 1926.

Jenisch, Erich. *Die Entfaltung des Subjektivismus: Von der Aufklärung zur Romantik*. Königsberg: Gräfe and Unzer, 1929.

Kahn-Wallerstein, Carmen. "Clemens Brentanos Verhängnis." *Schweizer Rundschau*, 50 (1950–1951): 611–619.

Kayser, Rudolf. *Arnims und Brentanos Stellung zur Bühne*. Diss. Würzburg. Berlin: W. Kuhlisch, 1914.

Kerr, Alfred. *Godwi: Ein Kapitel deutscher Romantik*. Berlin: Georg Bondi, 1898.

Killy, Walther. *Wandlungen des lyrischen Bildes*. 3rd ed. Göttingen: Vandenhoeck & Ruprecht, 1961.

Köpke, Rudolf. *Ludwig Tieck.* Leipzig: Brockhaus, 1855.

Korff, Hermann August. *Geist der Goethezeit.* Vol. 4. Leipzig: Koehler & Amelang, 1953.

Leoni, Editha. "Clemens Brentano und die deutsche Barocklyrik." Diss. Frankfurt am Main, 1932.

Mathes, Jürg. "Ein Tagebuch Clemens Brentanos für Luise Hensel." *Jahrbuch des Freien Deutschen Hochstifts* (1971), 198–310.

Mennemeier, Franz Norbert. "Rückblick auf Brentanos *Godwi.* Ein Roman 'ohne Tendenz.' " *Wirkendes Wort,* 16 (1966): 24–33.

Michels, Josef. *Clemens Brentano: Irrtum des Herzens—Einkehr bei Gott.* Münster in Westphalia: Regensbergsche Verlagsbuchhandlung, 1948.

Pfeiffer-Belli, Wolfgang. *Clemens Brentano.* Freiburg im Breisgau: Herder, 1947.

Politzer, Heinz. "Das Schweigen der Sirenen." *Deutsche Vierteljahrsschrift für Literaturwissenschaft und Geistesgeschichte,* 41 (1967): 444–467.

Preisendanz, Wolfgang. "Zur Poetik der deutschen Romantik, I: Die Abkehr vom Grundsatz der Naturnachahmung." In *Die deutsche Romantik.* Ed. Hans Steffen. Göttingen: Vandenhoeck & Ruprecht, 1967. Pp. 54–74.

Reed, Eugene. "The Union of the Arts in Brentano's *Godwi.*" *Germanic Review,* 29 (1954): 102–118.

Rehm, Walther. "Brentano und Hölderlin." *Hölderlin Jahrbuch* (1947), 127–178.

———. "Brentano und Hölderlin." In *Begegnungen und Probleme.* Bern: Francke, 1957. Pp. 40–88.

———. *Orpheus: Der Dichter und die Toten.* Düsseldorf: L. Schwann, 1950.

Rupprich, Hans. *Brentano, Luise Hensel und Ludwig von Gerlach.* Vienna: Österreichischer Bundesverlag für Unterricht, Wissenschaft und Kunst, 1927.

Schaub, Gerhard. *Le Génie Enfant. Die Kategorie des Kindlichen bei Clemens Brentano.* Berlin: Walter de Gruyter, 1973.

Schoeps, Hans-Joachim. "Clemens Brentano nach Ludwig von Gerlachs Tagebüchern und Briefwechsel." *Jahrbuch des Freien Deutschen Hochstifts* (1970), 281–303.

Scholz, Felix. *Clemens Brentano und Goethe.* Leipzig: Mayer and Müller, 1927.

Staiger, Emil. *Die Zeit als Einbildungskraft des Dichters.* 1939. Reprinted, Zurich: Atlantis, 1953.

Steig, Reinhold. *Achim von Arnim und die ihm nahe standen.* 3 vols. Stuttgart: J. G. Cotta'sche Buchhandlung, 1894–1913.

———. *Clemens Brentano und die Brüder Grimm.* Stuttgart and Berlin: J. G. Cotta'sche Buchhandlung, 1914.

———. "Schäfers Klagelied von Goethe." *Euphorion,* 2 (1895): 813–817.

Stopp, Elisabeth. "Brentano's *Chronika* and its Revision." In *Sprache und Bekenntnis. Sonderband des Literaturwissenschaftlichen Jahrbuchs: Hermann Kunisch zum 70. Geburtstag.* Ed. Wolfgang Frühwald and Günter Niggl. Berlin: Duncker and Humblot, 1971. Pp. 161–184.

————. "Brentano's 'O Stern und Blume'; Its Poetic and Emblematic Context." *Modern Language Review*, 67 (1972): 95–117.

Taeschler, Hans. *'Die Gründung Prags.' Eine Interpretation*. Diss. Zurich. Zurich: Juris, 1950.

Tucker, Harry. "Water as Symbol and Motif in the Poetry of Clemens Brentano." *Monatshefte*, 45 (1953): 320–323.

Tymms, Ralph. *German Romantic Literature*. London: Methuen, 1955.

Vordtriede, Werner. "Clemens Brentano's Novalis Experience." *Modern Language Quarterly*, 11 (1950): 73–78.

Wille, Klaus. *Die Signatur der Melancholie im Werk Clemens Brentanos*. Europäische Hochschulschriften, Reihe I, No. 36. Bern: Herbert Lang, 1970.

Willoughby, Leonard A. *The Romantic Movement in Germany*. London: Oxford, 1930.

Wollenberg, Friedrich W. *Brentanos Jugendlyrik: Studien zur Struktur seiner dichterischen Persönlichkeit*. Diss. Hamburg, 1961. Hamburg: Private Printing, 1964.

III. *Works on the Relationship of Music and Literature*

Benz, Richard. *Die Welt der Dichter und die Musik*. Düsseldorf: Diederichs Verlag, 1949.

Bernhardi, A. F. *Sprachlehre*. 2 vols. Berlin, 1803.

Böckmann, Paul. *Formensprache: Studien zur Literaturästhetik und Dichtungsinterpretation*. Hamburg: Hoffmann and Campe, 1966.

Brown, Calvin S. *Tones into Words*. Athens, Georgia: University of Georgia Press, 1953.

Dabney, J. P. *The Musical Basis of Verse*. 1901. Reprinted, New York: Greenwood, 1968.

Eliot, T. S. "Hamlet and His Problems." In *The Sacred Wood*. 3rd ed. London: Methuen, 1932. Pp. 95–103.

————. *On Poetry and Poets*. New York: Farrar, Straus and Cudahy, 1957.

Hassan, Ihab. *The Dismemberment of Orpheus*. New York: Oxford University Press, 1971.

Heller, Erich. *The Artist's Journey into the Interior*. New York: Random House, 1965.

Highet, Gilbert. *A Clerk at Oxenford*. New York: Oxford, 1954.

Hollander, John. *The Untuning of the Sky: Ideas of Music in English Poetry 1500–1700*. Princeton: Princeton University Press, 1961.

Ives, Margaret. "Musical Elements in Schiller's Concept of Harmony." *German Life and Letters*, 18 (1964–1965): 111–116.

————. *The Analogue of Harmony: Some Reflections on Schiller's Philosophical Essays*. Pittsburgh: Duquesne University Press, 1970.

Klein, Hans. "Musikalische Komposition in deutscher Dichtkunst." *Deutsche Vierteljahrsschrift für Literaturwissenschaft und Geistesgeschichte*, 8 (1930): 680–716.

Lanier, Sidney. *The Science of English Verse*. New York: Scribner, 1880.

Mittenzwei, Johannes. *Das Musikalische in der Literatur*. Halle/Saale: VEB Verlag Sprache und Literatur, 1962.

Newton, Douglas. "The Composer and the Music of Poetry." *The Score*, 1 (1948): 13–20.

Pater, Walter. "The School of Giorgione." In *Renaissance Studies in Art and Poetry*. London: Macmillan, 1925.

Peacock, Ronald. "Probleme des Musikalischen in der Sprache." In *Weltliteratur: Festgabe für Fritz Strich zum 70. Geburtstag*. Ed. Walter Henzen, Walter Muschg, and Emil Staiger. Bern: Francke, 1952. Pp. 85–100.

Reich, Willi. "Musik in der Literatur." *Stimmen*, 1 (1947): 377–381.

————, ed. *Musik in romantischer Schau: Visionen der Dichter*. Basel: Amerbach-Verlag, 1946.

Scher, Steven Paul. *Verbal Music in German Literature*. New Haven: Yale University Press, 1968.

Schneider, Wilhelm. *Ausdruckswerte der deutschen Sprache*. 1931. Reprinted, Darmstadt: Wissenschaftliche Buchgesellschaft, 1968.

Tiegel, Eva. *Das Musikalische in der romantischen Prosa*. Diss. Erlangen. Coburg: Tageblatt-Haus, 1934.

Walzel, Oskar. *Gehalt und Gestalt im Kunstwerk des Dichters*. 1929. Reprinted, Darmstadt: Wissenschaftliche Buchgesellschaft, 1957.

IV. Editions of Authors Cited (other than Brentano)

Biographische Porträts von Varnhagen von Ense. Leipzig: F. Brockhaus, 1871.

Eichendorff, Joseph von. "Brentano und seine Märchen." 1847. Reprinted in *Aurora*, 24 (1964): 14–20.

————. *Sämtliche Werke*. Ed. Wilhelm Kosch and August Sauer. Regensburg: J. Habbel, 1908 ff.

————. *Werke und Schriften*. Ed. Gerhart Baumann and Siegfried Grosse. Stuttgart: J. G. Cotta'sche Buchhandlung, 1957–1958.

Heine, Heinrich. *Sämtliche Werke*. Ed. Ernst Elster. Leipzig and Vienna: Bibliographisches Institut, n.d.

Herder, Johann Gottfried. *Sämtliche Werke*. Ed. Bernhard Suphan. Berlin: Weidmannsche Buchhandlung, 1877–1913.

Hölderlin, Friedrich. *Sämtliche Werke*. Ed. Friedrich Beißner. 6 vols. Stuttgart: Kohlhammer, 1943–1961.

Hoffmann, E. T. A. *E. T. A. Hoffmanns Werke*. Ed. Georg Ellinger. Berlin: Deutsches Verlagshaus Bong, n.d.

Hofmannsthal, Hugo von. "Ad me ipsum." *Neue Rundschau*, 65 (1954): 358–382.

————. *Gesammelte Werke in Einzelausgaben*. Ed. Herbert Steiner. Frankfurt am Main: S. Fischer, 1945 ff.

Kierkegaard, Søren. *Gesammelte Werke*. Jena: Eugen Diederichs, 1909–1938.

Kleist, Heinrich von. *Werke.* Ed. Erich Schmidt. Leipzig: Bibliographisches Institut, n.d.
Klopstock, Friedrich Gottlieb. *Ausgewählte Werke.* Ed. Karl A. Schleiden. Munich: Hanser, n.d.
Nietzsche, Friedrich. *Gesammelte Werke.* Ed. R. Oehler, M. Oehler, and F. Würzbach. Munich: Musarion Verlag, 1920–1929.
Novalis (Friedrich von Hardenberg). *Werke. Briefe. Dokumente.* Ed. Ewald Wasmuth. Heidelberg: Lambert-Schneider, 1953–1957.
Rilke, Rainer Maria. *Sämtliche Werke.* Ed. Rilke-Archiv. N.p.: Insel, n.d.
Schiller, Friedrich. *Werke.* Ed. Lieselotte Blumenthal and Benno von Wiese. Weimar: Hermann Böhlaus Nachfolger, 1943 ff.
Schlegel, Friedrich. *Kritische Friedrich-Schlegel-Ausgabe.* Ed. Ernst Behler. Munich: Ferdinand Schöningh, 1958 ff.
———. *Kritische Schriften.* Ed. Wolfdietrich Rasch. Munich: Hanser, 1964.
Schopenhauer, Arthur. *Schriften über Musik im Rahmen seiner Ästhetik.* Ed. Karl Stabenow. Regensburg: Bosse, 1922.
Schubart, Christian Friedrich Daniel. *Christian Friedrich Daniel Schubart: Ideen zu einer Ästhetik der Tonkunst.* Ed. Ludwig Schubart. 1806. Reprinted, Leipzig, 1924.
Tieck, Ludwig. *Schriften.* Berlin: G. Reimer, 1828–1854.
Wackenroder, Wilhelm Heinrich. *Werke und Briefe.* Ed. Friedrich von der Leyen. Jena: Eugen Diederichs, 1910.

V. General Reference Works

Beckson, Karl, and Arthur Ganz. *A Reader's Guide to Literary Terms.* New York: Noonday Press, 1960.
Brockway, Wallace, and Herbert Weinstock. *Men of Music.* New York: Simon and Schuster, 1939.
Burke, Kenneth. *The Philosophy of Literary Form.* 2nd ed. New York: Vintage Books, 1961.
Colum, Padraic. *Orpheus: Myths of the World.* New York: Macmillan, 1930.
Curtius, Ernst Robert. *Europäische Literatur und lateinisches Mittelalter.* 4th ed. 1948. Reprinted, Bern: Francke, 1963.
Einstein, Alfred. *Music in the Romantic Era.* New York: W. W. Norton, 1947.
Encyclopedia Britannica. Chicago: William Benton, 1971.
Goetschius, Percy. *Lessons in Musical Form.* Boston: n.p., 1904.
Grout, Donald Jay. *A History of Western Music.* New York: W. W. Norton, 1960.
Guthrie, W. K. C. *Orpheus and Greek Religion.* 2nd ed. London: Methuen, 1952.
Kayser, Wolfgang. *Das sprachliche Kunstwerk.* 6th ed. Bern: A. Francke, 1960.
Kluge, Friedrich. *Etymologisches Wörterbuch der deutschen Sprache.* 19th ed. Ed. Walter Mitzka. Berlin: W. de Gruyter, 1963.

Merker, Paul, and Wolfgang Stammler. *Reallexikon der deutschen Literaturgeschichte*. Ed. Werner Kohlschmidt and Wolfgang Mohr. 2nd ed. Berlin: Walter de Gruyter, 1955 ff.

Müller, Günther. *Geschichte des deutschen Liedes*. 1925. Reprinted, Munich: Wissenschaftliche Buchgesellschaft, 1959.

Muschg, Walter. *Tragische Literaturgeschichte*. 2nd ed. Bern: Francke, 1953.

Musiklexikon. Ed. Hans J. Moser. Berlin-Schöneberg: Max Hesse, 1935.

Paulys *Realencyclopädie der classischen Altertumswissenschaft*. Ed. Georg Wissowá. Stuttgart: J. B. Metzler, 1939.

Sachs, Curt. *The Rise of Music in the Ancient World*. New York: Norton, 1943.

Seyffert, Oskar. *Dictionary of Classical Antiquities*. Ed. Henry Nettleship and J. E. Sandys. 3rd ed. 1894. Reprinted, Cleveland: Meridian, 1961.

Sokel, Walter H. *The Writer in Extremis: Expressionism in 20th-Century German Literature*. Stanford, California: Stanford University Press, 1959.

Staiger, Emil. *Grundbegriffe der Poetik*. 4th ed. Zurich: Atlantis, 1959.

Webster's Third New International Dictionary of the English Language. Ed. Philip B. Gove. Springfield, Mass.: G. & C. Merriam, 1961.

Wellek, René, and Austin Warren. *Theory of Literature*. 3rd ed. New York: Harcourt, Brace & World, 1962.

Index

The following list consists of several different types of entry:

1. Factual data: the names of historical persons, mythological or biblical figures, works of art, music and literature (found under the name of their creator) actually mentioned in the text of this study. For the sake of the reader's convenience, the writings of Clemens Brentano have been divided into two categories, both arranged in alphabetical order:

a. individual works in the major genres (novel, stage pieces, etc.)

b. individual lyric poems (listed either by the title indicated in the text or by the first line when no authorized title is known—a procedure devised for the poems in *Werke* I, 1325–1333; for those lyrics not contained in *Werke* but only in Brentano's *Gesammelte Schriften*, volumes one and two, the titles given in the latter were used, even though it is well known that many of these stem from the editors rather than from the author)

2. General concepts intimately involved with Brentano's career (for example, "Catholic Church") or with his creative writings (such as "Distorting") which, nevertheless, are germane to this particular study of the poet in his capacity as the Orphean singer of German Romanticism.

3. Specific topics related to the prime focal point of this study: the complex relationship of a representative German Romanticist to the art of music. In this case, key words such as "music," "musical," "musicality," "'musicalization" as well as kindred terms (specific instruments, forms of composition, etc.) together with their respective cross-references will enable the reader concerned about musico-poetic correspondences to survey the phenomenon in a more or less systematic fashion. The basic problem with this type of entry, however, is the fact that the specific "key word" does not always appear in the text proper, but may be present in an implicit rather than an explicit form.

Adam, 58, 143
"Affektenlehre" (doctrine of the affections), 235
Agnes, Saint, 155
Alliteration, 220, 222, 229, 232, 233, 238
Amphion, 33, 46, 51
Angelic song, 135, 175–176, 245, 252; of Luise Hensel, 105–108
Animal performers, 70, 71, 94, 129, 142, 266, 276, 279; bear, 144–145; goat, 124; monkey, 142; pig, 279; stag, 192; unicorn, 146. *See also* Caterwauling
Apollinian, 68, 72, 118, 282

Apollo, relationship to Orpheus, 29–30, 65–66
Appearance ("Schein"), 84, 173, 191–192, 244, 246, 285; as a facet of harmony, 87–91. *See also* Discord, Harmony
Architecture (and music), 51, 82, 120, 145, 188, 192, 286–287
Argonauts, 30
Arion, 33, 46, 49–50, 68
Aristotle, views on musical instruments, 66, 67
Arnim, Bettina Brentano von, 21, 71, 85, 92, 93, 94, 102, 123, 124, 137–138,

142, 183, 187; her influence on Clemens' musical understanding, 14–16

Arnim, Ludwig Achim von, 15, 21, 23, 82, 85, 101, 103, 142, 160, 162, 201, 204, 207, 247, 263, 264, 293, 294

Art: absolute, 260–261, 262, 270; pictorial, 82, 84, 97, 148, 155, 156, 194–195, 247. See also Disease (and art)

Assonance, 229, 232

Augmentation, 233

Aurora, 177, 202

Avian song, 104, 113, 123, 124, 163, 170, 171, 187, 228–229, 244–245, 252, 276, 281–282; blackbird, 129; chickens, 124, 256, 257; cock (rooster), 125, 126, 146, 170, 246, 285; finch, 125, 126, 128, 276; lark, 125, 126, 153, 154, 256, 258, 288; owl, 125, 244, 279; quail, 125; raven, 186; robin, 125; siskin, 126; swallow, 125, 126, 127, 163; thrush, 126; titmouse, 126; turkey-cock, 276; vulture, 125, 127, 240, 244–245, 259, 260. See also Nightingale, Swan

Bachofen, Johann J., 65

Bagpipe, 41–43, 73, 139, 281. See also Instrumental symbolism, Woodwinds

Bass viol, 66, 71–72, 74, 196, 200, 241, 276. See also Instrumental symbolism, Stringed instruments

Bassoon, 66, 94, 207, 227. See also Instrumental symbolism, Woodwinds

Beethoven, Ludwig van, 14, 23, 24, 25, 202, 240–241, 251, 252–255, 259, 274, 287, 291, 294

Bernhardi, August F., 239

Brahms, Johannes, 14

Brass instruments, 66, 74, 75, 193. See also Instrumental Symbolism, Horn, Trombone, Trumpet

Brentano, Christian, 147, 150

Brentano, Clemens, editions of his works, 5–7; individual works: "Allerlei Gedanken bei Opern" (Various Thoughts at Operas), 25–27

Aloys und Imelde, 105 n. 54, 110, 127, 188, 201, 291, 294; music of love in, 112–114; philistine ethic in, 280–281

"Am Rhein, Am Rhein," 96–97

Blätter aus dem Tagebuch der Ahnfrau, 74, 84, 140, 146, 169, 174,

213, 295; refrains in, 171–172; sound symbolism of, 243–246

Briefe über das neue Theater, 81, 276

Die Chronika des fahrenden Schülers (revised version: *Aus der Chronika eines fahrenden Schülers*), 84, 160, 163–168, 294–295

Entweder wunderbare Geschichte von BOGS dem Uhrmacher oder . . . , 283–288, 290, 291, 293–294

Erklärung der Sinnbilder auf dem Umschlage dieser Zeitschrift, 32–33, 67, 82

Fanferlieschen Schönefüßchen, 127, 129, 144–145, 186, 278–279, 295

Geschichte vom braven Kasperl und dem schönen Annerl, 294

Gockel, Hinkel und Gackeleia (early version: *Gockel und Hinkel*), 76, 129, 140–141, 148, 160, 172, 177, 213, 242–243, 245, 281–282; nightingale song in, 130–131; revisions as religious contrafact of original, 168–174

Godwi oder Das steinerne Bild der Mutter, 43, 74, 81, 85, 110, 126, 140, 141, 145, 148, 174, 184–185, 188, 203, 252, 264, 274, 279, 286, 290, 291, 293; poem to Orpheus in 33–35; Orphean singer in, 38–40; "'Leier-Lyra" symbol in, 68–69; symbolism of stringed instruments versus winds in, 72–73; concept of harmony in, 88–96; Melos-Eros-Thanatos in, 114–121; the syn-aesthetic in, 189–195; refrain from the poem "Die lustigen Musikanten," 212–214; philistine music in, 275–276

Die Gründung Prags, 2, 33, 127, 134, 188, 294; lyre symbol in, 67–68; avian song in, 124–125; synaesthetic in, 201–202

Gustav Wasa, 75, 81, 145–146, 188, 293; synaesthesia in, 183–185; syn-aesthetic in, 195–200; function of the poem "Symphonie" in, 208–210, 236–237

Des Knaben Wunderhorn, 21, 22, 204, 206, 281 n. 6, 293

Das Leben unseres Herrn und Heilandes Jesu Christi (*Das Leben Jesu*), 143–144

"Lieblingslied der Geizigen," 291; plight of Ophean singer in, 277–278 elements of lyric musicality in, 288–289

Die lustigen Musikanten (as "Singspiel"), 101, 203, 274, 293; synaesthesia in, 185–186; philistine musicians in, 279–280

Die mehreren Wehmüller und ungarischen Nationalgesichter, 294; Michaly the violinist as Orphean performer in, 40–43

Myrtenfräulein, 125

Phaon und Sappho, 204

Der Philister vor, in und nach der Geschichte, 274, 290, 291

Ponce de Leon, 88, 110, 188, 200–201, 271, 275, 293; symbolism of double bass in, 71–72; Melos-Eros-Thanatos theme in, 111–112

Rheinmärchen (those dealing with Miller Radlauf and the House of Starenberg), 75, 124, 125, 129–130, 131, 134, 139, 275, 292, 295; Orphean performer in, 36–37; "Schwanenlied" in, 135–137; musicality of the lullaby in, 211–212; sound symbolism of the name Ameleya, 241–242

Romanzen vom Rosenkranz, 3, 40, 69–70, 73, 81–82, 105 n. 55, 108, 110 n. 68, 144, 151–152, 156, 161 n. 167, 166, 185, 186, 187, 210, 265, 275, 294; Rosadora-Biondette as Orphean figure in, 43–64; organ symbolism in, 76–80; swan song in, 133–134; dance symbolism in, 142–143; dilemma of the Orphean singer in, 174–177

Die Rose, 36, 293

Der Sänger, 67, 76, 87, 110 n. 68, 293; Orphean singer in, 37–38

Die Schachtel mit der Friedenspuppe, 97, 294

Der schriffbrüchige Galeerensklave vom Todten Meer, 294

Schneider Siebentot, 146, 295

Schnürlieschen, 141

Spenersche Zeitung, 25; Brentano's opera critiques in, 203–204

Die stumme Engländerin, 105 n. 55

Viktoria und ihre Geschwister, 75, 188, 202, 294; Brentano's original songs for, 16–19; "'Klangmalerei" in, 227–228

Brentano, Clemens, individual lyric poems arranged alphabetically either by title or first line in accordance with the listings found in W I, 1325–1333 or, if the poem is not included there, according to the information given in GS I–II:

"Der Abend," 185

"Abendständchen," 185

"Alhambra," 127

"Als hohe in sich selbst verwandte Mächte," 189–190, 251, 252

"An . . . nach ihren ersten Besuchen bei A. C. Emmerich," 151–152

"An Schinkel," 82, 286–287

"Auf dem Rhein," 126–127, 229, 244–245

"Auf einen grünen Zweig," 104, 128

"Blumen, still blühende!" 267

"Durch den Wald mit raschen Schritten," 160–163

"Durch die weite öde Wüste!" 157–158

"Ein Becher voll von süßer Huld," 267

"Eine feine reine Myrte," 109

"Einer Jungfrau bei dem Geschenk der Sakontala," 107

"Einsam will ich untergehn," 133, 213, 214, 218

"Die Einsiedlerin," 104

"Den ersten Tropfen dieser Leidensflut," 110

"Es ist der laute Tag hinabgesunken," 99–100, 264

"Frühes Lied," 151

"Frühlingsschrei eines Knechtes aus der Tiefe," 107, 260

"Gärtnerlied im Liedergarten der Liebe," 105 n. 55, 233

"Gesang der Liebe als sie geboren war," 100

"Die Gottesmauer" ("Draus bei Schleswig vor der Pforte"), 227, 232

"Guitarre und Lied," 215–218, 290

"Der heilige Solinus," 155

"Heimweh," 150

"Ich bin durch die Wüste gezogen," 105–106

"Ich darf mich wohl erfreuen," 151

"In das Stammbuch einer jungen Sängerin," 158–159

"Legende von der Heiligen Marina," 155–156, 295

"Lieb' und Leid im leichten Leben," 221–223, 264–265

"Lied beim Scharpiezupfen," 18, 20

"Lied vom Tod der A. C. Emmerich," 132–133

"Lied von eines Studenten Ankunft in Heidelberg," 96

"Die lustigen Musikanten," 74, 89–

91, 120, 203, 212–214, 221–222, 227, 233–234
"Meine Irrtümer in diesem Liede," 266–267
"Das Mosel-Eisgangs-Lied," 146
"Der Musikanten schwere Weinzunge," 291
"Nach großem Leid," 177–178
"Nachklänge Beethovenscher Musik," 251, 252–255, 260
"O kühler Wald," 229–230
"O schweig nur Herz," 106
"O Stern und Blume" [refrain], 172–174, 177–178, 213, 214–215
"O Traum der Wüste, Liebe, endlos Sehnen," 215, 218–220, 252, 256, 259–261
"Phantasie," 94, 207–208, 227, 237
"Schwanenlied," 135–137, 177, 223, 245, 251, 252
"Singet leise, leise, leise," 211–212, 234, 292
"Singweise zum wohlriechenden Franziskerl," 16, 17
"Der Spinnerin Nachtlied," 237–239
"Sprich aus der Ferne," 184–185
"Symphonie," 197–198, 199–200, 208–210, 236–237, 240, 251, 252, 260
"Text zum Oratorium von Ett," 108
"Theodor Körner an Viktoria," 19, 20
"Transitus Apostolorum," 97
"Treulieb, Treulieb ist verloren," 212
Trutznachtigall (adaptations)
  "Begierd' und Lobgesang des Heiligen Augustinus von der Herrlichkeit und Freud' des Himmlischen Paradeises," 152
  "Weihelied zum Ziel und End," 152–153
  "Zueignung," 154
  "Vom Gesange lust'ger Finken," 128–129
  "Das Waldvögelein" ("Es war ein frommer Ordensmann"), 154–155
  "Wenn der lahme Weber träumt, er webe," 74, 243, 252, 256–259, 288–289
  "Wie in Gewölben von Smaragd," 130
  "Wie man das Christkind beherbergen soll," 153
  "Worte am Hügel," 100
  "Zur Stunde, die in Sehnsucht zagt," 109–110
Brentano, Cunigunde (Kunigunde), 85
Brentano, Maximiliane, 13–14

Brentano, Sophie, 21
Bußmann, Auguste, 32–33, 103–104, 128, 130, 294

Calliope (Muse of Epic Song), 30
Canon, 196
Cantata, 21, 23, 171, 278
Castanets, 148
Catalani, Angelica, 169
Caterwauling ("Katzenmusik"), 41, 42–43, 57, 59, 124, 279, 281
Catholic Church, Brentano's relation to, 6, 46, 68, 76, 83–84, 86–87, 94, 108, 147, 148, 263, 294, 295
Chiasmus, 159, 162; tonal chiasmus, 232, 233–234
Chopin, Frédéric, 207
Christ, 44, 49, 62, 132, 144, 152, 159, 162–163, 240, 260; confrontation with Orpheus figure, 30–31; as object of religious verse, 153–154
Church bells, tolling of, 42, 61, 96, 129, 135, 163, 165, 170–171
Circe, 32–33
Cithara, 66
Clarinet, 14, 66, 199, 207, 227. See also Instrumental symbolism, Woodwinds
Contrafact, 157, 164, 168
Crisis: definition of, 1–2; of conscience, 3, 28–64, 65, 138, 174–177, 275; of identity, 3, 5–7; of communication, 4, 262–272, 290–291; of criticism, 8–12
Cygnus, 136, 137, 161. See also Stars and Constellations
Cymbals, 66, 73, 90, 213, 227

Dance, 3, 41, 42–44, 47, 57, 58, 65, 81, 89, 111, 112, 120, 122, 126, 160, 166, 190, 192, 197–198, 200, 201, 204, 209, 236, 237, 276, 285; dialectic of chaotic and cosmic forces in, 137–148, 282–284; Salome's, 143–144
Dante Alighieri, 162
David, 70 n. 10, 153, 278
Desert, image of, 105, 106, 128, 129, 136, 142, 157, 158, 190, 215, 218–220, 252, 256, 259–260
Devil, 42, 98–99, 144, 176, 285. See also Evil, forces of
Diepenbrock, Apollonia, 86
Diepenbrock, Melchior, 86
Diminution, 233, 234
Dionysus (Dionysos) and the Dionysian, 29, 66, 68, 72, 118, 143

Discord (dissonance, disharmony), 3, 87, 88, 89, 98, 112, 200, 278; in relationship to harmony, 80–84. See also Appearance, Harmony

Disease (and art), 72–73, 119

Distorting ("Entstellung") as poetic principle, 249–261, 267. See also Encoding

Doctor Faustus, 33

Double bass. See Bass viol, Instrumental symbolism, Stringed instruments

Dreams and dreaming, 123, 134, 135, 157, 174, 180, 215, 218–220, 229, 246, 252, 256, 258, 259, 288

Drum, 66, 75, 202, 227, 280

Duality (*coincidentia oppositorum*, ambivalence), 35, 44–45, 46, 57, 60, 68, 71, 74, 75, 78, 110, 116, 118, 136–137, 138, 147–148, 149–150, 156–159, 164–168, 169, 176, 177–178, 199, 214, 239, 244, 245, 269, 282, 283–287. See also Crisis of conscience, Dance

Echo, 54, 130, 191, 216, 229–230, 256

Education, 140–141

Eichendorff, Joseph von, 5 n. 3, 13, 180

Eliot, T. S., 9, 271

Emblem literature, 96

Emmerich, Anna K. (C.), 86, 131–133, 294, 295

Encoding, 270. See also Distorting

Enjambement, 208, 222

Erebus, 273, 275, 280

Ett, Kaspar, 108

Eurydice and Eurydicean figures, 29–30, 31–32, 33, 37–38, 43, 45, 52, 55, 56, 77, 80, 121, 138, 156, 192, 218

Eve, 57–58, 143

Evil, forces of, 37, 42, 45, 49, 56, 57, 160–161, 166, 167, 169, 171, 176, 242, 245. See also Devil

Fantasia, 207–208, 227, 237. See also Form, musico-poetic

Fantasy, clash with reality, 71–72, 74, 87, 104, 116, 160, 174, 241, 256, 258, 259, 262. See also Bass viol, Shawm

Fichte, Johann Gottlieb, 291

Finkenstein (sisters), 149

Fire imagery, 49, 80, 109, 134, 145–146, 155, 172, 174, 175, 192, 201, 219, 243, 244, 258, 281. See also Phoenix

Flageolet, 14. See also Instrumental symbolism, Woodwinds

Flower imagery, 39, 77, 101–102, 123, 124, 132–133, 160, 172, 174, 177–178, 183, 213, 214, 246, 267, 285

Flute, 48, 66, 72–73, 82, 89, 107, 116, 162, 166, 169, 185–186, 199, 201, 204, 207, 239, 287, 292. See also Instrumental symbolism, Woodwinds

Folk song, 6, 22

Form, musico-poetic in literature, 182, 206–220, 223–224, 247–248, 249, 261. See also Fantasia, Fugue

Fouqué, Friedrich de la Motte, 71

Freiligrath, Ferdinand, 142

Friendship, 95, 162. See also Harmony, socio-political

Fugue, 169–171, 275, 278. See also Form, musico-poetic in literature

"Gesamtkunstwerk" (total work of art), 47, 116, 117, 118, 156, 179, 188, 192, 197, 286. See also Syn-aesthetic

Gideon, 75

Goethe, Johann Wolfgang von, 13, 16, 22, 24, 117, 142, 188 n. 22, 212; *Faust*, 98; "Kennst du das Land," 22; "Schäfers Klagelied," 16; *Torquato Tasso*, 62, 110, 271; *Wilhelm Meisters Lehrjahre*, 210 n. 52, 212

Golden Age, the, 118, 122, 179, 184, 289

Görres, Joseph, 107

Gozzi, Gasparo, 24

Grillparzer, Franz, 27

"Grundvokale" ("Grundtöne"), 235–246, 289–290. See also "Klangsymbolik"

Guitar, 66, 76, 101–102, 103, 115, 119, 290; Brentano's performance on, 13–15; in poem "Guitarre und Lied," 215–218. See also Instrumental symbolism, Stringed instruments

Günderode, Karoline (Caroline) von, 126

Günderode, Minchen (Mienchen) von, 100–101

Hades, 29–30, 38, 51–52, 55, 150

Händel, Georg Friedrich, 278

Harmonica, 76, 193. See also Instrumental symbolism

Harmony, 3, 36, 50, 51, 65, 73, 80–99, 117, 118, 120, 122, 170–171, 183, 188, 202, 225, 236, 278, 284; aesthetic, 80–84, 179, 183, 184, 188; personal, 80, 85, 86, 87, 89–91, 92,

117, 141, 245, 278, 289; socio-political, 80, 92–97, 117, 202, 278; transcendental, 80, 97–99. See also Discord, Appearance

Harp, 37, 38, 39, 44, 47, 48–51, 52, 53–54, 57, 58–60, 62–63, 66, 67, 69 n. 6, 70–71, 72, 76–77, 79, 114, 122, 142, 153, 155, 157, 169, 175, 176, 241, 282, 284. See also Instrumental symbolism, Stringed instruments

Haydn, Franz Joseph, 209

Heine, Heinrich, 6 n. 6, 271

Hensel, Luise, 86, 103, 104, 127, 128, 129, 133, 136, 138, 149, 151, 152, 154, 213, 214, 241, 266, 294; as the angel in the desert, 105–108. See also Angelic song

Herder, Johann Gottfried, 121–122, 205

Hero (and Leander), 167

Herod, 143–144

Herodias, 143

Hirn, Frau, 147

Hoffmann, E. T. A., 9 n. 16, 12, 25, 27, 72, 205, 207, 253 n. 125, 266; Phantasiestücke in Callots Manier, 12, 207; Ritter Gluck, 253 n. 125

Hofmannsthal, Hugo von, 4, 262, 269, 271; Ad me ipsum, 269; Lord Chandos letter, 4, 262–272

Hölderlin, Friedrich, 1, 2, 27, 134–135, 278

Holofernes, 54

Horn (French, hunting, coachman's), 41, 48, 66, 74, 107, 130, 162, 170, 191, 192, 199, 201, 204, 207, 227, 280. See also Instrumental Symbolism, Brass instruments

Hügel, Baroness von, 100

Hundhausen, Gretchen (Gritha), 101

Imagery. See Musical imagery, Fire imagery, Flower imagery, Desert

Insect performers, 124–125, 129, 130, 187, 192, 284

Instrumental symbolism, 3, 37, 65, 66–80, 278, 289. See also Brass instruments, Stringed instruments, Woodwinds, Percussion, Orchestra, Organ (as well as individual instruments such as bass viol, violin, etc.)

Irony, 35, 53, 56, 73, 75, 96, 114, 117, 212, 254, 280, 285

Jacobi, Friedrich, 183

Jean Paul (Richter), 27

Jephthah's daughter, 47–48, 49, 54

Jew's harp, 76

John the Baptist, 143

Jonah, 288

Joshua, 75

Judas, 144

Judith, 47–48, 49, 54

Kempis, Thomas à, 82–83, 87

Key, musical (tonic and dominant), 236, 242. See also "Grundvokale"

Kierkegaard, Søren, 31–32, 88–89

"Klangmalerei" (onomatopoeia) 226–230

"Klangspiel" (sound play), 226, 230–234, 255

"Klangsymbolik" (sound symbolism), 226, 234–246, 289–290

Kleist, Heinrich von, 85, 187–188

Klopstock, Friedrich Gottlieb, 199, 247

Korbach, Benedikte, 101, 293

Kotzebue, August von, 184, 195–197, 200, 209

Kraus, Hannchen, 101, 102, 293

Lanier, Sidney, 99, 180–181

Laroche, Sophie von, 145

Lessing, Gotthold Ephriam, Laokoon, 91–92

Liederbuch für deutsche Künstler, 16, 20

Linder, Emilie, 97, 103, 105, 131, 213, 257, 258, 264, 267, 295; as the siren figure, 108–110

Liszt, Franz, 14

Lot (Biblical figure), 144

Love and music. See Melos-Eros-Thanatos

Luise, Queen of Prussia, 21, 23

Lullaby, 123–124, 125, 211–212, 292

Lully, Jean Baptiste de, 209–210

Lute, 38, 66, 72–73, 76, 102–103, 111, 112, 130, 160, 162, 184, 186, 226, 277, 278, 288, 289. See also Instrumental symbolism, Stringed instruments

Luther, Martin, 179

Lyra, 29–30, 37, 68–69. See also Lyre, Instrumental symbolism, Stars and constellations

Lyre, 29, 30, 32, 34, 36, 37, 40, 65, 66–70, 72, 78, 137, 143, 161, 167, 192, 218. See also Instrumental symbolism, Lyra, Stringed instruments

Madonna. See Virgin Mary

Magdalena, Mary, 144

Magic, 53, 54, 55, 57, 161, 166, 174, 180, 190, 206, 252, 257

Mann, Thomas, 72

Mara, Gertrud, 158–159

Marriage, 70, 96, 103, 104, 114, 120, 127, 130–131, 145, 146, 170, 279–280, 293, 294. *See also* Women in Brentano's life, Melos-Eros-Thanatos

Masks, 84, 88, 89, 90–91, 111, 112, 120, 141, 145, 173. *See also* Apearance, Singing-Weeping

Melos-Eros-Thanatos (music, love and death) complex, 3, 31, 36, 40, 41, 50–51, 65, 76–80, 99–121, 127, 130–131, 165–168, 197, 204, 216–220, 230, 252, 267; purely sensual eroticism, 50, 69–70, 143–144, 161, 279–281, 283. *See also* Marriage, Women in Brentano's life, Venus

Memnon, 202

Mereau, Sophie, 13 n. 40, 31–32, 34, 43, 85, 101, 102–103, 293

Meter, 220–222, 224, 234

Middle Ages, 43, 51, 52, 64, 91, 140

Minnesinger ("Minnesänger" and "Minnesang"), 26–27, 108, 179, 279

Minuet, 146, 147, 221

Modes of music: major, 72; minor, 182; Dorian, 235

Möhn, "Tante," 140–141, 293

Morpheus, 276

Moses, 177

Mousiké, 179–182, 188, 218, 226

Mozart, Wolfgang Amadeus, 24, 207, 209, 275–276, 291

Muses, 29, 60

Music: absolute, 26, 99, 111, 117, 181, 205, 225, 247, 254, 257, 274; power of, 1, 30, 33, 37, 38, 43, 44, 57, 65, 104, 113, 114, 116, 165–166, 168, 214, 244, 277, 278–279; ultimate mystery of, 22, 25, 26, 117, 205

"Musica Naturata-Musica Naturans," 65, 121–137, 281

Musical: composition (Brentano's), 13, 15–20, 28, 203, 274; criticism (Brentano's), 13, 15, 20–27, 28, 203–204, 274; imagery of lyric poetry, 182, 246–261. *See also* Music, Musicality, Musicalization, Instrumental symbolism

Musicality: Brentano's actual, 8, 12, 12–20, literary, 10–12, 28, 182; lyric, 204–261, 268, 288–290

Musicalization: of life, 3, 62, 64, 65–178, 277–286; of literature, 3–4,

179–261, 271, 286–290; of literary criticism, 8–12, 28. *See also* Music, Musical, Musicality

Napoleon, 75, 96, 147, 255

Narcissism, 133–134, 136, 161

Nature's music, 65, 121–237, 228, 281–282; trees and forests, 123, 131, 191, 228, 229–230, 245, 259; water music, 123–124, 125, 130, 135, 144, 145, 146, 167, 185, 186, 190, 204, 208, 228, 233, 242, 252, 254, 260, 265, 267, 275, 284, 287, 292. *See also* Avian song, Nightingale, Swan song

Nazarenes, 84, 97, 156

Niendorf, Emma von, 14, 263

Nietzsche, Friedrich, 10, 27

Nightingale, 47, 77, 81, 91, 107–108, 125, 129–133, 153, 154, 173, 176, 185, 237, 238, 239, 245, 256, 258, 259, 281, 288

Novalis (Friedrich von Hardenberg), 1, 2, 25, 28, 64, 122, 205, 206 n. 43, 210 n. 52, 224 n. 74

Oboe, 66, 73. *See also* Instrumental symbolism, Woodwinds

Odysseus, 109

Oigros, 30, 36

Onomatopoeia. *See* "Klangmalerei"

Opera, 25, 26, 44, 46, 47, 80, 100–102, 115, 120, 126, 134, 174, 179, 188, 190, 201, 203–204, 206, 285, 286. *See also* "Gesamtkunstwerk"

Opitz, Martin, 96

Orchestra, 48, 66, 67, 75–76, 93, 126, 192, 195, 196, 198, 199–200, 201

Organ, 66, 67, 76–80, 83–84, 118, 129, 130, 164–165, 169, 170–171, 176

Orpheus and Orphean figures in Brentano's works, 1, 2, 4, 27, 28–31, 32, 33, 35–36, 37, 38, 39, 40, 41–43, 44, 45, 46, 47, 49, 50, 51, 52, 55, 56, 57, 59, 61, 62, 63, 65, 66, 67, 70, 77–78, 82, 88, 98, 104, 114, 120, 121, 122, 129, 135, 136, 137, 138, 149, 150, 156, 167, 168, 169, 174, 176, 177, 179, 180, 188, 190, 195, 197, 200, 204, 206, 215, 218, 220, 225–226, 236, 243, 257, 261, 262, 271, 273, 275, 276–279, 280, 283–284, 285–286, 287, 290, 291, 292; as poetic symbol delineated by Walther Rehm, 1–2, 30–31, 44, 65, 80, 121–122, 137; Greek background, 28–31

Overbeck, Friedrich, 84
Overture, 197–200, 204, 208–210, 236
Ovid, 196

Paer (Paër), Ferdinando, 24, 25
Percussion instruments, 66, 67, 193, 214, 227–228. *See also* Instrumental symbolism, Piano
Persephone, 29, 52
Philistine, 4, 12, 24–25, 34, 74, 95, 140–141, 191, 195, 273–292
Philomela, 53
Phoenix, 80, 134
Piano, 13, 21, 86, 96, 102, 115, 198–199, 276. *See also* Percussion instruments
Pilgrim, as figure in Brentano's poetry, 105, 107, 108, 128, 156–158, 191
Pipe (musical instrument), 36, 37, 66–67, 72–74, 76, 91, 112, 213, 222, 228, 241, 242, 243, 275. *See also* Instrumental symbolism, Woodwinds
Plato (on musical instruments), 66–67
Polonaise, 138, 144. *See also* Dance
Polyptoton, 220
Proteus, 3, 5–7, 28

Reichardt, Johann Friedrich, 21–25, 274, 277
Reichenbach, Minna, 101, 293
Reichenbach (sisters), 89
Religious music, 3; Orpheus' cult of, 29; Judaeo-Christian, 30–31, 42, 44–64, 65, 76–80, 83–84, 86–89, 97–99, 105, 127, 129, 131–133, 147, 149–178, 199, 232, 284–285, 290
Renaissance, 30
Rhetoric and rhetorical devices, 84, 159, 162, 214, 218, 220, 222–223, 229, 232–234, 268. *See also* Alliteration, Assonance, Chiasmus, Diminution, Polyptoton
Rhythm, 205, 206, 220–224, 234
Rilke, Rainer Maria, *Sonette an Orpheus*, 1, 4, 261, 292
Ritter, Peter, 16, 101
Rondo, 218–219. *See also* Form
Runge, Philipp P., 187, 210, 278 n., 294

Salome, 143–144
Savigny, Friedrich Carl von, 85, 89, 98, 117
Schelling, Friedrich Wilhelm, 188 n. 22
Schiller, Friedrich von, 81, 85 n., 202–203, 205, 231, 247–248, 251; *Die Braut von Messina*, 202–203; *Ka-*

bale und Liebe, 203; "Über Matthisons Gedichte," 247–248; "Über naive und sentimentalische Dichtung," 247
Schinkel, Karl, 82, 188, 286–287
Schlegel, August Wilhelm, 188 n. 22, 225, 239
Schlegel, Friedrich, 64, 142, 180, 189, 210 n. 52
Schopenhauer, Arthur, 180, 188 n. 22
Schubart, Christian Friedrich Daniel, 66 n. 2
Schubart, Franz, 10–11, 207
Schumann, Robert, 11, 14, 207
Schwab, Herr, 76
Serenade, 201, 215–216, 280
Shakespeare, William, 99, 111, 255 n. 131, 273, 275; *The Merchant of Venice*, 273; *Twelfth Night*, 99
Shawm, 73, 74, 172, 227, 243, 244, 246, 258. *See also* Instrumental symbolism, Woodwinds
Singing. *See* Song, vocal
Singing-weeping, 88–91, 160, 162
Siren(s), 30, 41, 45, 48, 52, 105, 109–111, 115, 166–167
Solomon, 50
Sonata, 208–209, 236, 285. *See also* Form
Song, vocal, 29, 38, 41, 44, 47, 49, 55, 57, 58, 59, 60, 65, 79, 81, 83, 84, 86, 89–90, 100, 103, 111, 113, 115, 134, 163, 164, 165, 169, 170, 171, 175, 218, 239, 244. *See also* Song of Songs
Song form, 16–20
Song of Songs (Song of Solomon), 46, 50–57, 59, 61, 157, 166, 176
Sontag, Henriette, 158–159
Sound, patternings of in poetry, 182, 206, 211, 225, 246, 248. *See also* "Klangmalerei," "Klangspiel," "Klangsymbolik"
Spee, Friedrich von, *Trutznachtigall*, 152–154
Spontini, Gasparo, 14
Stars and constellations ("music of the spheres"), 29–30, 36, 37, 39, 45, 50, 58, 68, 69, 134, 135, 143, 161, 172, 173, 174, 177–178, 183, 213, 214, 215–216, 217, 218, 231, 233, 246, 253, 256, 257, 267, 285, 292. *See also* Lyra
Stein, Gertude, 220
Steinle, Eduard von, 33, 155
Stringed instruments, 37, 60–61, 66–67, 72–74, 76, 160, 168. *See also* Instrumental symbolism

Swan, swan song, 54, 106, 114, 125, 133–137, 157, 161, 177, 223, 233, 251, 252, 279. *See also* Avian song

"Sym-syndrome," 182

Symbol, Brentano's view of, 67–68, 187

Symbolists, 6–7, 181, 224 n. 73

Synaesthesia, 182, 183–186, 187, 189, 193, 196, 204, 286, 287–288

"Syn-aesthetic," 3–4, 182, 186–204, 206, 207, 287–288

Syzygy, phonetic (concealed alliteration), 232

Tambourine, 41, 69, 90, 148, 213, 221

Tannhäuser, 107–108

Tasso, Torquato, 190, 193, 271, 274

Theme and variations (as musico-poetic technique), 86, 102, 103–104, 126, 210–220, 237. *See also* Form, musico-poetic in literature

Thorough-bass, 15, 95–96

Threshold condition, 1, 2–4, 29, 31, 32, 34, 35, 38–39, 54, 55, 77–78, 98–99, 136, 137, 138, 164, 174, 177, 194–195, 214–215, 246, 261, 262, 271, 273, 275, 277, 286, 292

Tieck, Ludwig, 10, 21, 25, 28, 94, 204, 207, 209, 225, 226–227, 228 n. 84, 231

Todi, Luiza, 158–159

Tone play. *See* "Klangspiel"

Triangle (musical instrument), 66, 143

Trombone, 66, 74, 75, 199. *See also* Instrumental symbolism, Brass instruments

Trumpet, 66, 74, 75, 114, 126, 202, 228, 271, 280. *See also* Instrumental symbolism, Brass instruments

Vadutz, 259

Varnhagen von Ense, Karl, 113 n. 69

Varnhagen (von Ense), Rahel, 9, 93, 98, 176

Venus, 107–108, 118, 161, 283

Viola, 66. *See also* Instrumental symbolism, Stringed Instruments

Violin, 14, 40, 42–43, 58–59, 66, 100, 130, 141, 144, 169, 196, 275–276, 279–280, 286, 287, 289. *See also* Instrumental symbolism, Stringed instruments

Violoncello, 66. *See also* Instrumental symbolism, Stringed instruments

Virgin Mary, 77–78, 108, 152, 154–155

Wackenroder, Wilhelm Heinrich, 9 n. 16, 25, 28, 205, 228 n. 84

Wagner, Richard, 11, 27, 48, 195, 201, 204, 223, 235; *Die Meistersinger*, 201; *Tristan und Isolde*, 204, 223.

Walther von Klingen, 232 n. 91

Waltz, 58, 119, 139, 144, 147, 221. *See also* Dance

Wellington, Arthur Wellesley (Duke of), 75, 255

Welsch, Amalia, 100

Winkelmann, August, 33–34, 205

Winter, Peter von, 24

Winterwerber (School), 140

Woodwinds, 66–67, 72–74. *See also* Instrumental symbolism, Bassoon, Clarinet, Pipe, Shawm

Xylophone, 139

Zeitung für Einsiedler, 109, 294

Zither, 14, 66, 72, 81. *See also* Instrumental symbolism, Stringed instruments